Chris Notes!

A Set of Notes for Introductory Statistics

Dr. Chris O'Neal

ISBN: 978-0-578-56015-1

Table of Contents

Introduction

Welcome, and may I personally thank you for being so kind as to purchase these statistics notes. My main goal of writing them was to make the material in introductory statistics classes easier to understand, as it can most certainly be a little confusing at times. Many students in high school and university need to take this class as a requirement for their future studies, and so I wanted to help make this leg of their journey a little easier.

I have written these notes with clear definitions and formulas, along with plenty of helpful examples illustrating how everything works. As much as possible, I have explained everything in simple terms so that the reader can easily follow along. If you are like me and learn best from examples and graphs and even mnemonics, then you will love this book.

The material in these notes covers hopefully most or all of what you are expected to know in your introductory statistics class. Of course, your instructor might add or remove certain topics, so please remember to use your own assigned textbook as required, and treat my notes as a helpful supplement.

Many of the problems require making a sketch of the situation, often taking the form of drawing a bell curve (or the equivalent) and shading a section of it. Please do this as much as you can, as you will find that it is enormously helpful. Without such a diagram, it is too easy to get confused and make mistakes. Remember – when in doubt, draw it out!

Statistics is a subject that requires some sort of technology to compute some of the answers. In these notes we will concentrate on using the TI-84 graphing calculator. When applicable, I will show you different commands on this calculator and how they work with different topics. The calculator I used for writing these notes was a TI-84 Plus Silver Edition. Most of these commands are available on the TI-83 calculator as well, except for a small handful (and certain steps might need to be adjusted as well).

If your instructor has you use other programs to calculate answers (including SPSS, Minitab, StatCrunch, online calculators, or even tables), please reference your instructor's instructions on how to use those methods. We won't focus on using tables in these notes (with a couple of exceptions in the final chapter), but nevertheless you will find the most common tables in the appendices (after all, no statistics book is complete without setting the tables - as it were!)

The topics in this book are generally the ones you most likely will come across in your course. A few sections contain material that is either not always taught or is more advanced and may or may not be covered in an introductory class, and these sections contain an asterisk (*) next to the section name. You can either skip these sections as applicable, or you can read them anyway if you are up to the challenge! The appendices include a list of all the important formulas and TI-84 commands, along with the necessary statistics tables in the event you need to use them for your class.

A little bit about me - I have a PhD in statistics from the University of Georgia, and I work as a statistician for my main job. I am from England, as you might be able to tell from certain examples in these notes (for instance, the number of cups of tea a British person drinks per day!). And I really hope you enjoy using these "Chris Notes!" as much as I enjoyed writing them, and that you find them very helpful and, dare I say, enjoyable, to completing this required class.

Cheers!

Chris O'Neal

Chapter 1 – Introduction to Statistics and Interpreting Graphs

In this first chapter we learn some basic terms used in statistics, and we start to explore graphs and how to interpret them.

Section 1.1 – Introduction to Statistics

In this brief section we get acquainted with the general idea of what statistics is and when to use it.

DEFINITION

Statistics is the mathematical science of designing studies and experiments and then analyzing the resulting data. Simply put, a sample of subjects are studied, and then based on the results, a conclusion is made about the general population from which the subjects came.

For instance, we may want to know any of the following:

1) The average number of movies that people watch in one month.
2) The most common color of a car.
3) The proportion of people who own a dog.

ETYMOLOGY

The word statistics comes from the Latin *statisticum*, which meant "of the state." In 1749, Gottfried Achenwall introduced the word *Statistik* into German to discuss data analysis of the state. The man whom we can thank for introducing the word into the English language was Sir John Sinclair, a Scottish politician. From 1791 to 1799, he published the *First Statistical Account of Scotland*, which discussed life in Europe during the industrial and agricultural revolutions.

Of course, we cannot possibly survey everybody in the whole population since this is too time-consuming and costly. This is where statistics comes in. (One exception is the United States census, which is sent to everybody in the country every ten years.) Statistics involves surveying only a handful of people, all randomly selected from the population, and then using the results in that sample to make a conclusion about the population.

The goal of these statistics notes is to present the topics usually covered in an introductory statistics class in an easy-to-understand way, along with plenty of examples. Since every statistics class involves computational steps, we need to have some set guidelines on how to handle these calculations. There are many technologies available to students (graphing calculators, Excel, statistical programs, and websites), and usually one or two are chosen for a classroom.

As mentioned in the introduction, in these notes we will use the TI-84 graphing calculator. When appropriate, I will show you which commands are useful. If you have a different graphing calculator or a different version of the TI-84, you might need to adjust some of the steps. Usually by convention we will compute all intermediate calculation steps using all decimal places the calculator shows because rounding to fewer decimals could cause round-off error further in a problem.

When a TI-84 command can be used, I will show you how to do the problem by hand using formulas before showing you how the command works. Why, you may ask? If I were to just tell you the calculator command without walking you through what is going on behind the scenes, you might become too dependent on the calculator. Sooner or later, you are going to come across a problem with just enough information that the calculator cannot be used in the usual way, and so you would have to understand how the problem really works. Believe me, you will be thankful you tried at least some problems by hand!

Lastly, you will discover that I particularly love studying the etymology of different words, or in other words whether the words come from Latin or ancient Greek, and what they originally meant. While these tidbits are obviously not essential to know for the course, they add in an extra flavor that hopefully you will enjoy. I also love mnemonics whenever possible as they can be great tools to remember certain points, so when I see an opportunity for one, you will be presented with it. Enjoy these notes!

Section 1.2 – Populations versus Samples

For the following definitions, keep in mind as an example predicting the outcome of an election.

DEFINITION

The **population** is the total set of subjects in which we are interested.

A **sample** is a selected subset of the population for which we have data available.

A **subject** is an individual that is in the sample.

A **parameter** is a numerical value that summarizes something in the population.

A **statistic** is a numerical value that summarizes something in the sample.

For instance, suppose there is an election coming up in the United Kingdom, and we want to know what percentage of people will vote for a specific candidate. To investigate, we randomly sample 1000 people and ask them whether they plan to vote for that candidate.

1) The population is all people in the United Kingdom who are eligible to vote.
2) The sample is the 1000 people who were randomly selected.
3) An individual person who was randomly chosen for the sample is a subject.
4) The parameter of interest is the percentage of people in the United Kingdom who will vote for the candidate.
5) The statistic of interest is the percentage of people in the sample of 1000 selected people who will vote for the candidate.

Here is a Venn diagram illustrating the concepts.

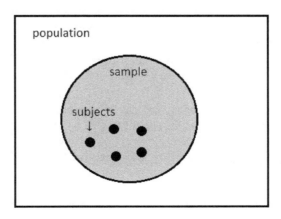

Of course, there are many possible different samples that can be drawn from the population, so two different researchers doing the same study will almost certainly pick two different groups of people. That means that sample averages will differ, depending on which subjects are chosen.

EXAMPLE

There are 1300 students enrolled in organic chemistry at a specific college one semester, and we would like to know the proportion of these students that are freshmen. Suppose it is too hard to survey all 1300 students, so instead we draw a random sample of size 100. We ask each of these 100 students whether they are freshmen. We then find the proportion in this sample that are freshmen.

1) The population is all 1300 students taking organic chemistry.
2) The sample is the 100 organic chemistry students who were randomly selected.
3) An individual organic chemistry student who was randomly chosen for the sample is a subject.
4) The parameter of interest is the proportion of all 1300 organic chemistry students who are freshmen.
5) The statistic of interest is the proportion of the 100 randomly selected organic chemistry students who are freshmen.

Δ

ETYMOLOGY

The word population comes from the Latin *populus*, which meant "people," while the word sample comes from the Old French *essample*, which meant "example." Subject derives from the Latin *sub-* and *jacere* (meaning "under" and "throw"), which combined resulted in *subjectus*, or "brought under" (as in certain material is brought under a specific topic, or subject). Lastly, the word parameter is from the Greek $\pi\alpha\rho\acute{\alpha}$- and $\mu\acute{\epsilon}\tau\rho o\nu$, which meant "beside" and "measure."

NOTATION

When we talk about the mean (or proportion) of a sample versus that of a population, we use different symbols to distinguish which one we are using.

Population mean (parameter)	μ (pronounced "mu")
Sample mean (statistic)	$\overline{x}$ (pronounced "x-bar")
Population proportion (parameter)	p (you know how to pronounce this!)
Sample proportion (statistic)	$\hat{p}$ (pronounced "p-hat")

MNEMONIC

Population and parameter both begin with P, while sample and statistic both begin with S. This is an easy way to remember which letter goes with which word!

EXAMPLE

A certain lottery scratch-off card has a probability of 0.20 of being a winner, with $1.05 as the average amount won. We play 50 such cards and discover that a proportion of 0.22 of them are winners, with the average winnings being $1.75.

The population proportion of scratch-off cards that are winners is 0.20. This is a parameter because it describes the population, and therefore we write $p = 0.20$.

The population mean amount won on a scratch-off card is $1.05. This is a parameter because it describes the population, and therefore we write $\mu = \$1.05$.

The sample proportion of scratch-off cards that are winners is 0.22. This is a statistic because it describes the sample of 50 cards, and therefore we write $\hat{p} = 0.22$.

The sample mean amount won on a scratch-off card is \$1.75. This is a statistic because it describes the sample of 50 cards, and therefore we write $\overline{x} = \$1.75$.

Δ

DEFINITION

A statistic is **descriptive** if it summarizes the actual data in the sample.

We can use a statistic to make a conclusion, or inference, about the population based on the sample. A statistic that makes a conclusion about the population is **inferential**.

EXAMPLE

In the same example as above, suppose 40 out of 100 organic chemistry students selected were freshmen, and therefore the percentage of people in the sample who are freshmen is 40%. Using a certain test, we conclude that out of all organic chemistry students, between 36% and 44% are freshmen.

The percentage in the sample is 40%, which summarizes what we see in the sample. This statistic is descriptive for that reason. Using the new notation, we would say $\hat{p} = 0.40$ (because if the percentage is 40%, then the proportion is 0.40).

The conclusion is that between 36% and 44% of all organic chemistry students are freshmen. This statistic makes a conclusion about the population and is therefore inferential.

Δ

EXAMPLE

In a sample of 500 college students, we discover that the majority of students in the sample attend football games. We conclude that the majority of all students at this college attend football games.

The observation that the majority of the selected 500 students attend football games is descriptive since it describes the sample. The conclusion that the majority of all students attend football games is inferential since it describes the population based on what was seen in the sample.

Δ

Section 1.3 – Categorical Data versus Quantitative Data

This section discusses types of variables.

DEFINITION

A **variable** is a characteristic of interest that we are studying for statistical analysis.

In this class, the variable of interest is usually a number, but there are occasions when it is a non-numeric quality. Thus, there are two types of variables: categorical and quantitative.

DEFINITION

A variable of interest is **categorical** (sometimes also called **qualitative**) if it can be summarized as a word, category, or some physical attribute. You cannot take the average of a categorical variable.

EXAMPLE
The following are all examples of categorical variables because they cannot be expressed as numbers. They represent some sort of physical attribute.

1) A person's eye color (blue, green, etc.).
2) A football player's position (quarterback, punter, receiver, etc.).
3) A movie's genre (horror, action, romance, comedy, etc.).
4) A living organism's classification (archebacterium, eubacterium, protist, fungus, plant, animal).
5) A child's dream job (policeman, firefighter, author, etc. – for some reason you never hear children saying that they want to be statisticians when they grow up!).

Δ

DEFINITION
A variable of interest is **quantitative** (sometimes also called **numerical**) if it can be summarized as a number, and furthermore we can report statistics such as an average, maximum, etc.

The following are examples of quantitative variables because they can be expressed as numbers:

1) The speed of a boat, in knots.
2) The oven temperature, in Fahrenheit, needed for a recipe.
3) A person's annual salary, in dollars.
4) The number of children a person has.
5) The number of gallons of water in a swimming pool.

Δ

Furthermore, quantitative variables can be further grouped into discrete and continuous variables. This distinction will be important later in the course.

DEFINITION
A quantitative variable is said to be **discrete** if it can only take on a countable number of values. Usually this variable would be equal to a whole number only.

A quantitative variable is **continuous** if it can have any number of decimals.

This can be a little tricky to discern, so here are some examples. A good rule of thumb is to ask yourself whether the item could realistically take decimal values. If not, it must be discrete.

EXAMPLE
The following are all discrete variables:

1) The number of living grandparents a person has (0, 1, 2, 3, or 4 – whole numbers).
2) The number of customers entering a shop in an hour (0, 1, 2, 3, etc.).
3) The number of hits needed to sink a game piece in Battleship (2, 3, 4, or 5).
4) The number of goals a soccer team scores in a match (0, 1, 2, 3, etc.).
5) The number of times per month the fire alarm goes off in a dormitory.

And now here are some continuous examples.

1) A person's height, in inches (could be 60.1, or 60.11, or 72.335, so theoretically we could have all sorts of decimals here).

2) The length of a jellyfish's tentacles, in millimeters.
3) The volume of oil in a barrel, in cubic feet.
4) The time taken to run a mile, in seconds.
5) The mass of a subatomic particle, in kilograms.

Δ

Ask yourself questions like this: can you have, say, 2.18129 grandparents alive? Not exactly! That means that the variable "number of living grandparents" cannot be continuous; it must be discrete. Similarly, imagine the look on your opponent's face if you were to suggest that they had achieved 1.94673 hits and sunk your destroyer! Again, we are talking about a discrete variable.

On the other hand, can you have 15.2135 cubic feet of oil in a barrel? Of course, this is theoretically possible. That means that that variable is continuous.

EXAMPLE
Label each of the following as categorical or quantitative, and if the latter, discrete or continuous:

A) The number of diamonds in a five-card poker hand.
B) The brand of a refrigerator.
C) The used condition of a textbook.
D) The time taken to swim one lap.
E) A zip code.

Solution: For part A, the number of diamonds in a poker hand is obviously a number, so it is quantitative. A standard five-card hand can have 0, 1, 2, 3, 4, or 5 diamonds, but you cannot have a decimal number of diamonds. This is discrete.

In parts B and C, a refrigerator brand is a name (Frigidaire, GE, Whirlpool, etc.) and not a number, so this is categorical. Similarly, the condition of a textbook (new, like new, good, acceptable) is categorical because it is a physical attribute that is not numeric.

The time to swim a lap can be expressed as a number, in seconds, so part D is quantitative. Since one can swim a lap in a decimal number of seconds, it is also continuous.

Lastly, in part E, a zip code is a number, so it is … categorical! Why is it categorical when it is a number? The answer is because a zip code, although represented by a number, is really a geographical region. Does it make sense to average zip codes? No, doing so has no value. (By a similar argument, phone number area codes are also categorical.)

Δ

ETYMOLOGY
The word variable comes from the Latin *varius*, which meant "diverse." Categorical derives from the Greek κατηγορία meaning "statement" (as in an accusation), while quantitative's root is the Latin *quantus* for "how much." Finally, the words discrete and continuous come from the Latin *discretus* (meaning "separate") and the Latin *con-* and *tenere* (meaning "hold together").

Section 1.4 – Frequencies, Proportions, and Percentages
The next topic deals with proportions and percentages. We can easily compute these, and given one, we

can quickly derive the other. Consider the following three definitions.

DEFINITION

The number of observations within a specific category is called the **frequency**.

The proportion of observations (or alternatively, the percentage of observations) within a specific category is called the **relative frequency**.

A **frequency table** lists the number of observations (the frequencies) for each category of data.

Just to be clear, here are a couple more definitions:

DEFINITION

A **proportion** is equal to the frequency in one category divided by the total sample size. It is always between 0 and 1, inclusive:

$$\text{proportion} = \frac{\text{frequency}}{\text{sample size}}$$

A **percentage** is equal to a proportion times 100, so it is always between 0% and 100%, inclusive:

$$\text{percentage} = \frac{\text{frequency}}{\text{sample size}} \times 100$$

On your homework, quizzes and tests, it is very important to note whether the question is asking for a proportion or a percentage!

ETYMOLOGY

The words "frequency," "proportion," and "percentage" come from the Latin *frequens*, *pro portione*, and *per centum*, which meant "frequent," "in respect of a person's share," and "by the hundred," respectively.

EXAMPLE

We have a group of 300 people classified by what continent they are from. The data are given below (let's assume that nobody was born on Antarctica!):

N. America	S. America	Europe	Africa	Asia	Australia
103	22	110	12	33	20

We want to turn these into proportions, followed by percentages. Remember, a proportion is frequency divided by total sample size (here 300), so the proportion for North America would be

$$\frac{103}{300} = 0.34333$$

Using the same computation techniques, the resulting proportions for each continent are:

N. America	S. America	Europe	Africa	Asia	Australia
0.34333	0.07333	0.36667	0.04	0.11	0.06667

If we wanted percentages, then the answers would be equal to those in the above table, each multiplied by 100 (so the decimal goes two places to the right).

N. America	S. America	Europe	Africa	Asia	Australia
34.333%	7.333%	36.667%	4%	11%	6.667%

Δ

EXAMPLE
Suppose we had a group of 440 people, and we were told that 20% of them were European. How do we compute the frequency? Recall the technique from high school algebra:

$$440 \times 0.20 = 88$$

To double-check this answer, note that $88/440 = 0.20$, which is 20%.

How many Australian people would we have if we were told that 35% of these 440 were from down under? We need to compute 35% of 440, which is

$$440 \times 0.35 = 154$$

Δ

Section 1.5 – Describing Data Using Graphs
We need to have some methods of displaying graphical summaries of our data in an aesthetically pleasing manner; in other words, so a layman can read the chart and understand what it is saying (and at the same time minimizing boredom!). However, the choice of graph comes down to whether the data are categorical or quantitative, as well as whichever type makes the most visual sense.

SUMMARIZING CATEGORICAL DATA
When the data are categorical, there are three main types of graphs we can make. For these three graphs, keep in mind the continent data example, repeated below for convenience.

N. America	S. America	Europe	Africa	Asia	Australia
103	22	110	12	33	20

Categorical Graph 1: Pie Chart
In a **pie chart**, we have as many slices of the "pie" as we do categories. Each slice's size is representative of that category's percentage of the sample, so a larger slice will represent a larger chunk of the sample. Similarly, the smallest slice will be the category with the fewest number of people. (Rumor has it that pie charts are popular with bakers!) Here is a pie chart for the continent data above.

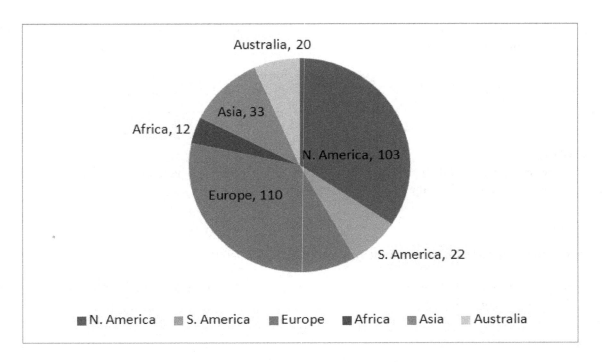

The numbers around the pie indicate each category's frequency. One drawback to a pie chart is that without the legend's numbers, it would not be obvious which category – North America or Europe – was larger, since at first glance the two slices are roughly the same size.

Categorical Graph 2: Bar Graph

A **bar graph**, or **bar chart**, illustrates the data by plotting categories side-by-side on the horizontal axis, and the frequencies (or relative frequencies) on the vertical axis. This means that the higher the bar, the more subjects in that category. Thus, to determine which category has the largest frequency, we need only choose the category with the highest bar. Here are the same continent data:

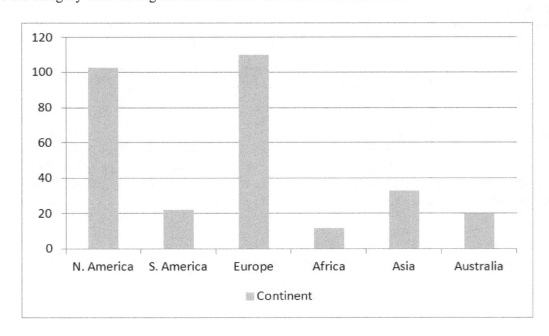

Hence, the drawback to pie charts is fixed with a bar graph – it is now clear that Europe has the most number of subjects, with North America a close second.

Categorical Graph 3: Pareto Graph
Sometimes a bar graph is arranged from highest to lowest frequencies. Such a bar graph is called a **Pareto graph** (named after the French economist Vilfredo Pareto). The following graph is similar to the bar graph above, only with the categories arranged from highest frequency (Europe) to lowest (Africa).

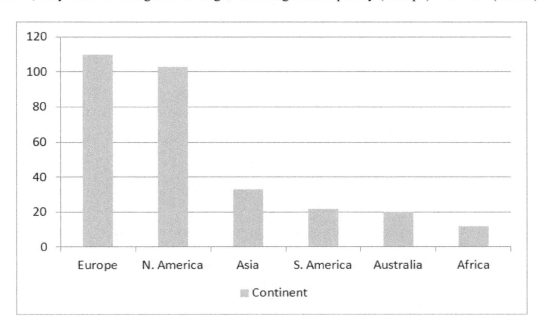

SUMMARIZING QUANTITATIVE DATA
As with categorical data, there are numerous ways of summarizing data that are numerical. We begin with the dot plot.

Quantitative Graph 1: Dot Plot
In a **dot plot**, we plot our numbers as follows. We graph along the horizontal axis the numbers used, and above each number we plot one dot for each occurrence of that number in the data set. Here is a sample dataset of test scores in a class.

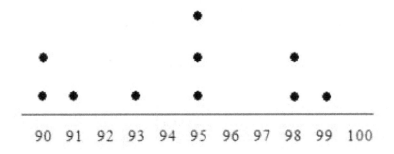

There are ten dots, so there are ten total tests. To work out how many students scored 91, observe that 91 has one dot above it, representing one score. Similarly, three students scored 95 because there are three dots above 95. On the other hand, no students scored a 97 since the 97 column has no dots.

Quantitative Graph 2: Histogram

A **histogram** is the quantitative equivalent of a bar graph. The "categories" on the horizontal axis are now numerical values, or they can even be intervals of numerical values. For instance, here is a dataset recording some seventh graders' IQ scores.

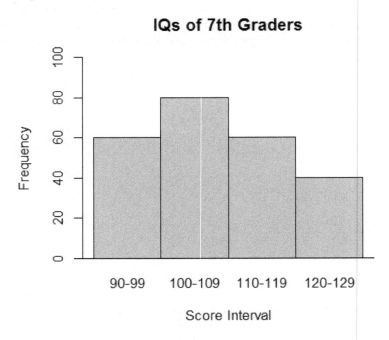

A) How many total students are in the sample?
B) How many students have an IQ between 100 and 119?
C) What is the percentage of students having an IQ between 90 and 109?

For part A, using the y-axis frequencies as a guide, there are $60 + 80 + 60 + 40 = 240$ total students.

For part B, we want to see how many students fall between 100 and 119. Note that this includes two intervals, $100 - 109$ and $110 - 119$, so we need to add their frequencies. Thus, there are $80 + 60 = 140$ such students.

As for part C, we first need the number of students with an IQ is between 90 and 109. Again, this encompasses two intervals, $90 - 99$ and $100 - 109$, so there are $60 + 80 = 140$ such students. To compute the percentage, we find the proportion (or relative frequency) and multiply it by 100:

$$\frac{140}{240} \times 100 = 58.333\%$$

Quantitative Graph 3: Stem and Leaf Plot

The final type of chart worth considering is called a **stem and leaf plot**. Recall that the ones-place digit of a number is the rightmost digit. (For example, the ones-place digit of 167 would be 7.)

What we do is create a "vertical bar chart" with the stem being the whole number except for the ones-place digits. We later plot the ones-place digits alongside the appropriate location on the stem, in ascending order. This may be hard to visualize, so here is an example. Consider the following selling prices on eBay for a specific item:

199   210   210   223   225   225   225   228   232   235

Since the minimum response is 199 and the maximum is 235, that means the stem will consist of 19, 20, 21, 22, and 23. (Note that no numbers here begin with 20, but we include it anyway instead of skipping it.) These are the resulting numbers when the ones-place digits are discarded. The lowest is 19 and the highest is 23, so we also list all numbers in between.

Next, we take each ones-place digit and plot it alongside its corresponding stem, going in ascending order. This means that 19's only "leaf" is 9 because of the number 199. 21's leaves are 00 (because there are two occurrences of 210).

There are five numbers whose first two digits are 22: 223, 225, 225, 225, and 228. When we "peel off" the 22 from each number, we are left with 3, 5, 5, 5, and 8. Thus, the 22 row has the leaves 35558.

Lastly, the last two numbers start with 23, and the remaining digits are 2 and 5. That means that the 23 row has leaves 25. The complete stem and leaf plot looks like this:

$$
\begin{array}{r|l}
19 & 9 \\
20 & \\
21 & 0 \\
22 & 35558 \\
23 & 25 \\
\end{array}
$$

Notice the absence of leaves on row 20. This is because there was no number that began with 20. When this happens, we still must write that number on the stem; we just leave the leaf area blank. It would be incorrect to put a 0 on that row because that would imply the number 200 was in the data set, which it is not.

EXAMPLE
The following data represent the length of an eruption (in seconds) for a random sample of eruptions of "Old Faithful," a geyser at Yellowstone National Park. Draw a stem and leaf plot.

110	99	112	108	109
108	106	113	97	102
76	97	104	114	107

Solution: First, it would be helpful to rearrange the data from lowest to highest.

76	97	97	99	102
104	106	107	108	108
109	110	112	113	114

19

If we examine all the numbers except for the rightmost digit, we are left with the numbers 7, 9, 10, and 11. This means that the "stem" will consist of the numbers 7 − 11 (and this includes 8, even though no observation starts with 8).

Only one number starts with 7 (the 76), so the only "leaf" on that row is 6. Next, we have three numbers beginning with 9 (97, 97, and 99), so the leaves are 779. Continuing in this fashion, we arrive at the following stem-and-leaf plot:

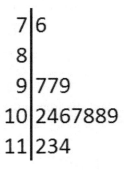

$$\begin{array}{c|l} 7 & 6 \\ 8 & \\ 9 & 779 \\ 10 & 2467889 \\ 11 & 234 \end{array}$$

Δ

Section 1.6 – Shapes of Histograms

When data are quantitative and displayed as a histogram, they often take specific visual shapes. This can tell us a lot about the nature of the data, and it will be important to note the general shape for future computations. There are three important types of shapes to consider, and they are explained below.

ETYMOLOGY

The word histogram has an uncertain etymology. One possibility is that it comes from the Greek ἱστός (meaning "mast") and γραμμα (meaning "drawing"), where the word "mast" refers to those on a ship. As the mast on a ship rises vertically, so do the bars on a histogram. However, another explanation is that the English mathematician Karl Pearson coined the word from "historical diagram."

Histogram Shape 1: Symmetrical

A **symmetrical distribution** is one where the left side of the distribution is a mirror image of the right side. It does not have to be a perfect mirror image; if the data look approximately symmetrical, then we can say that it is symmetric. Additionally, if the data take on a "bell curve shape" as in the graph below, then the data are also **normal**. This means that the data look a little like an upside-down bell.

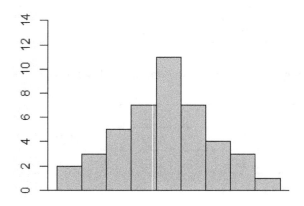

Histogram Shape 2: Skewed Left

A **skewed left distribution** is one where the left tail of the distribution is longer than the right tail. Put another way, most of the data are on the right side of the graph, creating a longer left tail.

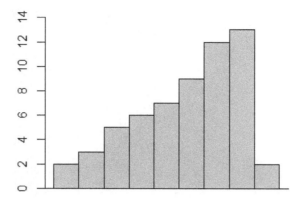

Histogram Shape 3: Skewed Right

A **skewed right distribution** is one where the right tail of the distribution is longer than the left tail. Put another way, most of the data are on the left side of the graph, creating a longer right tail.

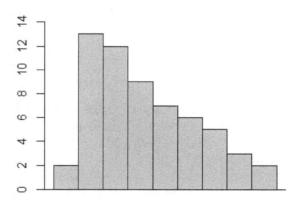

Sometimes data are represented by "smooth" curves rather than as raw histograms, such as the one below representing a skewed right curve.

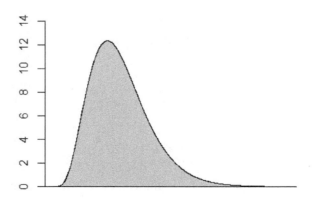

EXAMPLE

Consider the following histogram of more IQ scores, this time of 9th graders. Like in a previous example, the scores are divided into intervals.

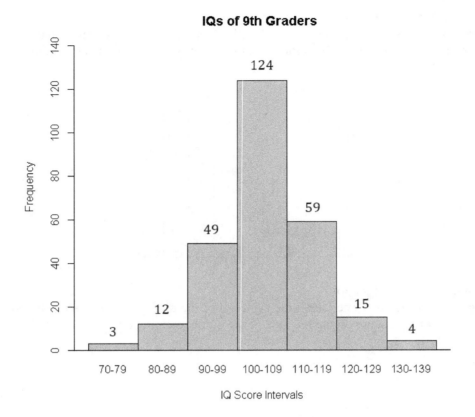

A) How many students were sampled?
B) Which interval has the highest frequency? What is its frequency?
C) Which interval has the lowest frequency? What is its frequency?
D) What is the relative frequency of an IQ between 100 and 129?
E) Describe the shape of the distribution.

Solution: For part A, we just need to add all the frequencies that have very kindly been listed on the histogram:

$$3 + 12 + 49 + 124 + 59 + 15 + 4 = 266 \text{ total students}$$

The interval with the highest frequency is $100 - 109$, and its frequency is 124. (Take care not to confuse the interval with the frequency!) Similarly, the interval with the lowest frequency is $70 - 79$, with a frequency of 3.

The relative frequency of an IQ between 100 and 129 is asking for the proportion rather than the frequency itself. There are $124 + 59 + 15 = 198$ students with an IQ within this range, and so the relative frequency would be

$$\frac{198}{266} = 0.74436$$

As for the shape of the distribution, the left side is almost a mirror image of the right (not exactly but very close). That means that it is approximately symmetric. Furthermore, since a lot of data are in the middle and the rest are in "tails" on the graph, the data are approximately normal.

Δ

In introductory classes, usually distributions that are symmetric are also normal. In general, this is not always necessarily the case. Consider the following graph:

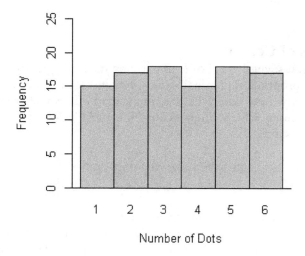

This graph represents 100 rolls of a dice and the recorded numbers 1 through 6. It is approximately symmetric because the left side is almost a mirror image of the right, but it is not normal because the data do not take on a bell curve. (This type of dataset follows what is known as a uniform distribution.) However, in this class, when we encounter symmetric data, it will almost always be normal.

Chapter 2 – Summary Statistics

In this chapter we begin to learn how to compute basic summary statistics for quantitative data, thereby laying the foundation for future chapters.

Section 2.1 – Measures of Center

Up until now we have covered several ways of summarizing data graphically with charts. The next step is to summarize them using appropriate numerical values. For instance, it is usually of interest to know the average of a dataset, or to know how much the data are spread out. Sometimes we care to know specific percentiles, or we want to know which point occurs the most often. Thus, there are many different numerical ways to summarize data.

On that note, it is important to realize that the following only applies to quantitative data, not categorical!

DEFINITION

The **average**, or the **mean**, is a measure of the center of a dataset, the central tendency. To compute the mean, add up all the values of the dataset and divide by the number of these values. As a formula, suppose the data values are x_1, x_2, and so on up to x_n, so there are n data points. The mean is computed as

$$\text{mean} = \frac{x_1 + x_2 + \cdots + x_n}{n}$$

Using mathematical summation notation (Σ, the uppercase Greek letter "sigma" used to indicate that we are adding a series of numbers), the mean is also

$$\text{mean} = \frac{\sum x_i}{n}$$

EXAMPLE

To compute the mean of the dataset $\{2, 4, 7, 8, 9\}$, we first note that there are $n = 5$ data points. We add them and divide by 5:

$$\text{mean} = \frac{2 + 4 + 7 + 8 + 9}{5} = \frac{30}{5} = 6$$

The average, or mean, of this dataset is 6.

Δ

There are two different symbols we can use to denote the mean, and it depends whether we are talking about the whole population or just a sample.

NOTATION

The symbol for the population mean is μ (pronounced "mu").
The symbol for the sample mean is $\bar{x}$ (pronounced "x-bar").

Which symbol do we pick? If we were given all the data for a whole population, we would use μ. If we were given a sample of data, as in the previous example (and most examples in this class), we would use $\bar{x}$. In the previous example, we would write $\bar{x} = 6$.

DEFINITION

The **median** is the data value that occupies the middle position when the data are ranked in ascending order (from smallest to largest). The median separates the bottom 50% of the data from the top 50% of the data. The following steps will compute the median:

Step 1: Arrange the data from smallest to largest.

Step 2: Note whether n (the number of data values) is odd or even.

Step 3: If n is odd, then there is one unique middle data value, and it lies in the $\left(\frac{n+1}{2}\right)$ ranked position.

Step 4: If n is even, then there are two middle data values in the $\left(\frac{n}{2}\right)$ and $\left(\frac{n}{2}+1\right)$ ranked positions. The median is the average of those two middle observations.

EXAMPLE

Going back to the dataset $\{2, 4, 7, 8, 9\}$, the data are already in ascending order. There are five observations, an odd number, so the median is one unique value. It occurs in the $(5 + 1)/2 = 3$ position, the third number, so the median is 7.

Next, suppose the dataset is instead $\{2, 4, 7, 8, 9, 12\}$. Now there are $n = 6$ observations, an even number, so there are two middle values. The ranks of interest are $6/2 = 3$ and $(6/2) + 1 = 4$, and the data values 7 and 8 correspond to the third and fourth ranks, respectively. The median is the average of 7 and 8, which is $(7 + 8)/2 = 7.5$.

Δ

DEFINITION

The **mode** is the data value that occurs the most frequently, or has the highest frequency. To be clear, the mode is <u>not</u> equal to the highest frequency; the mode is the data value corresponding to the highest frequency. The mode can be computed with either quantitative or categorical data.

If there is a tie (two different numbers each occurring the most often), then the dataset has two modes and is said to be **bimodal**.

EXAMPLE

Suppose we open 10 bags of M&Ms and count the number of M&Ms inside each bag. Let's compute the mean, median, and mode by hand. The counts are as follows:

$$32, 34, 38, 29, 36, 32, 35, 31, 34, 32$$

Solution: Since we need to compute the median by hand, let's go ahead and arrange these data in ascending order:

$$29, 31, 32, 32, 32, 34, 34, 35, 36, 38$$

There are ten values, so $n = 10$ and the mean is

$$\bar{x} = \frac{29 + 31 + 32 + 32 + 32 + 34 + 34 + 35 + 36 + 38}{10} = \frac{333}{10} = 33.3$$

The median can be computed using the technique above. Note that $n = 10$ is even, and so we will need to find the two middle values and average them. The ranks of interest are $10/2 = 5$ and $(10/2) + 1 = 6$, or the fifth and sixth ranks. These correspond to 32 and 34, so the median is

$$\text{median} = \frac{32 + 34}{2} = 33$$

If you don't like that method of finding the median, you can also cross out the outermost numbers on the left and right side, two at a time, and work your way in until you arrive at the middle values:

$$\cancel{29}, 31, 32, 32, 32, 34, 34, 35, 36, \cancel{38}$$
$$\cancel{29}, \cancel{31}, 32, 32, 32, 34, 34, 35, \cancel{36}, \cancel{38}$$
$$\cancel{29}, \cancel{31}, \cancel{32}, 32, 32, 34, 34, \cancel{35}, \cancel{36}, \cancel{38}$$
$$\cancel{29}, \cancel{31}, \cancel{32}, \cancel{32}, \boxed{32, 34}, 34, \cancel{35}, \cancel{36}, \cancel{38}$$

In which case, you can find the median once again by averaging the two middle values:

$$\text{median} = \frac{32 + 34}{2} = 33$$

Finally, the mode is the number that occurs the most frequently. Here 32 appears the most often, three times, so the mode is 32 (and not three).

Δ

EXAMPLE
Suppose we now open an eleventh bag and discover that it contains 34 M&Ms. What is the mode now?

Solution: We first list the data (with the extra 34 already added):

$$29, 31, 32, 32, 32, 34, 34, 34, 35, 36, 38$$

This time 32 occurs three times, but 34 also occurs three times, both more than the other counts. We have a tie! There are two modes, 32 and 34, so this dataset is bimodal.

Δ

EXAMPLE
Examining the bar graph from the continent data shown earlier, find the mode.

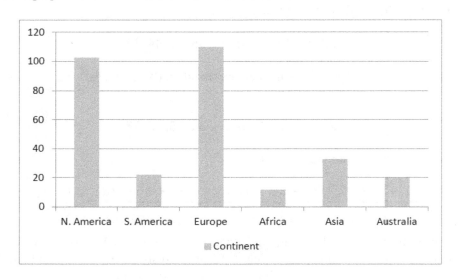

Solution: The mode, by definition, is the number (or category) that occurs the most frequently. Europe has the highest frequency, so the mode is Europe. Note that even though these data are categorical, we can still compute the mode. Again, the mode is not the frequency of the category, but rather the name of the category (Europe).

Δ

EXAMPLE
The following is a list of animals found on a farm:

8 Horses	32 Chickens	2 Dogs	15 Cows	2 Cats

If possible, compute the mean, median, and mode of this dataset.

Solution: At first glance, you may be tempted to say that the data are $8, 32, 2, 15,$ and 2, in which case there are five values, so we can find all three statistics…right? Not so fast! The data are in fact categorical. That means that Horse appears 8 times, Chicken appears 32 times, and so on. In other words, the beginning and end of the dataset look like this (the middle rows have been omitted):

Horse	Horse	Horse	Horse	Horse
Horse	Horse	Horse	Chicken	Chicken
Chicken	Chicken	Chicken	Chicken	Chicken
…	…	…	…	…
Cow	Cow	Cow	Cow	Cow
Cow	Cow	Cow	Cat	Cat

To compute the mean, you would literally add up all animals and divide by the grand total, so you would add Horse + Horse + Horse + …, and hopefully you can see that this is nonsense! Thus, it is not possible to compute the mean, and for the same reason the median. (The official reason is because the data are categorical rather than quantitative.) Remember: do not count your chicks before they hatch!

However, we can compute the mode; it is the category with the highest frequency. That honor goes to Chicken, with the highest frequency of 32. The mode is Chicken.

Δ

Soon we will see the first feature of the TI-84 graphing calculator, which will compute all the necessary numbers in an instant. (Think of the effort needed to compute, say, the median by hand in a large dataset – you would be late home for dinner!)

EXAMPLE
Consider the eBay selling prices data from Section 1.5:

$$210 \quad 225 \quad 232 \quad 235 \quad 225 \quad 225 \quad 199 \quad 210 \quad 228 \quad 223$$

Let's first rearrange this set into ascending order. This is mandatory if we want to compute the median by hand.

$$199 \quad 210 \quad 210 \quad 223 \quad 225 \quad 225 \quad 225 \quad 228 \quad 232 \quad 235$$

The mean is found by adding up all these numbers and dividing by the sample size, here 10, so we have

$$\frac{199 + 210 + 210 + 223 + 225 + 225 + 225 + 228 + 232 + 235}{10} = \frac{2212}{10} = 221.2$$

The median is the middle-most point, but since we have an even number of values, we take the average of the two middle points (the 5th and 6th ones):

$$\require{cancel}$$

~~199~~, 210, 210, 223, 225, 225, 225, 228, 232, ~~235~~
~~199~~, ~~210~~, 210, 223, 225, 225, 225, 228, ~~232~~, ~~235~~
~~199~~, ~~210~~, ~~210~~, 223, 225, 225, 225, ~~228~~, ~~232~~, ~~235~~
~~199~~, ~~210~~, ~~210~~, ~~223~~, $\boxed{225, 225}$, ~~225~~, ~~228~~, ~~232~~, ~~235~~

$$\frac{225 + 225}{2} = 225$$

The mode is the highest occurring number, which is also 225 (it occurs three times, more than any other number).

Δ

ETYMOLOGY

The word mean comes from the Proto-Indo-European *medhyo-*, which meant "middle." In the mathematical context, it was first used circa 1300 to describe a musical tone intermediate between two other tones. The words median and mode come from the Latin *medianus* and *modus*, which meant "of the middle" and "measure," respectively.

Meanwhile, the word average has an interesting origin. It originates from the Arabic عوار (pronounced "awar"), meaning "damage to goods." This word represented a fee that was paid to ship goods. However, it later was used as a term for the financial cost from goods that were damaged or lost at sea. Specifically, in the late 16th century, it referred to how such a financial loss was allocated between the owners of the goods that were damaged and the owners of the vessel transporting the goods. Later, in the mid 18th century, this definition led to the general idea of calculating the mathematical mean.

While we are on the subject of etymology, the word *data* is the plural of *datum*, which is Latin for "that is given." Hence, you would say "The data are collected" and not "The data is collected."

In general, don't worry about the odd/even rules of determining a median, for the graphing calculator will do all the dirty work for us. Here is how we use it to compute the summary statistics.

TI-84 COMMAND: SUMMARY STATISTICS

To find the summary statistics for a dataset, first put them into a list by pressing $\boxed{\text{STAT}}$, choosing Option 1: *Edit ...*, and typing the numbers into the L_1 column.

Next, from the home screen, press $\boxed{\text{STAT}}$, scroll right to CALC, and choose Option 1: $1 - Var\ Stats$. Press $\boxed{\text{2nd}}$ and $\boxed{1}$ to type L_1, and press $\boxed{\text{ENTER}}$. You will see a long list of summary statistics – much easier than computing them by hand! The following list summarizes what they are, and some terms are more important than others.

For this section, the two important figures from this list are $\bar{x}$ (sample mean) and *Med* (median). You will meet most of the others later in this chapter. Note that the mode is not computed; you have to find that value yourself.

$$\overline{x} = \text{sample mean}$$
$$\Sigma x = \text{sum of all data points}$$
$$\Sigma x^2 = \text{sum of all squared data points}$$
$$Sx = \text{sample standard deviation (Section 2.3)}$$
$$\sigma x = \text{population standard deviation (DO NOT USE THIS)}$$
$$n = \text{sample size}$$
$$minX = \text{minimum (Section 2.5)}$$
$$Q_1 = \text{lower quartile (Section 2.5)}$$
$$Med = \text{median}$$
$$Q_3 = \text{upper quartile (Section 2.5)}$$
$$maxX = \text{maximum (Section 2.5)}$$

EXAMPLE

Going back to the M&M example from earlier, here were our counts:

$$32, 34, 38, 29, 36, 32, 35, 31, 34, 32$$

Enter these numbers into the L_1 list on the TI-84. You do not have to arrange the data in ascending order. Next, use the $1 - Var\ Stats$ command, and you will see $\overline{x} = 33.3$ and $Med = 33$, which match what we found by hand earlier.

Δ

DEFINITION

An **outlier** is a data point that is ridiculously far away from the other data points. It is much higher or lower than one would expect.

EXAMPLE

Consider the data $0, 0, 0, 3, 3, 4, 6, 6, 99$. The number 99 is an outlier since it is much higher than the other numbers. (Later in this chapter you will learn two techniques that will test for outliers.)

Δ

The presence of outliers can really upset the mean of a dataset because the mean takes into account all the data points. Therefore, if there is a rather high value, it will pull the average up (and by the same token, an incredibly low number will pull down the mean). Thus, reporting the mean in a dataset with outliers can be deceptive since most points are not like the outliers.

What do we do to correct this dilemma? Luckily, it turns out that the median is resistant to outliers, whereas the mean is sensitive to them. In other words, the median does not change if there is an outlier present. The reason for this is because outliers, if they exist, are always at the tail ends of the dataset, but the median is right in the center. That means that the median never interacts with the outliers.

As a consequence, if there are no outliers, then you can go ahead and use the mean, as usual. However, if outliers are present, it is more appropriate to use the median as the measure of the average rather than the mean since the median will be more representative of the sample, and inferentially, the population.

EXAMPLE

Consider the selling prices of houses in the state of Georgia. We would expect the majority to be between, say, $100,000 and $300,000, but there are also a few million-dollar homes. Obviously few of these happen, so those are upper outliers. If we compute the mean, then these unusually high prices pull up the average, making it no longer truly reflective of the "real" average selling price.

It would make more sense to instead report the median selling price, since this value is guaranteed to be in the center of the dataset and consequently paint a more accurate picture. For instance, it may turn out that the median selling price is $230,000, whereas the mean might have been $600,000! Clearly the median is more reliable in a situation like this since it is located in the main cluster of the data.

Δ

DEFINITION
A data distribution is **symmetric** if it is mound-shaped, or bell-shaped.

The distribution is **skewed left** if when sketched, the left tail is longer than the right tail. This means there are some extreme lower outliers.

The distribution is **skewed right** if when sketched, the right tail is longer than the left tail; therefore there are some extreme upper outliers.

Here are sample sketches of all three distributions above.

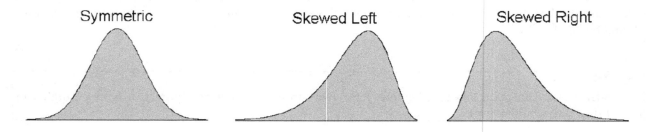

Symmetric   Skewed Left   Skewed Right

Remember: <u>a distribution is skewed in the direction of the longer tail.</u>

EXAMPLE
The ages of residents at a retired home would be skewed left since they would mostly be elderly, but with the occasional younger person staying too. The presence of a few low age values is what makes the left tail longer.

Earthquake magnitudes could be considered skewed right. Usually they are just barely noticeable, if at all (low magnitude), but every once in a great while we will experience a powerful earthquake (high magnitude). These events are rare and therefore extend the right tail.

Δ

ETYMOLOGY
The word symmetric comes from the Greek σύν and μέτρον, which meant "with" and "measure." In contrast, skew comes from the Old French *eschiver*, which meant "eschew." The word outlier is formed from the words "out" and "lie. It was first used circa 1600 to mean a stone that had been removed but left unused.

It turns out that there is a direct connection between skewness and the relationship between the mean and the median. Since the mean is the numerical average and the median the halfway point, it should make sense that for a symmetric distribution, the mean and median are approximately equal.

However, when the distribution is skewed left, the lower outliers pull down the mean, causing the mean to be smaller than the median. Similarly, a distribution that is skewed right has upper outliers that pull up the mean, making the mean higher than the median. We therefore have the following results:

Shape	Outcome
Skewed Left	Mean < Median
Symmetric	Mean = Median
Skewed Right	Mean > Median

This characterization works both ways. That is, given the distribution's shape, we can tell which statistic is larger, but also if we were told that, say, the mean was smaller than the median, then we can immediately conclude that the distribution must have been skewed left. Remember the following points:

1) The table above.
2) The mean is sensitive to outliers, but the median is resistant.
3) When outliers are present, it is better to use the median as the measure of the center.

MNEMONIC
First write "mean" and "median" in that order, alphabetical order. Suppose that the mean is less than the median, or mean < median. Observe that the < symbol looks a little like an L, for Left Skewed. Now suppose that the mean is greater than the median, or mean > median. Observe that the > symbol, when drawn a certain way, looks a little like the top-right piece of an R, for Right Skewed:

EXAMPLE
Consider a sample of people who are members of MENSA, an organization for highly intelligent people (so if you don't know what MENSA is, then you probably don't qualify to join!). We record from each person selected the age at which they first joined. The mean age is 21 and the median age is 28. What shape would you expect this data set to exhibit? Which number would you use as the measure of the center?
Solution: Observe that the mean of 21 is less than the median of 28. If these two numbers were very close together (for instance, 21 and 22), then an argument could be made for symmetry, but here 21 is quite a bit less than 28. When the mean is less than the median, the distribution is therefore skewed left.

This should not come as much of a surprise because although the majority of people would join MENSA as adults, once in a while you might come across a teenager or even a child who qualifies to join. However, these younger ages are obviously more rare than "adult ages," which means we might have some lower outliers, suggesting a longer left tail, or a distribution that is skewed left.

Thus, when it comes to using a number as a measure of the center of this distribution, it would be best to use the median of 28.

Δ

EXAMPLE
Suppose we are studying the lengths of earthworms. We know the mean is 120 millimeters and that the

distribution is symmetric. What is the median?

Solution: Since the distribution is symmetric, the mean and median are approximately the same. Since the mean is 120 mm, the median is approximately 120 mm also.

Δ

Before moving on, we need to address the question: when is the mode ever used? While it is interesting to know what response is recorded the most often, with numerical data the mean and median are generally of more interest, although it is certainly possible to compute the mode.

However, the mode is far more useful for categorical data because you cannot compute a numerical mean out of physical attributes. In fact, the mode is the only one of the above statistics that can be computed, given categorical data. For instance, with the continent data from Chapter 1, the mode would be Europe since that category has the highest frequency.

EXAMPLE
Given the following graphs, match them with the correct summary statistics.

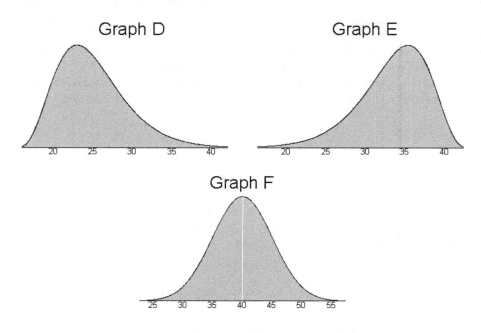

Dataset	Mean	Median	Graph
A	40	40	
B	29	34	
C	31	25	

Solution: Starting with the easy one, notice that Dataset A has equal mean and median, so it must be symmetric. The only symmetric graph is Graph F.

Dataset B has a mean less than the median. That means that we are looking for a left-skewed diagram, and so we pick Graph E.

Dataset C has a mean greater than the median, so we need a right-skewed diagram. The only right-skewed diagram is Graph D.

Dataset	Mean	Median	Graph
A	40	40	F
B	29	34	E
C	31	25	D

Δ

Section 2.2 – Computing Mean and Median in a Frequency Table

We have seen how to compute the mean and median on a graphing calculator, but sometimes the data are presented in a frequency table. In which case, there is a process to compute the mean and median given such a table. Here is an example of how this works.

Suppose 201 British people are surveyed and asked how many cups of tea they drink per day. The results are as follows.

Cups of Tea	Frequency
1	30
2	102
3	36
4	33
Total	201

Before we go further, stop and remember this – whatever the mean and median are, they have to be between 1 and 4, no less or higher (so if you end up with an average of, say, 50.25, you definitely went wrong somewhere). Don't let the frequency column confuse you; that column just tells you how many times the numbers 1, 2, 3, and 4 appear.

Here is how we compute the mean: we multiply each pair of numbers in all rows. In other words, we compute 1×30, and then 2×102, and so on, then add up the results. Finally, we divide by the sample size to turn it into an average.

$$\overline{x} = \frac{1 \times 30 + 2 \times 102 + 3 \times 36 + 4 \times 33}{201} = \frac{474}{201} = 2.35821$$

To get the median, notice the data are in ascending order, and we need to find the halfway point. Half of 201 is 100.5, so (as an approximation) we need to find where subject #101 is located. The median will be the number of cups of tea (and not the frequency).

Is the median in row 1? Well, we need 101 subjects, but we only come up to 30, so we have not yet covered 101. The median is therefore not 1.

After row 2, we have covered 30 + 102 = 132 subjects, so we have now past subject #101. The median is therefore 2.

By the way, the mode is the number that occurs the most frequently in the table. The response 2 occurs 102 times, more than 1, 3, and 4 occur, and so the mode is 2 (and not 102).

Next, suppose we move 20 of the subjects in row 1 into row 4. That is, the sample size is still 201, but some subjects have changed location in the table (20 subjects that had previously recorded one cup of tea now claim four). The new table looks like this:

Cups of Tea	Frequency
1	10
2	102
3	36
4	53
Total	201

Let's re-compute the mean and median. The updated mean is

$$\overline{x} = \frac{1\times10 + 2\times102 + 3\times36 + 4\times53}{201} = \frac{534}{201} = 2.65672$$

The mean has, of course, increased. What about the median? The median will still be around subject #101, and we need to find in which row that falls. Is the median in row 1? We need 101 subjects, but we only come up to 10, so we have not yet covered 101. The median is therefore not 1.

After row 2, we have covered $10 + 102 = 112$ subjects, so we have now past #101. The median is therefore 2 … and it has not changed even though we manipulated the tail ends of the dataset!

Note that if we instead moved around some data in the center, then there is a good chance the median could change, simply because the center of the ordered data has been meddled with. The point is that if extreme tail-end data are changed, that is when the median likely stays the same.

Section 2.3 – Measures of Spread

We have discussed in considerable detail measures of central tendency of datasets. Another item of interest is how much the data are spread out, as this gives us some clues to the overall shape of a distribution. First, here is a simple definition that is just the difference between the smallest and largest points.

DEFINITION

The **range** is the difference between the largest and the smallest data values. It is computed as

Range = Maximum Value − Minimum Value

We can also talk about deviations from the mean.

DEFINITION

A **deviation from the mean** is the difference between a given data value x_i and the mean $\overline{x}$. Given a specific data value, the deviation is computed as

$$x_i - \overline{x}$$

For example, consider the data $\{2, 6, 7, 9, 11\}$. First, the mean is

$$\overline{x} = \frac{2 + 6 + 7 + 9 + 11}{5} = \frac{35}{5} = 7$$

The range is the highest value minus the lowest value, so

$$\text{range} = 11 - 2 = 9$$

There are five data points (call them x_1, x_2, x_3, x_4, and x_5), so there are a total of five deviations, one per data value. The deviation for the first value of 2 is $2 - 7 = -5$. Repeating these differences for the other values, we have

$$x_1 - \overline{x} = 2 - 7 = -5$$
$$x_2 - \overline{x} = 6 - 7 = -1$$
$$x_3 - \overline{x} = 7 - 7 = 0$$
$$x_4 - \overline{x} = 9 - 7 = 2$$
$$x_5 - \overline{x} = 11 - 7 = 4$$

We can also draw these conclusions:

1) If the data point has a negative deviation, it is below the mean (for instance, 2 is lower than the mean of 7).
2) If the has a zero deviation, it is exactly equal to the mean (for instance, 7 happens to be equal to the mean of 7).
3) If the data point has a positive deviation, it is above the mean (for instance, 9 is higher than the mean of 7).

Computing the deviations brings us to the next definition.

DEFINITION

The **sample variance** is a measure of how spread apart the data values are. The higher the variance, the more the data are spread apart. The lower the variance, the closer together the data. To compute it, you square all the individual deviations, add them, and divide by $n - 1$. Sample variance is denoted by s^2 (pronounced s-squared), and the formula is

$$s^2 = \frac{\sum (x_i - \overline{x})^2}{n - 1}$$

In an introductory statistics class, we will usually be more concerned with standard deviation because it is easier to interpret visually.

DEFINITION

The **sample standard deviation** is also a measure of how spread apart the data values are. The higher the standard deviation, the more the data are spread apart. The lower the standard deviation, the closer together the data. As we shall see, standard deviation is easier to see on a graph of data than variance is, which is why we will focus on it instead.

To compute it, you square all the individual deviations, add them, divide by $n - 1$, and then finally take the positive square root. Sample standard deviation is denoted by s, and the formula is

$$s = \sqrt{\frac{\sum(x_i - \overline{x})^2}{n - 1}}$$

We note the fact that s is the positive square root of s^2 because in a regular algebra class, when you take the square root of a number, you usually write "$\pm$" next to it to indicate a positive and negative answer. However, standard deviation is always a nonnegative value, so we will always take the positive square root.

ETYMOLOGY

The words variance and deviation come from the Latin *variare* and *deviare*, which meant "to change" and "to turn aside," respectively.

EXAMPLE

Going back to the dataset $\{2, 6, 7, 9, 11\}$, the mean is $\overline{x} = 7$. Here are the individual deviations again:

$$x_1 - \overline{x} = 2 - 7 = -5$$
$$x_2 - \overline{x} = 6 - 7 = -1$$
$$x_3 - \overline{x} = 7 - 7 = 0$$
$$x_4 - \overline{x} = 9 - 7 = 2$$
$$x_5 - \overline{x} = 11 - 7 = 4$$

To compute sample standard deviation, we square each deviation, add them, divide by $n - 1$, and finally square root the result. We are going to explicitly list each step, so you have a good idea of how to do this by hand. (My apologies – the next two minutes are not going to be particularly enjoyable!) First, let's square each deviation:

$$(x_1 - \overline{x})^2 = (2 - 7)^2 = (-5)^2 = 25$$
$$(x_2 - \overline{x})^2 = (6 - 7)^2 = (-1)^2 = 1$$
$$(x_3 - \overline{x})^2 = (7 - 7)^2 = 0^2 = 0$$
$$(x_4 - \overline{x})^2 = (9 - 7)^2 = 2^2 = 4$$
$$(x_5 - \overline{x})^2 = (11 - 7)^2 = 4^2 = 16$$

We then add all the squared deviations and divide by $n - 1$. Since there are five data values, $n - 1 = 5 - 1 = 4$.

$$\frac{\sum(x_i - \overline{x})^2}{n - 1} = \frac{25 + 1 + 0 + 4 + 16}{4} = \frac{46}{4} = 11.5$$

Finally, standard deviation is equal to the square root of the result above, so

$$s = \sqrt{\frac{\Sigma(x_i - \overline{x})^2}{n - 1}} = \sqrt{11.5} = 3.39116$$

Δ

The good news is that the graphing calculator will easily compute standard deviation for us, so we do not have to go through this agony each time. It is still helpful, though, to understand the mechanics of how the formula works.

As stated earlier, the higher the variance and standard deviation, the more the data values are spread apart. The lower the variance and standard deviation, the less they are spread apart.

EXAMPLE
Suppose five students take Test A and five more students take Test B, and the scores are as follows:

Test A:	15	57	81	89	96
Test B:	74	78	79	83	84

Which set of test scores has a larger standard deviation and why?

Solution: We could compute the two different standard deviations, but we do not need to. The Test B scores are not very spread out since the scores only range from 74 to 84. In contrast, the Test A scores are a lot more spread out, since they range from 15 to 96. That means that Test A has a larger standard deviation. (If you bother to compute the standard deviations, you will find that Test A's is 32.87552 and Test B's is 4.03733. However, you can just make the above argument to avoid computing them.)

Δ

Recall that we can denote the mean by two different symbols depending on whether we are talking about the population mean (μ) or the sample mean ($\overline{x}$). The same is true for the standard deviation.

NOTATION
The symbol for the population standard deviation is σ (pronounced "sigma," a lowercase Greek letter, not to be confused with Σ, the uppercase Greek letter for "sigma").
The symbol for the sample standard deviation is s (I do believe you know how to pronounce this!)

MNEMONIC
Note that you generally use Greek letters for population parameters (μ for mean and σ for standard deviation) and Latin letters for sample statistics ($\overline{x}$ for mean and s for standard deviation). To remember this, you usually don't know much about the population, so it's all Greek to you! (The only exception we have seen so far is with proportions, where we use p for the population and $\hat{p}$ for the sample.)

Whenever we calculate standard deviation using the graphing calculator, we are calculating the sample standard deviation, s.

TI-84 COMMAND: SAMPLE STANDARD DEVIATION
To find the standard deviation for a dataset, first put them into a list by pressing $\boxed{\text{STAT}}$, choosing Option 1: *Edit* ..., and typing in the numbers into the L_1 column.

Next, from the home screen, press $\boxed{\text{STAT}}$, scroll right to CALC, and choose Option 1: $1 - Var\ Stats$. Press $\boxed{\text{2nd}}$ and $\boxed{1}$ to type L_1, and press $\boxed{\text{ENTER}}$. You will see a long list of summary statistics just as we saw earlier. The fourth statistic listed is Sx, this is the sample standard deviation you need.

Be aware that the fifth statistic listed is σx. This can best be described as the standard deviation assuming that the list entered is the whole population instead of just a sample. DO NOT USE THIS NUMBER – USE Sx INSTEAD!

EXAMPLE

Going back to the data $\{2, 6, 7, 9, 11\}$, we already computed $s = 3.39116$. Entering these five numbers into the L_1 list on the TI-84 and doing the $1 - V\square r\ Stats$ command, we discover that $Sx = 3.391164992$, which matches what we found but with more decimals provided. (Again, do not pick σx!)

$$\Delta$$

Now that we have seen how to compute standard deviation, we next learn what it means graphically. As mentioned earlier, it is a measure of how little or how much the data are spread out. Generally speaking, the closer all the data points are together, the smaller the standard deviation. In contrast, when the data are more spread out, the standard deviation increases, as in the following graphs:

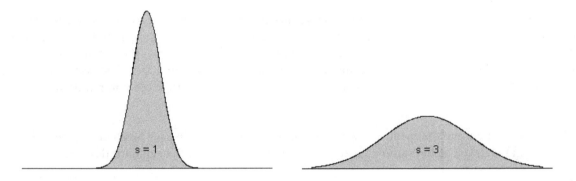

EXAMPLE

Here is an interesting example when we are given two graphs with no numbers given, and yet we need to deduce which graph has the higher spread. Each square represents some data value (so five per graph).

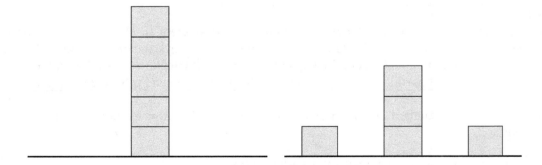

On the left graph, all five points are equal, so they all have zero deviation from the mean. Thus, the left graph has no spread. This represents the extreme case when $s = 0$; that indicates that all data values are equal to one another. On the right, the mean is clearly in the center, so we have two points that are some distance away from the mean. Let's mark them with lines.

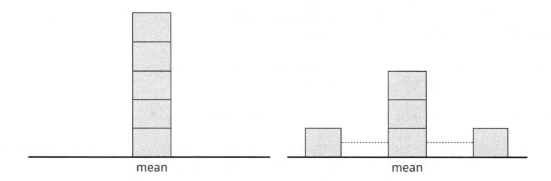

Thus, the right graph has a higher standard deviation.

Here is another example with a new dataset of five points, along with the same graph we just saw.

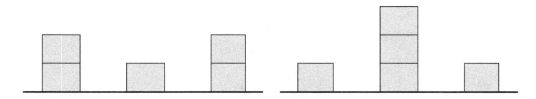

For the left graph, the mean is still in the center. This time we have four squares that are some distance away, in comparison with the right graph with only two squares. This tells us that the left graph must have the higher standard deviation.

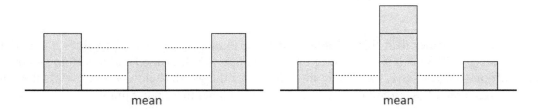

Δ

Section 2.4 – The Empirical Rule

We now introduce a useful rule that is used to find specific percentages of data values. The twist is that this rule only works for bell-shaped (normal) distributions.

DEFINITION

If a distribution is bell-shaped (meaning it is symmetric and looks a bit like an upside-down bell in shape), it is possible to approximate the percentage of data that lie within one, two, and three standard deviations on either side of the mean. We use the **Empirical Rule** to approximate these percentages. The rule goes like this:

Approximately 68% of the data values lie within one standard deviation of the mean. This means that about 68% of the data fall between $\mu - \sigma$ and $\mu + \sigma$.

Approximately 95% of the data values lie within two standard deviations of the mean. This means that about 95% of the data fall between $\mu - 2\sigma$ and $\mu + 2\sigma$.

Approximately 99.7% of the data values lie within three standard deviations of the mean. This means that about 99.7% of the data fall between $\mu - 3\sigma$ and $\mu + 3\sigma$.

Let's repeat the Empirical Rule in words. Provided the data are bell-shaped...

1) Approximately 68% of the data will lie within 1 standard deviation of the mean (on both sides).
2) Approximately 95% of the data will lie within 2 standard deviations of the mean.
3) Approximately 99.7% of the data can be expected to lie within 3 standard deviations of the mean.

Here are some helpful graphs illustrating what is going on here. First, if μ is the mean and σ is the standard deviation, then going out one standard deviation on both sides means we find the values $\mu - \sigma$ and $\mu + \sigma$. The Empirical Rule tells us that about 68% of the data will fall between those two limits.

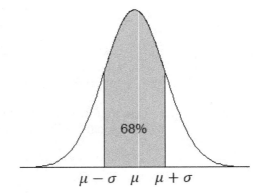

However, we can go further than this. If 68% of the distribution is between the values $\mu - \sigma$ and $\mu + \sigma$, then $100\% - 68\% = 32\%$ is left over. Since the distribution is bell-shaped and therefore symmetric, that means that half of 32%, or 16%, must be in the left area of the graph (below $\mu - \sigma$), while the remaining 16% is in the right area of the graph (above $\mu + \sigma$). So let's label that on the graph:

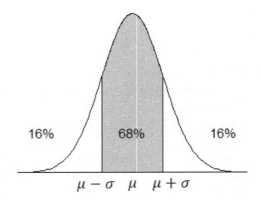

Next, if we go out two standard deviations on both sides, that means we find the values $\mu - 2\sigma$ and $\mu + 2\sigma$. The Empirical Rule tells us that about 95% of the data will fall between those two limits.

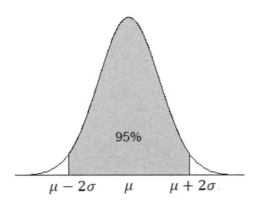

If 95% of the distribution is between the values $\mu - 2\sigma$ and $\mu + 2\sigma$, then $100\% - 95\% = 5\%$ is left over. That means that half of 5%, or 2.5%, must be in the left area of the graph (below $\mu - 2\sigma$), while the remaining 2.5% is in the right area of the graph (above $\mu + 2\sigma$).

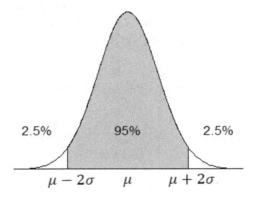

Finally, if we go out three standard deviations on both sides, that means we find the values $\mu - 3\sigma$ and $\mu + 3\sigma$. The Empirical Rule tells us that about 99.7% of the data will fall between those two limits.

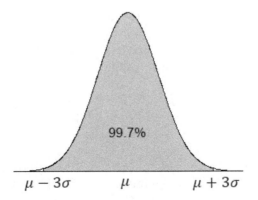

If 99.7% of the distribution is between the values $\mu - 3\sigma$ and $\mu + 3\sigma$, then $100\% - 99.7\% = 0.3\%$ is left over. That means that half of 0.3%, or 0.15%, must be in the left area of the graph (below $\mu - 3\sigma$), while the remaining 0.15% is in the right area of the graph (above $\mu + 3\sigma$).

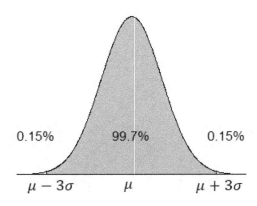

Some examples are definitely in order here!

EXAMPLE

The weight of an adult zebra is bell-shaped with mean 700 pounds and standard deviation 70 pounds. Assuming these population parameters, find the lower and upper limits between which we have approximately 68%, 95%, and 99.7% of all zebra weights.

Solution: First, $\mu = 700$ and $\sigma = 70$. (We use the Greek letters since we are talking about the population, so these are parameters.) About 68% of zebra weights lie within one deviation of the mean, so we need to compute $\mu - \sigma$ and $\mu + \sigma$:

$$(\mu - \sigma, \mu + \sigma) = (700 - 70, 700 + 70)$$
$$= (630, 770)$$

This means that approximately 68% of all adult zebras have a weight between 630 pounds and 770 pounds. Next, going out two deviations from the mean results in about 95% of the zebra weights:

$$(\mu - 2\sigma, \mu + 2\sigma) = (700 - 2 \times 70, 700 + 2 \times 70)$$
$$= (700 - 140, 700 + 140)$$
$$= (560, 840)$$

Thus, approximately 95% of all adult zebras have a weight between 560 pounds and 840 pounds. Finally, going out three deviations from the mean results in about 99.7% of the zebra weights:

$$(\mu - 3\sigma, \mu + 3\sigma) = (700 - 3 \times 70, 700 + 3 \times 70)$$
$$= (700 - 210, 700 + 210)$$
$$= (490, 910)$$

About 99.7% of all adult zebras have a weight between 490 pounds and 910 pounds. Consequently, would it be unusual to have an adult zebra weighing more than 910 pounds? Since this falls in the region above 910 (remember, that small area is only 0.15% of all weights!), the answer is most certainly yes.

The following bell curve illustrates where the mean and the one, two, and three deviation cutoffs fall.

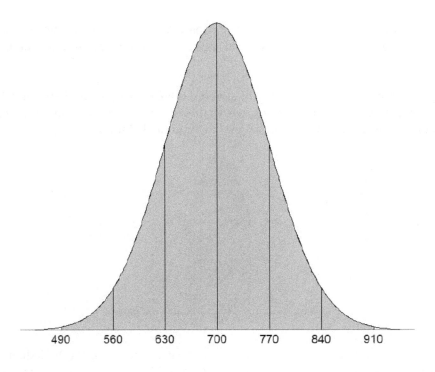

490   560   630   700   770   840   910

Δ

EXAMPLE

In a certain country, the heights of men are bell-shaped with a mean of 65 inches and a standard deviation of 4 inches.

A) Approximately what percentage of men have a height between 57 inches and 73 inches?
B) Approximately what percentage of men have a height between 65 inches and 69 inches?
C) Approximately what percentage of men have a height between 57 inches and 77 inches?

Solution: This question turns up the heat a little and requires us to think carefully. First, we have $\mu = 65$ and $\sigma = 4$. So that we have them available, let's go ahead and compute the one, two, and three deviation intervals:

$$(\mu - \sigma, \mu + \sigma) = (65 - 4, 65 + 4)$$
$$= (61, 69)$$

$$(\mu - 2\sigma, \mu + 2\sigma) = (65 - 2 \times 4, 65 + 2 \times 4)$$
$$= (65 - 8, 65 + 8)$$
$$= (57, 73)$$

$$(\mu - 3\sigma, \mu + 3\sigma) = (65 - 3 \times 4, 65 + 3 \times 4)$$
$$= (65 - 12, 65 + 12)$$
$$= (53, 77)$$

These intervals tell us the following:

1) About 68% of all male heights in this country fall between 61 and 69 inches.
2) About 95% of all male heights in this country fall between 57 and 73 inches.
3) About 99.7% of all male heights in this country fall between 53 and 77 inches.

With all that said, let's turn back to the questions. For part A, having a height between 57 and 73 inches happens to correspond to our two-deviation interval, and so about 95% of all male heights in this country fall between 57 and 73 inches.

Matters start to get trickier in part B. We know that about 68% of heights fall between 61 and 69, but the question is asking for between 65 and 69. As we shall see later in these notes, drawing sketches will GREATLY help in solving certain problems, so let's get into the habit now:

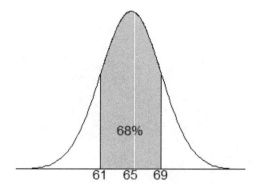

Note that the mean of 65 falls in the middle of the curve (it has to since the bell-shaped distribution is symmetric). That means that the mean evenly cuts the 68% middle region into two regions of 34% each. In other words, 34% of heights fall between 61 and 65, while the remaining 34% fall between 65 and 69, as in the updated sketch:

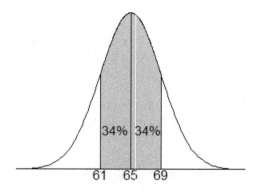

Finally, we can answer part B. About 34% of all male heights in this country fall between 65 and 69 inches.

Part C is also a mindbender. We are concerned with the limits 57 and 77, but notice that these correspond to the lower limit of the 95% interval and the upper limit of the 99.7% interval. What should we do? Again, make sketches! Here are sketches of the 95% region (with 2.5% on both sides) and the 99.7% region (with 0.15% on both sides).

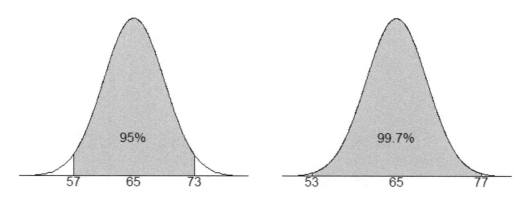

Now let's make a sketch of what we wish to find. We need the percentage between 57 and 77:

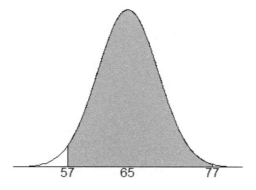

Notice that our graph can be split into three regions: the left, the middle (the one we want), and the right. All three percentages must add to 100%, and so if we can figure out the percentage of heights that fall in the left and right sides, we can get the middle by subtraction. For the left side, we determined that 2.5% fall below 57, so let's update our sketch with that information.

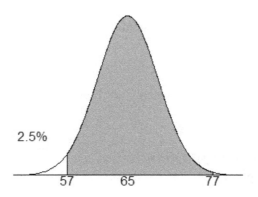

Next, for the right side, we determined that 0.15% fall above 77, so let's update our sketch again:

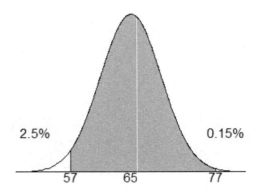

If the left region is 2.5% and the right region is 0.15%, then that means that the middle region must be equal to

$$100\% - 2.5\% - 0.15\% = 97.35\%$$

Our final sketch looks like this:

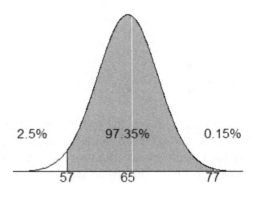

The answer to part C is that about 97.35% of all male heights in this country fall between 57 and 77 inches.

$$\Delta$$

Here is a catchphrase you will be hearing periodically in these notes: "When in doubt, draw it out!"

Section 2.5 – Position of Values in Quantitative Data

This section focuses on finding percentiles and using them to test for outliers.

DEFINITION

The pth **percentile** is the value such that $p\%$ of all the observations in the dataset fall below or at that value. This also means that the other $(100 - p)\%$ of the observations in the dataset fall above that value.

A data value's percentile tells you approximately what percentage of the data is less than that value. For example, if a value X lies at the 30th percentile, then approximately 30% of the data values are less than that value, and approximately 70% of the data values are higher than that value, as in the following sketch.

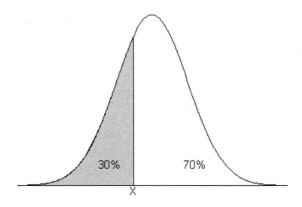

EXAMPLE

If Matt graduated at the 78th percentile in a class of 876, approximately how many students ranked below Matt?

Solution: Since Matt is the 78th percentile, by definition 78% of the 876 students ranked below him. We compute 78% of 876:

$$876 \times 0.78 = 683.28$$

Rounding to the nearest whole number, approximately 683 students ranked below Matt.

Δ

EXAMPLE

Suppose Sarah graduated at the 89th percentile in a class of 500. Approximately how many students ranked above Sarah?

Solution: First, we want to find where the 89th percentile is, which means we should find how many students scored below the 89th percentile. By definition, this would be 89% of 500, and so

$$500 \times 0.89 = 445$$

However, be careful, because the question is asking for the number of students scoring *above* Sarah, whereas a percentile measures the number of students *below*. There are approximately 445 students that rank below Katie, and so there are approximately 55 students that rank above Katie. This was computed as

$$500 - 445 = 55$$

Δ

EXAMPLE

Let's make things a little tougher, eh? Katie graduated 28th from the top in a class of 239. What is her percentile?

Solution: This question wants to know what the percentile is for Katie. That means that, given that Katie is at the pth percentile, what is p (the whole number). It would first help to find out what percentage of students rank below her, as that is the definition of a percentile.

Given that Katie graduated 28th from the top of 239 students, we first compute $239 - 28 = 211$. This means that given 239 students, if Katie is number 28, then 211 students rank below her.

Now, the question is what percentage of 239 is 211? We compute

$$\frac{211}{239} = 0.88285$$

This translates into 88.285%, or 88% when rounded to the nearest whole number. Remember we are looking for the percentile itself, so this means that the answer is 88.

Δ

DEFINITION

The **quartiles** are specific percentiles that are useful. Each dataset has three quartiles of interest that we can use for further analysis.

The **first quartile (Q_1)** is the value such that 25% of the data are smaller than Q_1 (which means that 75% are larger). This is the 25th percentile and is also called the **lower quartile**.

The **second quartile (Q_2)** is the value such that 50% of the data are smaller than Q_2 (which means that 50% are larger). This is the 50th percentile and also the median.

The **third quartile (Q_3)** is the value such that 75% of the data are smaller than Q_3 (which means that 25% are larger). This is the 75th percentile and is also called the **upper quartile**.

Although their definitions are self-explanatory, let's throw in two more that we need for creating plots.

DEFINITION

The **maximum (Max)** is the data value that is the largest in the dataset, and the **minimum (Min)** is the data value that is the smallest in the dataset.

ETYMOLOGY

The words minimum and maximum come from the Latin *minimus* and *magnus*, which meant "smallest" and "large," respectively. Due to the Latin declensions of these words, the English plurals are minima and maxima. The word quartile comes from the Latin *quartus*, which meant "fourth."

The following is an example of a **box-plot** with the percentage cutoffs. (It is also sometimes called a **box-and-whisker** plot.) The box is drawn from the lower quartile to the upper quartile, with a vertical line at the median. Next, the "whiskers" are drawn from the lower quartile to the minimum and from the upper quartile to the maximum (unless there are outliers, which we will get to in a little bit).

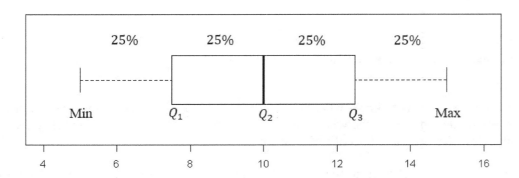

Again, note that Q_1 is the same as the 25th percentile, Q_2 is the same as the median, and Q_3 is the same as the 75th percentile.

The following procedure describes how to find the quartiles by hand. But don't worry – the TI-84 will compute them faster, and you will see how to do that next!

FINDING QUARTILES
The quartiles can be found by hand using the following steps.

Step 1: Arrange the data in order from smallest to greatest.
Step 2: Find the median using earlier techniques. This is Q_2.
Step 3: Look at the lower half of the observations. The median of this set of observations is the 25th percentile, Q_1.
Step 4: Look at the upper half of the observations. The median of this set of observations is the 75th percentile, Q_3.

Note that this procedure works assuming there is an even number of data points. If there is an odd number, slightly different techniques may be used, but don't worry about that – using the graphing calculator is much easier!

TI-84 COMMAND: FINDING QUARTILES
To find the quartiles for a dataset, first put them into a list by pressing STAT, choosing Option 1: *Edit* ..., and typing in the numbers into the L_1 column.

Next, from the home screen, press STAT, scroll right to CALC, and choose Option 1: $1 - Var\ Stats$. Press 2nd and 1 to type L_1, and press ENTER. Now scroll down to the last few stats, and you will see the minimum ($minX$), lower quartile (Q_1), median (Med), upper quartile (Q_3), and maximum ($maxX$).

EXAMPLE
The following data represent the hemoglobin (in grams per deciliter) for 20 randomly selected dogs. Determine the minimum, the maximum, and the quartiles.

5.2	7.7	7.8	8.8	8.9
9.3	9.3	9.5	9.6	9.9
10.0	10.1	10.2	10.6	10.6
11.2	11.6	12.9	13.0	13.1

Solution: We first find the answers by hand for illustration purposes, and then we repeat them with the TI-84. First, notice that the data have already been arranged in ascending order. The minimum is 5.2 and the maximum is 13.1.

Since there are $n = 20$ observations, an even number, the median is an average of the 10th and 11th data points, so

$$Median = \frac{9.9 + 10.0}{2} = 9.95$$

To find the lower quartile, we treat the lower half of the data (the first 10 values) as its own dataset.

5.2	7.7	7.8	8.8	8.9
9.3	9.3	9.5	9.6	9.9

The median of these ten numbers occurs at the average of the 5th and 6th data points, so

$$Q_1 = \frac{8.9 + 9.3}{2} = 9.1$$

To find the upper quartile, we treat the upper half of the data (the last 10 values) as its own dataset.

10.0	10.1	10.2	10.6	10.6
11.2	11.6	12.9	13.0	13.1

The median of these ten numbers occurs at the average of the 5th and 6th data points, so

$$Q_3 = \frac{10.6 + 11.2}{2} = 10.9$$

Next, on the TI-84, type the twenty numbers into the L_1 list. Press $\boxed{\text{STAT}}$, scroll right to CALC, and choose Option 1: $1 - Var\ Stats$. The calculator gives the same values as we found by hand:

$$minX = 5.2$$
$$Q_1 = 9.1$$
$$Med = 9.95$$
$$Q_3 = 10.9$$
$$maxX = 13.1$$

Δ

Repeating the definition from earlier, an outlier is an extreme observation that occurs due to errors in measuring the variable, or data entry, or from errors in sampling. An outlier might also be a genuinely correct value that simply occurs much lower or higher than expected for specific reasons. It is now time to learn the first of two methods that tests for the presence of outliers in a dataset.

OUTLIER TEST 1: USING BOX-PLOTS

The following steps describe how to use a box-plot to check for the presence of outliers in a dataset.

Step 1: Determine the lower and upper quartiles (Q_1 and Q_3) of the dataset.
Step 2: Compute the **interquartile range (IQR)**, which is the difference between the upper and lower quartiles:

$$IQR = Q_3 - Q_1$$

Step 3: Compute the lower threshold $Q_1 - (1.5 \times IQR)$. If a data value is less than this lower threshold, it is a potential outlier.
Step 4: Compute the upper threshold $Q_3 + (1.5 \times IQR)$. If a data value is greater than this upper threshold, it is a potential outlier.

EXAMPLE
The following data represent the hemoglobin (in grams per deciliter) for 20 randomly selected dogs. Test to see if there are any potential outliers.

5.2	7.7	7.8	8.8	8.9
9.3	9.3	9.5	9.6	9.9
10.0	10.1	10.2	10.6	10.6
11.2	11.6	12.9	13.0	13.1

Solution: In the previous example, we had determined that $Q_1 = 9.1$ and $Q_3 = 10.9$. This means that the interquartile range is

$$IQR = Q_3 - Q_1 = 10.9 - 9.1 = 1.8$$

The lower and upper thresholds are

$$\text{Lower Threshold} = Q_1 - (1.5 \times IQR) = 9.1 - (1.5 \times 1.8) = 6.4$$
$$\text{Upper Threshold} = Q_3 + (1.5 \times IQR) = 10.9 + (1.5 \times 1.8) = 13.6$$

Thus, if there are any data points below 6.4 or above 13.6, they are potential outliers. Are there any values below 6.4? The only point is 5.2, so this is a potential outlier on the lower side. Are there any values above 13.6? Since the highest point is 13.1, which is not above the upper threshold, there are no upper outliers.

Δ

DRAWING A BOX-PLOT

The **five-number summary** refers to the minimum, lower quartile, median, upper quartile, and maximum. Having found these numbers, a box-plot is drawn using the following steps.

Step 1: Draw a box starting at Q_1 and ending at Q_3.
Step 2: Inside the box, draw a vertical line at the median. It will not necessarily be right in the middle of the box.
Step 3: Draw a line from Q_1 to the smallest data point that is not an outlier, and draw a small vertical line at that point.
Step 4: Draw a line from Q_3 to the largest data point that is not an outlier, and draw a small vertical line at that point.
Step 5: If there are any data points that are outliers, mark them with an asterisk (∗).
Step 6: This step is optional, but draw using dashed lines the lower and upper thresholds that denote where outliers would fall. This is simply a visual guide and is not required.

EXAMPLE

Using the previous example with hemoglobin in dogs, we had

$$\text{Min} = 5.2 \qquad Q_1 = 9.1 \qquad \text{Median} = 9.95 \qquad Q_3 = 10.9 \qquad \text{Max} = 13.1$$

We also determined that the lowest value, 5.2, was a potential lower outlier. This means that the lowest observation that is not an outlier is 7.7. That means that the box-plot looks like this:

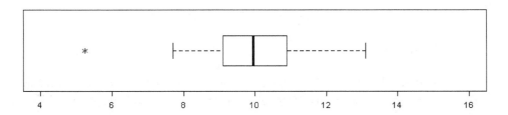

If we choose to include the thresholds as visual guides, then the box-plot looks like this:

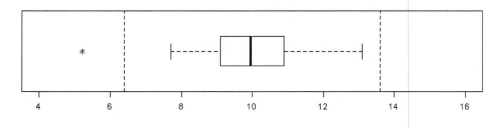

Δ

EXAMPLE
The following table shows the average distance from each planet to the sun. Even though their distance varies depending where they are in their orbits, the numbers below represent the average distance away (in astronomical units, or AUs). One AU is equal to the average distance from the Earth to the sun (approximately 93 million miles). Even though Pluto is arguably no longer a planet (depending who you ask), it is still included in the chart.[1] Draw a box-plot of the distances, and test to see if there are any outliers in this dataset.

Planet	Average Distance to Sun (in AU)
Mercury	0.387
Venus	0.722
Earth	1
Mars	1.52
Jupiter	5.2
Saturn	9.58
Uranus	19.2
Neptune	30.1
Pluto	39.5

Solution: Using the $1 - Var\ Stats$ command on the TI-84, the five-number summary is

$$minX = 0.387$$
$$Q_1 = 0.861$$
$$Med = 5.2$$
$$Q_3 = 24.65$$
$$maxX = 39.5$$

This means that the interquartile range is

$$IQR = Q_3 - Q_1 = 24.65 - 0.861 = 23.789$$

The lower and upper thresholds are

$$\text{Lower Threshold} = Q_1 - (1.5 \times IQR) = 0.861 - (1.5 \times 23.789) = -34.8225$$
$$\text{Upper Threshold} = Q_3 + (1.5 \times IQR) = 24.65 + (1.5 \times 23.789) = 60.3335$$

This means that if there are any data points below −34.8225 or above 60.3335, they are potential outliers. Are there any values below −34.8225? The lowest point is 0.387, which is not below the lower threshold, so there are no lower outliers. Are there any values above 60.3335? Since the highest point is 39.5, which is not above the upper threshold, there are no upper outliers either.

The box-plot therefore looks like this:

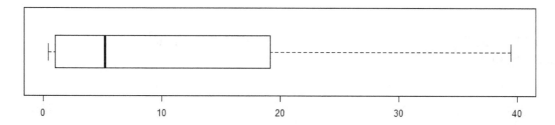

If we choose to include the thresholds as visual guides, then the box-plot looks like this:

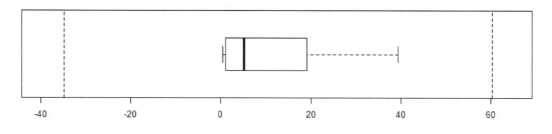

Δ

The final note in this section is that generally we can roughly guess the shape of the distribution based on the shape of the box-plot.

DISTRIBUTION SHAPE BASED ON BOX-PLOT

If the median is near the center of the box and the left and right outer lines are approximately equal in length, the distribution is approximately symmetric.

If the median is to the right of the center of the box, or the left outer line is much longer than the right outer line, the distribution is skewed left.

If the median is to the left of the center of the box, or the right outer line is much longer than the left outer line, the distribution is skewed right.

Of course, if the skewed distribution features some lower or upper outliers, then we should instead consider the distance from the edge of the box to the last outlier rather than just the outer line alone.

As you can imagine, if we have box plots from two different datasets side by side, we can easily compare their shapes to guess which one is more skewed.

EXAMPLE
Look at the box-plots from the previous two examples. The first box-plot features a lower outlier. Also notice that the median is somewhat to the right of the center of the box. These features suggest that the hemoglobin distribution is skewed left.

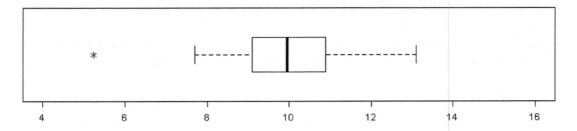

The second box-plot has no outliers, but observe that the right line is much longer than the left line. This distribution is obviously skewed right.

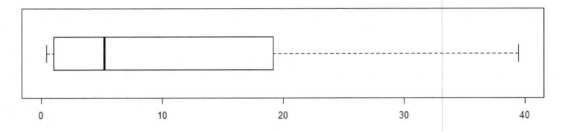

The following box-plot is an example of one representing an approximately symmetric distribution.

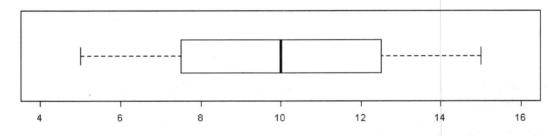

Δ

Section 2.6 – Z-Scores

This final section discusses a new measure of how far away from the mean a data point falls.

DEFINITION

A data value's **Z-score** is the position that value has relative to the mean, measured in standard deviations. Put another way, the Z-score is the number of standard deviations the data value is above or below the mean. It is computed as

$$Z = \frac{\text{(data value)} - \text{(mean)}}{\text{standard deviation}}$$

The notation for the mean and standard deviation changes depending whether we are working with a sample or a population, but it always comes down to the above general formula. If we are working with a sample, the Z-score formula is

$$Z = \frac{x - \bar{x}}{s}$$

If we are working with a population, the Z-score formula is

$$Z = \frac{x - \mu}{\sigma}$$

If the Z-score is positive, then the value is above the mean.
If the Z-score is equal to 0, then the value is equal to the mean.
If the Z-score is negative, then the value is below the mean.

EXAMPLE

From samples taken from a certain region, the average $20 - 29$ year-old man is 69.2 inches tall, with a standard deviation of 3.0 inches, while the average $20 - 29$ year-old woman is 64.3 inches tall, with a standard deviation of 2.7 inches.

   A) Find the Z-score for a 75-inch man.
   B) Find the Z-score for a 70-inch woman.
   C) Who is relatively taller, a 75-inch man or a 70-inch woman? (N.B. this means who has the higher Z-score, not necessarily the higher height!)

Solution: For part A, the data value is 75, and we need to use the population mean and standard deviation of 69.2 and 3.0, respectively. The Z-score is

$$Z = \frac{x - \mu}{\sigma} = \frac{75 - 69.2}{3.0} = 1.93333$$

This means that a 75-inch man is 1.93333 standard deviations above the mean (because the Z-score is positive).

Next, for part B, the data value is 70, and we need to use the population mean and standard deviation of 64.3 and 2.7, respectively. The Z-score is

$$Z = \frac{x - \mu}{\sigma} = \frac{70 - 64.3}{2.7} = 2.11111$$

This means that a 70-inch woman is 2.11111 standard deviations above the mean (because the Z-score is positive).

For part C, who is relatively taller, a 75-inch man or a 70-inch woman? If we had asked for which one is taller, then the answer would obviously be the man as he is five inches taller than the woman. However, the question is who is *relatively taller*, which means who has the larger Z-score. The answer is the 70-inch woman. This is because when the woman is compared to the population of women, and the 75-inch man is compared to the population of men, the woman is a greater extent taller in her population than the man is in his.

In this way, by **standardizing** the data values of 75 and 70 inches, we can more easily compare two values together that came from different populations.

Δ

DEFINITION
When we **standardize** data values, we subtract off their mean and divide the result by their standard deviation. In other words, a data point's Z-score is equal to the standardized data point.

In Section 2.5, we saw the first method to check for outliers that involved a box-plot analysis. It worked regardless of the shape of the data. There is a second outlier test we show next, but this one only works for bell-shaped (normal) data.

OUTLIER TEST 2: USING Z-SCORES FOR BELL-SHAPED DATA
If a dataset is bell-shaped (normally distributed), a specific data value is considered to be a potential outlier if it falls more than three standard deviations from the mean. In other words, if the Z-score is less than −3 or greater than 3, the data point is a potential outlier.

To summarize everything about Z-scores:

1) A Z-score is the number of standard deviations above/below the mean the data point lies.
   a) If the Z-score is negative, the data point is below the mean.
   b) If the Z-score is 0, the data point is equal to the mean.
   c) If the Z-score is positive, the data point is above the mean.
2) The data point is a potential outlier (provided the distribution is bell-shaped) if...
   a) The Z-score is less than −3, or
   b) The Z-score is greater than 3.

EXAMPLE
Assume that male heights in a certain region are normally distributed with mean 69.2 inches and standard deviation 3.0 inches.

A) Would a male with a height of 58 inches be considered a potential outlier?
B) What about a male with a height of 62 inches?
C) What is the Z-score for a male whose height is 1.5 standard deviations below the mean? Find this height.

Solution: For part A, we first compute the Z-score:

$$Z = \frac{x - \mu}{\sigma} = \frac{58 - 69.2}{3.0} = -3.73333$$

This Z-score is below −3, and so this male would be a potential outlier. For the 62-inch male,

$$Z = \frac{x - \mu}{\sigma} = \frac{62 - 69.2}{3.0} = -2.4$$

This Z-score is not below −3 anymore, so this male is not a potential outlier.

Part C looks tricky, as there does not seem to be enough information to solve it. However, look at it again. The definition of a Z-score is the number of standard deviations away from the mean a point falls. To say a point is 1.5 standard deviations above the mean is to say that the Z-score is positive 1.5.

That means that a point that is 1.5 standard deviations below the mean has a Z-score of negative 1.5 (the negative sign indicates that it is below the mean). Thus, $Z = -1.5$. The next question is what height corresponds to this Z-score. We can use the Z-score formula in reverse to solve for x, the data value:

$$-1.5 = \frac{x - 69.2}{3.0}$$
$$-4.5 = x - 69.2$$
$$64.7 = x$$

A male of height 64.7 inches is 1.5 standard deviations below the mean, with a Z-score of -1.5.

Δ

Chapter 3 – Association, Correlation, and Regression

In Chapter 3 we explore the relationships between two variables, first quantitative and later categorical.

Section 3.1 – Basic Definitions of Association

The following terms are used throughout this chapter, so we launch the chapter by defining them, along with some examples.

DEFINITION

A **response variable** is a variable that can be explained by some other variable. That is, it is determined by another variable. When graphing data, the response variable goes on the y-axis (the vertical axis,) so it is the y-variable.

An **explanatory variable** is a variable that explains, or affects, the response variable. When graphing data, the explanatory variable goes on the x-axis (the horizontal axis), so it is the x-variable.

EXAMPLE

The number of hours you study for an exam affects your score on that exam. Thus, the explanatory variable is the number of hours spent studying for the test. The response variable is the score on the test.

Δ

DEFINITION

An **association** exists between two variables if a specific value for one variable is more likely to occur with certain values of the other variable.

EXAMPLE

If we do not spend much time preparing for an exam, then we probably will not perform particularly well, and our score will likely be low. If we spend a long time studying, then our score will likely be high. This means that there is an association between the number of hours spent studying and the test score.

Δ

DEFINITION

A **lurking variable** is another variable that is somehow related to the explanatory and/or the response variables, but it is not the variable being studied.

EXAMPLE

In the same example, a lurking variable could be the number of hours of sleep you get the night before taking the exam. The amount of sleep can also affect how well you will do on the test.

Δ

EXAMPLE

In general, the more years a person works for a company, the higher their salary will be. We need to determine the explanatory variable, the response variable, whether there is an association, and what a lurking variable could be here.

Solution: The number of years worked for a company seems to have an impact on the salary. Thus, the explanatory variable is the number of years worked for the company. The response variable is the salary. The way the statement is worded, there does appear to be an association between the two variables. A lurking variable would be something that could affect the salary even though it is not being considered at the moment, such as a person's performance on their job.

Δ

Section 3.2 – Association Between Two Quantitative Variables

We now take a closer look at association. When both the explanatory and response variables are quantitative, we can mathematically compute a value for the association between the variables, as well as graph the two variables on the same plot. The association is either going to be positive, negative, or zero, and the graph will follow specific corresponding patterns.

DEFINITION

A **scatterplot** is a graphical display for two quantitative variables. The explanatory variable goes on the x-axis (horizontal), and the response variable goes on the y-axis (vertical). The points are not connected when the graph is drawn.

MNEMONIC

One way to remember which variable goes where is that "explanatory" contains the letter x, so it goes on the x-axis!

EXAMPLE

Suppose we have the following data:

X	1	2	3	4	5	6	7	8
Y	1	3	4	5	8	6	7	9

By plotting each x against the corresponding y, we obtain the following scatterplot:

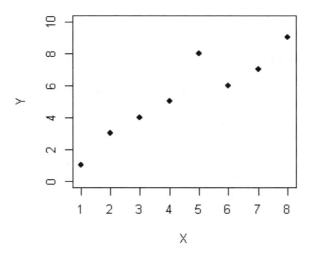

Scatterplot of X versus Y

We should notice two things from this scatterplot. First, whatever the relationship is among the eight points, it definitely has a positive trend. This means that as x increases, y tends to increase. Second, should we draw a line of best fit (we will get to this in a little bit), it will not be perfect since we cannot fit a straight line through all points, but it should certainly come close to doing so.

Δ

59

EXAMPLE
Here is another set of points. We now build and examine the scatterplot for trends.

X	1	2	3	4	5	6	7	8
Y	15	11	4	10	6	3	6	2

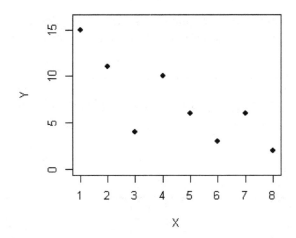

What do you notice? This scatterplot shows negative trend now. This means that as x increases, y tends to decrease. In addition, because the points are more spread out, it is going to be tougher to find a "good" line of best fit through them. Thus, the relationship here should be weaker than that from the previous example.

Δ

EXAMPLE
Here is a dataset that has neither positive nor negative trend.

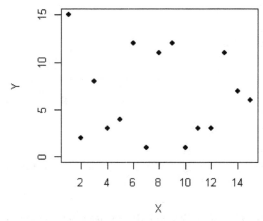

X	1	2	3	4	5	6	7	8	9	10	11	12	13	14	15
Y	15	2	8	3	4	12	1	11	12	1	3	3	11	7	6

Do you see why? The seemingly randomness of all the points makes it difficult to compute a good line of best fit through them. Whatever the optimal fit is, it clearly will not be strong. Also, the points do not appear to exhibit positive or negative trend; rather, their randomness suggests no trend at all.

Δ

Based on these examples, we now write down what each type of association tells us.

DEFINITION
Consider two variables x and y.

1) The variables have **positive association** if as x increases, y increases.
2) The variables have **negative association** if as x increases, y decreases.
3) The variables have **no association** if as x increases, there is no definite increase or decrease in y.

EXAMPLE
Given the followings pairs of variables, determine the type of association.
   A) The weight of a car and miles it gives to the gallon.
   B) The speed of a car and distance required coming to a complete stop.
   C) The weight on a bar and number of repetitions a weightlifter can achieve.
   D) The temperature outside and a student's grade on a test.

Solution: The solutions are as follows.

   A) Generally the heavier the car, the more gasoline it uses, which means it would go less miles to the gallon. Thus, the car's weight and its miles per gallon are negatively related.
   B) The faster you drive a car, the greater the distance required coming to a complete stop. These variables have positive association.
   C) The heavier the weight on a bar, the more difficult it is for a weightlifter to lift. This means that generally the number of repetitions would decrease. Thus, these variables have negative association.
   D) The outside temperature clearly has nothing to do with a student's test grade, so these variables have no association.

Δ

We can now state the association between two variables. However, what if we want to take it one step further and determine if there is a *linear* relationship between the variables? The answer is that we calculate what we call correlation. To be clear, two variables that have an association have some sort of relationship. Correlation measures to what extent that association is linear. (It is possible the variables might be related in some other way, such as parabolic.)

DEFINITION
Two variables x and y are said to have **linear correlation** if the data tend to follow a straight-line path on a scatterplot, or are close to a straight line.

1) The variables have **positive correlation** if as x increases, y increases.
2) The variables have **negative correlation** if as x increases, y decreases.
3) The variables have **no correlation** if as x increases, there is no definite increase or decrease in y, or in other words there is no linear relationship between x and y.

Further, correlation can be further described as **strong correlation** or **weak correlation**.

The following diagram gives examples of each type of correlation: positive and negative, strong and weak, none whatsoever.

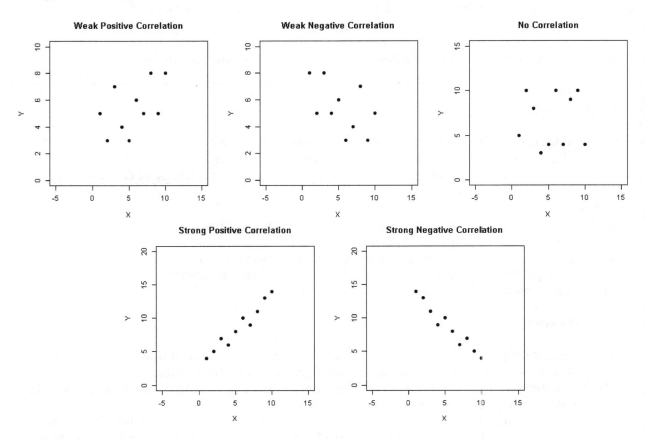

We now state and explain the equation used to compute correlation.

DEFINITION

Correlation (r) is the numerical measure of the strength of the linear relationship between two variables x and y. The equation is

$$r = \frac{\sum \left(\frac{x_i - \bar{x}}{s_x} \right) \left(\frac{y_i - \bar{y}}{s_y} \right)}{n - 1}$$

The letters are defined as follows:

x_i = all individual explanatory variables
y_i = all individual response variables
$\bar{x}$ = the mean of all x's
$\bar{y}$ = the mean of all y's
s_x = the standard deviation of all x's
s_y = the standard deviation of all y's
n = the sample size

Correlation is denoted by the letter r because it was first studied by pirates... RRRRRR!!! (Just kidding!) Normally the first letter of correlation (the c) would be used, except in mathematics c often denotes a constant. The next letter, o, is too easily confused with zero, so the letter after that is r.

If you look at the correlation formula, the contents of the summation formula are literally the Z-scores of the individual x's and y's. This means that another way to define the equation is

$$r = \frac{\sum Z_x Z_y}{n - 1}$$

EXAMPLE

Consider the following data of the speed of a car (in mph) and the required distance to come to a complete stop (in feet). We want to compute the correlation by hand. (Don't worry – the graphing calculator will compute it as well!) The point of this example is so you can get the hang of what the formula is doing.

Speed	Distance
15	44
25	85
50	229
70	388

Solution: First, we compute the numbers we need – the averages, standard deviations, and sample size:

$$\bar{x} = 40 \qquad \bar{y} = 186.50 \qquad n = 4$$
$$s_x = 24.83277404 \qquad s_y = 156.0096151$$

Next, we compute the individual Z-scores for the four x values and the corresponding y values.

$$Z_x = \frac{x - \bar{x}}{s_x} = \frac{15-40}{24.83277404} = -1.006734083 \qquad Z_y = \frac{y - \bar{y}}{s_y} = \frac{44-186.50}{156.0096151} = -0.9134052405$$

$$Z_x = \frac{x - \bar{x}}{s_x} = \frac{25-40}{24.83277404} = -0.6040404498 \qquad Z_y = \frac{y - \bar{y}}{s_y} = \frac{85-186.50}{156.0096151} = -0.6506009257$$

$$Z_x = \frac{x - \bar{x}}{s_x} = \frac{50-40}{24.83277404} = 0.4026936332 \qquad Z_y = \frac{y - \bar{y}}{s_y} = \frac{229-186.50}{156.0096151} = 0.2724191068$$

$$Z_x = \frac{x - \bar{x}}{s_x} = \frac{70-40}{24.83277404} = 1.2080809 \qquad Z_y = \frac{y - \bar{y}}{s_y} = \frac{388-186.50}{156.0096151} = 1.291870599$$

We then compute the products of the Z-scores for each of the four data points. To do this, we multiply Z_x by Z_y for each data value. It would be easier to do this in a table to summarize our results:

Speed	Distance	Z_x	Z_y	$Z_x Z_y$
15	44	-1.0067340830	-0.9134052405	0.9195561872
25	85	-0.6040404498	-0.6506009257	0.3929892758
50	229	0.4026936332	0.2724191068	0.1097014399
70	388	1.2080809000	1.2915870590	1.5603416567

Now all we need to do is add up the Z-score products and divide by $(n-1)$:

$$r = \frac{\sum Z_x Z_y}{n-1} = \frac{0.9195561872 + 0.3929892758 + 0.1097014399 - 1.5603416567}{4-1}$$

$$= \frac{2.98258856}{3} = 0.99420$$

Here is a scatterplot of the data. Judging by where the points fall, the data show positive association, and the points definitely show a linear trend. This means that the correlation is strong and positive. In fact, a correlation of 0.99420 is clearly positive, and as we are about to see, it is also extremely strong!

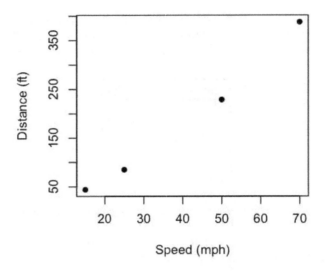

Δ

Soon we will see how to use the TI-84 to compute correlation so that you don't have to worry about messy hand computations. Before we present how to do that, we first need to discuss linear regression because the TI-84 command that does that for us also computes correlation, so we delay that discussion until Section 3.3.

The following list of properties is everything you could possibly want to know about correlation.

PROPERTIES OF THE LINEAR CORRELATION COEFFICIENT (r)

Property 1: r must always be between -1 and 1, or in other words $-1 \leq r \leq 1$.
Property 2: $r > 0$ indicates a positive linear relationship. If $r = 1$, then there is perfect positive correlation.
Property 3: $r < 0$ indicates a negative linear relationship. If $r = -1$, then there is perfect negative correlation.
Property 4: If $r = 0$, then there is no linear relationship between the two variables.
Property 5: A value of r close to 1 or -1 indicates a strong linear relationship, while a value of r close to zero represents a weak linear relationship.
Property 6: The sign of correlation coincides with the sign of the regression equation (coming up in Section 3.3).
       a) If correlation is positive, then the regression line has a positive slope.
       b) If correlation is negative, then the regression line has a negative slope.

Property 7: Correlation is unit-less.
Property 8: Correlation does not change if the two variables change order.
Property 9: Correlation only measures the degree of <u>linear</u> association.
Property 10: Unfortunately correlation does not prove that one variable <u>causes</u> the other to happen; it only suggests an association.

Let's discuss these points further.

Property 1: Mathematically, correlation always has to be between -1 and 1, including the endpoints. This means that $-1 \leq r \leq 1$.

Property 2: If correlation is positive $(r > 0)$, then the two variables x and y have a positive linear relationship. If correlation happens to be exactly positive 1 $(+1)$, it means the variables have perfect positive correlation.

Property 3: If correlation is negative $(r < 0)$, then the two variables x and y have a negative linear relationship. If correlation happens to be exactly negative 1 (-1), it means the variables have perfect negative correlation.

Property 4: If correlation is exactly equal to 0, then the two variables x and y have no linear relationship.

Property 5: If correlation is close to 1 or -1, then the two variables x and y have a strong linear relationship. For example, if two variables have correlation 0.90 and two other variables have correlation -0.90, they both have an equally strong linear relationship, just in opposite directions.

On the other hand, if correlation is close to 0 (on either side), then the two variables x and y have a weak linear relationship. For example, a correlation of 0.10 would be weak because it is close to 0, but so would a correlation of -0.05.

Property 6: In the next section, we will study regression equations, which represent the line of best fit through the data. If one were to draw a line of best fit through the points, the slope would either be positive or be negative. If that line has positive slope, then correlation is positive. If that line has negative slope, then correlation is negative.

Property 7: Correlation does not have units; it is just a number. For example, the problem in the previous section concerned using the speed of a car (in mph) to predict the stopping distance (in feet). The units for x were miles per hour, and the units for y were feet. However, the correlation of 0.99420 was just that number. It was not 0.99420 mph, feet, feet/mph, etc. The reason is because in the correlation formula, the units all cancel out each other.

Property 8: Suppose the correlation between two variables x and y is r. Now suppose we interchanged the variables and instead wanted to compute the correlation between y and x. It turns out that the correlation would still be r, so it would not change. For example, returning to the previous problem, imagine we instead wanted to use the stopping distance to predict the speed of the car. The correlation would still be 0.99420.

Property 9: Correlation will only tell us to what extent two variables have a *linear* relationship. A strong correlation (close to 1 or -1) means that the variables have a strong relationship, one that is linear. A weak correlation (close to 0) means that the variables have a weak linear relationship. However, that does not prove that there is no relationship at all; it is possible that the variables have a non-linear relationship. We could detect this by examining a scatterplot.

Property 10: If correlation is strong between two variables, it means that higher values of x tend to occur at the same time as higher (or lower) values of y. However, that does not necessarily prove that x causes y to behave a certain way; it simply means that there is an association. Put another way, correlation is not proof of causality.

The following chart illustrates where strong, weak, and "moderate" correlation fall on a number line. Note that there is no official rule on what number to cross when going from weak to moderate, or moderate to strong. We arbitrarily choose 0.3 and −0.3 for the weak/moderate line, and 0.7 and −0.7 for the moderate/strong line. The point is not where the thresholds fall, but how close to 1, −1, or 0 the correlation falls.

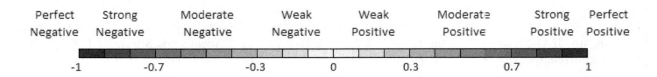

EXAMPLE
Which of the following are the strongest and the weakest correlations?

$$0.80, \quad -0.34, \quad 0.67, \quad -0.92, \quad 0.04, \quad -0.12$$

Solution: This problem is easier than it looks. What makes it look confusing is the presence of some negative signs. The strongest correlation is the one that is closest to either 1 or −1, *regardless of the positive or negative sign.* That number is −0.92.

The weakest correlation is the one that is closest to 0, on either side of it (meaning it could be positive or negative). That number is 0.04.

If you are still confused by this, temporarily ignore any negative signs (in mathematical terms this is called taking the absolute value). Doing so produces

$$0.80, \quad 0.34, \quad 0.67, \quad 0.92, \quad 0.04, \quad 0.12$$

Looking at this altered set of numbers, it quickly becomes apparent that the largest is 0.92 (which was originally −0.92, the strongest), and the smallest is 0.04 (which was originally still 0.04, the weakest).

Δ

A note about Property 9: correlation will only pick up whether there is a linear relationship. However, it is possible that the data are still related some other way. Consider the following scatterplot. If we compute correlation for these data, it turns out to be 0.0828, suggesting little to no linear association. And in fact there is no linear association, but the data are clearly related ... a parabola runs through them. (Don't you worry – this is out of scope for these notes!) The point is this: to have a correlation near 0 implies that there is no <u>linear</u> relationship, but it would be naïve to claim that the data are not related in <u>any</u> way.

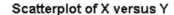

Scatterplot of X versus Y

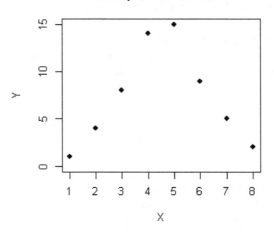

Δ

EXAMPLE

Consider the four scatterplots below. Each has a different correlation, and the possible correlations are 0.52, 0.03, −0.35, and −0.97. We need to match each plot with the correct correlation.

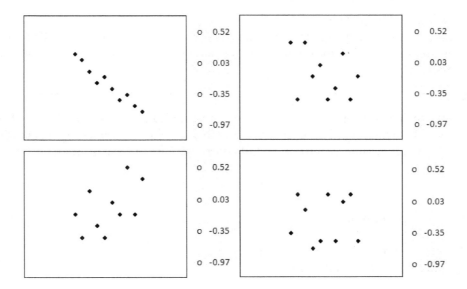

Solution: There is a three-step technique for doing this:

1) First identify the plots that clearly show positive trend. Separate these from those with negative trend.
2) Given the positive plots, make a judgment call on which one looks the strongest and which is the weakest.
3) Repeat Steps 1 and 2 with the plots that show negative trend.

In Step 1, we see that the bottom left plot has some positive association. The top left plot clearly has negative trend. The top right plot appears to be have negative association, although the points are spread out, giving a weak trend. The bottom right plot seems to have little to no association since the points have no apparent pattern. Looking at the numbers for correlation, there are two plots with positive correlation, one of which is the bottom left, and so the bottom right plot must be the other one (even though the correlation would be very weak and close to zero on the positive side).

In Step 2, we examine the two plots on the bottom, the ones identified as having a positive correlation. The bottom left plot clearly has stronger association than the bottom right. This means that the bottom left plot will have a correlation that is closer to +1. The bottom right plot's correlation will be positive as well, although since this one is weaker, it will be close to 0.

That said, one of the choices is 0.52 and another choice is 0.03, so it quickly becomes apparent that the bottom left plot's correlation is 0.52 and the bottom right plot is matched with 0.03.

Next, the top two plots have negative trend. In Step 3, we decide that the top left plot has stronger association than the top right plot. That means that the top left plot's correlation will be closer to −1 than the top right's correlation. The two choices are −0.35 and −0.97, and so the top left plot's correlation must be −0.97. That leaves −0.35 for the top right plot.

This could be a statistician's party game: Pin the Correlation on the Scatterplot!

Δ

Section 3.3 – Linear Regression

To predict the response variable using the explanatory variable, we create what is called a regression line. This line helps us predict the value for the response variable y as a straight-line function of the value x of the explanatory variable.

DEFINITION

Linear regression, or just **regression**, is the act of mathematically finding the line of best fit through given data points. The resulting line goes by a number of names, including **regression equation**, **regression line**, **linear regression equation**, and of course the **line of best fit**. It takes the form

$$\hat{y} = a + bx$$

The letters are defined as follows:

$\hat{y}$ = the predicted response for data point x. It is pronounced "y-hat."
a = the intercept (also called the y-intercept)
b = the slope
x = the data point of interest

By convention, we draw the y with a hat over it to distinguish the predicted response ($\hat{y}$) from the actual, observed response (y). In other words, given a known x value, what is the expected response value we should observe, based on what the regression equation tells us?

That predicted answer is $\hat{y}$ (again, it is pronounced "y-hat"). To find it, simply plug in the given x value into the regression equation. Compare this to the y (with no hat) in a known data point (x, y) that was used to find the regression equation. That is the difference between y and $\hat{y}$.

Of course, as you have probably already guessed by looking at the previous scatterplots, a line of best fit is practically never a perfect fit. Where a response is predicted to be may not always lie right on the regression line, and it may not even come close. However, as long as the line is a relatively good fit (with strong correlation), it will give useful predictions for future points.

While we are on this subject, let's discuss the difference between where a point actually falls and where it was predicted to fall.

DEFINITION

The **residual** of y is the difference between the (known) observed value of y and the predicted value $\hat{y}$ according to the regression equation:

$$\text{residual} = y - \hat{y} = \text{observed} - \text{predicted}$$

Notice that a residual can be positive or negative.

The following graph shows an example of a regression equation and two observations (the black dots), one above the regression equation (with a positive residual) and one below the regression equation (with a negative residual).

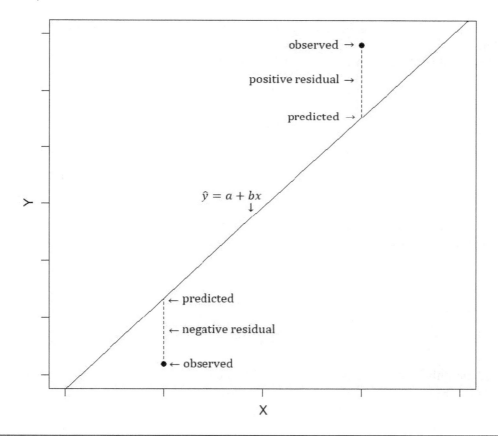

MNEMONIC

The definition of residual, "observed" minus "predicted," is in alphabetical order, if you need a way to remember the order of subtraction!

Let's now look at an example of how regression works. We will see how to compute the regression equation afterwards.

EXAMPLE
Suppose we want to model a regression equation to predict the average monthly cost of car insurance (in dollars) based on the number of accidents the client has had within the past two years. In other words, given number of recent car accidents (x), we wish to predict the monthly car insurance cost (y). After analyzing some available data, we obtain the following equation:

$$\hat{y} = 37.11 + 39.82x$$

A) What is the predicted monthly cost of insurance for someone who has had 2 car accidents?
B) Suppose from known data we were told that someone who had 2 car accidents actually paid $101. Calculate that person's residual.
C) Now find the predicted cost and residual for a person who has had 6 accidents if the observed value for such a client was $296.

Solution: For A, we have $x = 2$ that we can substitute into the regression equation:

$$\hat{y} = 37.11 + 39.82(2) = 116.75$$

This means that the predicted monthly cost $(\hat{y})$ for someone with 2 accidents is $116.75. Now for part B, we know that one specific client with 2 accidents paid $101. This is y because it is an observed value. The residual is equal to observed minus predicted (again, alphabetical order!), so we have

$$\begin{aligned} \text{residual} &= \text{observed} - \text{predicted} \\ &= y - \hat{y} \\ &= 101 - 116.75 \\ &= -15.75 \end{aligned}$$

The residual for this client is $-$$15.75. That means that the client paid less than what they were predicted to pay.

For part C, we repeat the steps for someone who has had 6 accidents and paid $296, so the data point is $(6, 296)$, or $x = 6$ and $y = 296$. The regression equation is

$$\hat{y} = 37.11 + 39.82(6) = 276.03$$

The residual is then

$$\begin{aligned} \text{residual} &= \text{observed} - \text{predicted} \\ &= 296 - 276.03 = 19.97 \end{aligned}$$

The predicted monthly cost would be $276.03, and this client has a residual of $19.97. That means that the client paid more than what they were predicted to pay.

Δ

Here is a plot of the previous example's regression equation (the solid line), as well as the two used points and their residuals (distance indicated by the dashed lines). As you can see from the graph...

1) Residuals can be positive (above the regression line), meaning the observed point was higher than we expected, or...
2) Residuals can be negative (below the regression line), in which case the observed point fell below where we predicted it to be.

3) If a residual is exactly zero (right on the regression line), the observed point happened to be right where we predicted it to fall. In practice, this rarely happens.

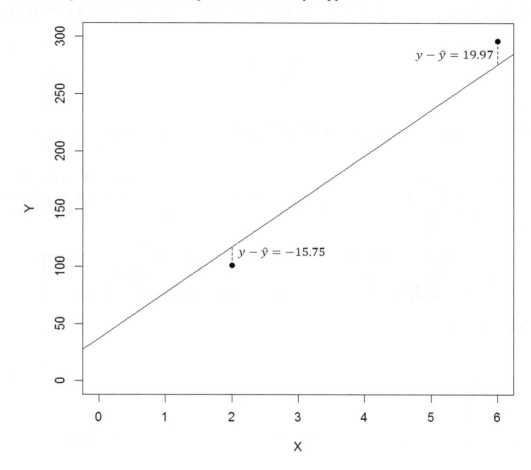

Let's restate the definition of a residual to include the interpretations.

DEFINITION
The **residual** of y is the difference between the (known) observed value of y and the predicted value $\hat{y}$ according to the regression equation: $$\text{residual} = y - \hat{y} = \text{observed} - \text{predicted}$$ A positive residual means that the observed point was higher than expected, or that the observed point was underestimated. A negative residual means that the observed point was lower than expected, or that the observed point was overestimated.

Now, exactly how do we compute the regression equation? Let's first see how to compute it by hand, and then we will go to the TI-84.

71

FORMULAS FOR REGRESSION FORMULA

Suppose we have n pairs of points (x, y) and wish to fit the regression equation $\hat{y} = a + bx$ through them. The slope b and the intercept a can both be computed using the following relatively simple formulas:

$$b = \frac{\sum(x_i - \overline{x})(y_i - \overline{y})}{\sum(x_i - \overline{x})^2}$$
$$a = \overline{y} - b\overline{x}$$

Here $\overline{x}$ is the sample mean of the x data points and $\overline{y}$ is the sample mean of the y data points.

EXAMPLE

Let's try just one example where we compute the coefficients by hand. Consider the following five data points showing the weight of a weight-lifting bar (x) and the number of repetitions a specific person was able to achieve with the given weight (y). Build a linear regression equation through the five pairs of data points using the formulas.

Weight (X)	30	50	55	80	65
Number of Reps (Y)	25	22	20	8	17

Solution: First let's compute the sample means:

$$\overline{x} = \frac{30 + 50 + 55 + 80 + 65}{5} = 56$$
$$\overline{y} = \frac{25 + 22 + 20 + 8 + 17}{5} = 18.4$$

The next step is to compute each $(x_i - \overline{x})$ and $(y_i - \overline{y})$ so that we can subsequently compute $(x_i - \overline{x})(y_i - \overline{y})$ and $(x_i - \overline{x})^2$.

$(x_i - \overline{x})$	$(y_i - \overline{y})$	$(x_i - \overline{x})(y_i - \overline{y})$	$(x_i - \overline{x})^2$
30 - 56 = -26	25 - 18.4 = 6.6	-26 x 6.6 = -171.6	$(-26)^2 = 676$
50 - 56 = -6	22 - 18.4 = 3.6	-6 x 3.6 = -21.6	$(-6)^2 = 36$
55 - 56 = -1	20 - 18.4 = 1.6	-1 x 1.6 = -1.6	$(-1)^2 = 1$
80 - 56 = 24	8 - 18.4 = -10.4	24 x -10.4 = -249.6	$24^2 = 576$
65 - 56 = 9	17 - 18.4 = -1.4	9 x -1.4 = -12.6	$9^2 = 81$

We need to find the sums of the $(x_i - \overline{x})(y_i - \overline{y})$ and $(x_i - \overline{x})^2$, so

$$\sum(x_i - \overline{x})(y_i - \overline{y}) = (-171.6) + (-21.6) + (-1.6) + (-249.6) + (-12.6) = -457$$
$$\sum(x_i - \overline{x})^2 = 676 + 36 + 1 + 576 + 81 = 1370$$

The b coefficient for the slope is then

$$b = \frac{\sum(x_i - \overline{x})(y_i - \overline{y})}{\sum(x_i - \overline{x})^2} = -\frac{457}{1370} = -0.3335766423$$

Using this b, we can now get a:

$$a = \overline{y} - b\overline{x} = 18.4 - (-0.3335766423 \times 56) = 37.08029197$$

The regression equation is therefore (rounded to five decimals)

$$\hat{y} = 37.08029 - 0.33358x$$

Δ

Not exactly a pleasant experience, is it? Fortunately the TI-84 will compute the regression equation for us, so let's learn that next.

TI-84 COMMAND: LINEAR REGRESSION AND CORRELATION

First, enter your x data into L_1 and your y data into L_2. Recall that to do this, press $\boxed{\text{STAT}}$, choose Option 1: $Edit$ ..., and then enter the numbers into the two lists.

When your lists are ready, press $\boxed{\text{STAT}}$, scroll right to CALC, and select Option 8: $LinReg(a + bx)$. Type L_1, the comma button, L_2, and press $\boxed{\text{ENTER}}$. The resulting output contains the following:

$y = a + bx$, the chosen regression equation.
a, the intercept.
b, the slope.
r^2, the square of correlation – we won't use this term in these notes.
r, the correlation.

Note: If you don't see r listed, there is a simple trick you can do. Go into the Catalog (press $\boxed{\text{2nd}}$ and $\boxed{0}$), scroll down to $DiagnosticOn$, and press $\boxed{\text{ENTER}}$ twice. When you see "Done" on the home screen, you are all set and should not have to do this again. Now repeat the above steps and you should now see r.

Note: There is also Option 4: $LinReg(ax + b)$ which may also be used. Just keep in mind that using this option, the letters a and b have been reversed to represent the slope and intercept, respectively. For consistency, I recommend just sticking with Option 8: $LinReg(a + bx)$.

EXAMPLE
Using the previous example, enter the sets of numbers into L_1 and L_2. Choosing Option 8: $LinReg(a + bx)$ results in the following output:

$$a = 37.08029197$$
$$b = -0.3335766423$$
$$r = -0.9491956454$$

The regression coefficients match what we computed by hand. The correlation is $r = -0.9491956454$, which is very close to -1, indicating a strong negative relationship between the weight of the bar and the number of repetitions made.

Δ

We have talked about what a regression equation is, how to use it, and how to compute it. What is just as important is being able to interpret the slope and intercept correctly, in the context of the problem. Here are the techniques, but they will make more sense given an actual scenario.

INTERPRETATION OF THE REGRESSION EQUATION
Recall that the regression equation is $\hat{y} = a + bx$.

The slope b tells us that a unit increase in x causes the predicted response, on average, to increase or decrease by b units. The response increases when the slope is positive, and it decreases for a negative slope. (The part "on average" is important to include because not all subjects will behave in this manner; it just represents an average increase or decrease.)

The intercept a tells us what the predicted response, on average, would be when x is equal to 0 units. Depending on the context, it may or may not have a practical interpretation.

To review from algebra, the following are examples of what positive and negative slopes look like.

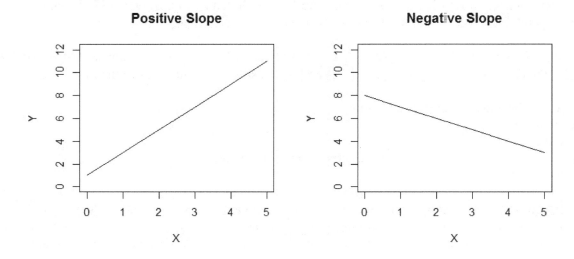

MNEMONIC
To remember which line in the above graphs goes with positive and negative slope, look at the negative slope line. The capital letter N features a diagonal line going to top left to bottom right – which is exactly what a line with negative slope looks like!

EXAMPLE
Consider the previous example, where x = weight of the bar (in pounds) and y = number of repetitions. The regression equation (to five decimals) was $\hat{y} = 30.08029 - 0.33358x$. (Note: we are defining the weight of a bar to be equal to the bar's own weight plus any additional weight attached.)

    A) What is the slope? Interpret that value.
    B) What is the intercept? Interpret that value.
    C) Predict the y value when x is 80 pounds.
    D) Compute and interpret the residual for $x = 80$.

Solution: For part A, the slope is -0.33358, and it is negative. This means that for every unit increase in x, y is expected to decrease by 0.33358 units on average. In the context of this problem, for every

74

additional pound of weight increase, the number of repetitions is expected on average to decrease by 0.33358.

Part B asks for the intercept, which is 30.08029. The intercept is the expected y-value when $x = 0$. In the context of this problem, if we lift a weight bar that weighs 0 pounds, we can expect, on average, to lift it 30.08029 times.

But then you have to stop and ask yourself, does that make practical sense? Does it make sense to lift a weight bar that weighs 0 pounds? Absolutely not! What do you say? Here we go…

RUBBISH!!!

The point of this example is to show that the intercept does not always make practical sense, so the answer is that the intercept has no practical interpretation. Now, for certain mathematical reasons we will not go into, the equation still requires the intercept to be there; it just does not have a feasible interpretation. (It would be incorrect to drop it and say $\hat{y} = -0.33358$.)

For part C, when x is 80 lb, the predicted response is

$$\hat{y} = 30.08029 - 0.33358(80) = 10.39389$$

Given a bar that weighs 80 pounds, one can expect, on average, to be able to do 10.39389 repetitions. For part D, recall from the previous example's table the observation ($x = 80$, $y = 8$). That means that the residual is

$$\text{residual} = \text{observed} - \text{predicted}$$
$$= 8 - 10.39389 = -2.39389$$

The residual is negative, so for the observation $(80, 8)$, the regression equation overestimates the number of repetitions (although it is reasonably close).

Δ

ETYMOLOGY
You are probably familiar with the abbreviation "lb" for pounds. It comes from the Latin expression *libra pondo*, which meant "pound weight." The abbreviation therefore comes from the word meaning "weight" rather than "pound!" Also, the Latin plural of *libra* is *librae* (not *libras*). This means that in spite of what people tend to use in everyday language, one should never write "lbs" for pounds. (Note that earlier we wrote 80 lb; that is in fact the correct way to write it.)

EXAMPLE
An analysis says that we can use the length of an alligator (in feet) to predict its weight (in pounds). The equation turns out to be $\hat{y} = 10 + 40x$.

   A) Find the expected weight of an alligator that is 10 feet long.
   B) Interpret the slope and the intercept.
   C) What can you say about correlation?

Solution: For part A, given that $x = 10$, we have

$$\hat{y} = 10 + 40(10) = 410$$

An alligator that is 10 feet long is, on average, expected to weight 410 pounds.

For part B, the slope is positive 40. This means that for every additional foot in length, an alligator's weight is expected, on average, to increase by 40 pounds. An intercept of 10 literally means that an alligator that is 0 feet long will, on average, weight 10 pounds. Does that make sense? No! What do you say?

RUBBISH!!!

That was another example where the intercept has no practical interpretation. As for part C, we clearly do not have enough information to compute the correlation (we need the data for that). However, observe that the slope is positive. Recall from our discussion of correlation that the sign of correlation matches the sign of the slope. Thus, whatever the correlation is, we at least know that it is positive. (We do not, however, have enough information to tell whether it is strong or weak.)

Δ

EXAMPLE
We want to investigate whether height above sea level (in feet) has an effect on surrounding temperature (in Fahrenheit) on a certain mountainous island. Analysis provides the following regression equation: $\hat{y} = 80 - 0.05x$.

A) Write out what x and y are in this problem.
B) Interpret the slope and the intercept.
C) Is correlation positive or negative here?
D) Would it be acceptable to use this equation to predict the surrounding temperature at 30,000 feet?

Solution: For part A, we are using sea level to predict temperature on the island. This means that x is sea level (in feet) and y is surrounding temperature (in Fahrenheit).

For part B, the slope is -0.05. This means that for every additional foot above sea level, the surrounding temperature is expected to decrease, on average, by 0.05°F. The intercept is 80, and this means that for zero feet above sea level (in other words, right at sea level), the surrounding temperature, on average, is 80°F. Does that make sense? In this example, it does make intuitive sense because at least part of an island would likely be at sea level.

Noting that the slope of the regression equation is negative, part C says that correlation is also negative.

Regarding part D, an island is expected to have much of its land at or somewhat above sea level. The regression equation would be reliable to use between 0 feet and a certain realistic measurement, provided the correlation is high. However, a height of 30,000 feet is far too high to be realistic for an island (as a comparison, Mount Everest, the tallest mountain in the world, is just over 29,000 feet tall!) Thus, it would be unreasonable to use the regression equation to predict the temperature at such an extreme height.

Δ

DEFINITION
A linear regression equation is considered reliable for predicting a response within the range of given x values in the data. However, it is dangerous to predict outside this range, since we do not know if the linear pattern continues. The incorrect act of doing this is called **extrapolation**.

EXAMPLE

Suppose we analyze some data and find that there is a linear association between a year (1900 − 2000) and population size (in billions). That may be true in this examined time frame, but we do not know if the same trend will continue in the year 3000. Thus, while we can use the regression equation to predict within the years 1900 through 2000, it is not a good idea to predict outside that interval.

Δ

EXAMPLE

A company wants to use the percentage of its profits it donates to charity per year to predict the number of dollars it will get back in taxes. It is discovered that for every percentage increase in profits donated, the company is expected to get back an extra 52 dollars on taxes.

A) What are the explanatory and response variables?
B) What is the slope?
C) Write down the regression equation if the intercept is 1000.
D) Can we tell if correlation is positive or negative? Strong or weak?
E) Predict the number of dollars the company gets back in taxes if it donates 18% of its profits to charity.
F) Choose the best answer:
   i. The intercept has no interpretation in this context.
   ii. For every extra $1000 the company donates, it can expect to get another $52 back on its taxes.
   iii. The company can expect to get back only $1000 on taxes if it does not donate any of its profits.
G) Choose the best answer:
   i. When the company donates 30 percent of its profits, it should get back approximately $52 more dollars than it would have done had it donated only 29 percent.
   ii. For every $52 donated, the company should get back an extra percentage of its profits.
   iii. The slope has no practical interpretation.

Solution: In part A, the study is whether the percentage of its profits the company donates can predict the number of dollars it will get back in taxes. Thus, x is the percentage of profits donated to charity in a given year, and y is the amount (in dollars) the company receives back in taxes.

For parts B and C, the slope is positive 52. It is positive because when donations increase, taxes back increase as well. If the intercept is 1000, the regression equation becomes $\hat{y} = 1000 + 52x$.

Regarding part D, since the slope is positive, correlation is positive as well. We cannot tell whether correlation is strong or weak without having the actual dataset.

For part E, to predict the number of dollars the company receives back in taxes when they donate 18% of their profits to charity, we note that x is a percentage amount. Thus, we compute

$$\hat{y} = 1000 + 52(18) = 1936$$

The answer is that when the company donates 18% of the profits, on average they will receive $1,936 back in taxes.

Parts F and G discuss interpreting the intercept and the slope. Before we confuse ourselves with the possible choices, let's interpret them in our own words. The intercept of 1000 says that when the company donates 0%, or nothing, it will receive back $1,000 in taxes on average. Does that make sense? Yes, it is possible for a company to donate nothing to charity (although that is not necessarily a good idea). With that in mind, let's look at the choices again:

    i.   The intercept has no interpretation in this context.
    ii.   For every extra $1000 the company donates, it can expect to get another $52 back on its taxes.
    iii.   The company can expect to get back only $1000 on taxes if it does not donate any of its profits.

Choice (iii) most closely matches our interpretation.

As for the slope of positive 52, this means that for every additional percentage of donated profits, the company will receive, on average, an extra $52 back in taxes. Here are the choices again:

    i.   When the company donates 30 percent of its profits, it should get back approximately $52 more dollars than it would have done had it donated only 29 percent.
    ii.   For every $52 donated, the company should get back an extra percentage of its profits.
    iii.   The slope has no practical interpretation.

The slope always has an interpretation, so choice (iii) is not the answer. At first glance, neither of the remaining choices matches our stated interpretation. However, choice (i) involves a comparison between 29 percent and 30 percent. This is an increase of one percentage point, which results in an average of $52 extra. Although phrased in an unusual way, choice (i) is the correct answer.

Δ

EXAMPLE
Suppose we want to know if the length of a song (in seconds) has an effect on the amount of computer memory it takes up (in megabytes). An estimated equation turns out to be $\hat{y} = 0.21 + 0.02x$.

    A) What are the explanatory and response variables?
    B) Interpret the slope and intercept.

Solution: The study is whether the length of a song can predict the computer memory used. Thus, for part A, x is the length of a song (in seconds), and y is the computer memory (in megabytes) it takes up.

For part B, the slope is 0.02, which means that when a song is one second longer, it is expected, on average, to take up an additional 0.02 megabytes. The intercept is 0.21, which literally means that a song that is 0 seconds in length would, on average, take up 0.21 megabytes. Does that make sense? No – a song that is 0 seconds long would be nonexistent and therefore take up no space! The intercept is meaningless here. What do you say?

RUBBISH!!!

Δ

Section 3.4 – Association Between Two Categorical Variables

Up until now we have been studying association between two quantitative variables. This final section explores the association between two categorical variables. Although we cannot use regression equations, we can at least compute a different measure of how closely the two variables are related.

DEFINITION

A **contingency table** (also called a **two-way table**) is a table that relates two different categorical variables. Each box inside the table is a **cell** that represents a specific "level" of the variable.

For instance, suppose we have the following data:

	Left-Handed	Right-Handed
Male	260	620
Female	240	580

The two variables are gender (male, female) and writing preference (left-handed, right-handed). These are categorical variables because they are not numbers.

Which is the explanatory variable and which is the response? Ask yourself the following questions. Could a person's gender possibly influence which hand they write with? It is certainly possible. Could a person's hand preference for writing possible influence their gender? No, that does not make sense! This means that the explanatory variable is gender, and the response variable is writing preference.

By convention, in these notes we will always put the explanatory variable on the side of the table (across the rows) and the response variable on the top of the table (across the columns).

Continuing the example above, we need to include the totals for each row and column:

	Left-Handed	Right-Handed	Total
Male	260	620	880
Female	240	580	820
Total	500	1200	1700

We can use the table to answer questions like the following. How many males are in this sample? We look at the row total of males, of which there are 880. How many right-handed people are there in this sample? We look at the column total for right-handed people, and there are 780.

Rather than ask about counts, we can calculate proportions from the table. For instance, if we want to know the proportion of people in the data that are male, there are 880 males out of 1700 subjects, and so the answer is $880/1700 = 0.51765$. If we need the proportion of right-handed subjects, there are 1200 out of 1700, making the answer $1200/1700 = 0.70588$.

We can go further and calculate **conditional proportions**, which are proportions for values of one variable given that the other variable is a specific value. That means the denominator of the fraction will no longer be equal to the grand total number, but instead a row total or column total. Let's answer the following questions:

A) What proportion of the male subjects are right-handed? Left-handed?
B) What proportion of the female subjects are right-handed? Left-handed?

To find the proportion of male subjects who are right-handed, we first note that there are 880 males, of which there are 620 who are right-handed. Thus, the answer is 620/880 = 0.70455. If we instead need the proportion of males who are left-handed, the answer would be 260/880 = 0.29545.

Similarly, to find the proportion of female subjects who are right-handed, there are 820 females, of which 580 are right-handed. That means the answer is 580/820 = 0.70732. To get the proportion of females who are left-handed, the answer is 240/820 = 0.29268.

Let's create a new table with these conditional proportions for categories of the response variable.

	Left-Handed	Right-Handed
Male	0.29545	0.70455
Female	0.29268	0.70732

Since the proportions in each row are very similar to each other, we say that there is **no association** between gender and whether a person is left-handed or right-handed. In other words, based on our sample, gender does not seem to affect/explain whether someone is left-handed or right-handed.

For instance, we can say that if a person is male, there is a 0.70455 chance that he will be right-handed. If a person is female, there is a 0.70732 chance that she will be right-handed. Since these two proportions are so similar to each other, we conclude that gender does not appear to affect whether someone is left-handed or right-handed.

Now, this is a hunch we have just by looking casually at the numbers. We now introduce a better quantification of association that uses the conditional proportions.

DEFINITION

Given a table of conditional proportions, we can compute **relative risk**, the comparative odds for each group. Relative risk is defined as the conditional proportion for one group divided by the conditional proportion for another group. Formally, we compute

$$\text{Relative Risk} = \frac{\text{Conditional proportion for first group (larger proportion)}}{\text{Conditional proportion for second group (smaller proportion)}}$$

By convention, we put the larger conditional proportion on the numerator and the smaller conditional proportion on the denominator.

INTERPRETATION OF RELATIVE RISK

Relative risk indicates how many times more likely the outcome is for the first group than the second group. The following facts are true:

1) Relative Risk ≥ 1.
2) When the numerator and denominator conditional proportions are very similar, relative risk is very close to 1.
3) When the numerator conditional proportion is a lot larger than the denominator conditional proportion, relative risk is quite a bit larger than 1.

You probably have heard on the news a phrase like "This group of people is 3 times as likely to do a certain activity as another group of people." They are talking about relative risk!

EXAMPLE
Consider the conditional proportions table we made above.

	Left-Handed	Right-Handed
Male	0.29545	0.70455
Female	0.29268	0.70732

Let's compute the relative risk for males and females on the likelihood of being left-handed. To do this, we go to the left-handed column (which, not so coincidentally, is the left column!). Since the proportion for males is higher, we put that one on the numerator:

$$\text{Relative Risk} = \frac{0.29545}{0.29268} = 1.00946$$

This means that a male is only 1.00946 times more likely to be left-handed than a female is. Notice that since we did male followed by female in the formula, we keep the same order in the interpretation.

Let's now find the relative risk for males and females on the likelihood of being right-handed. Looking in the right-handed column, we put the conditional proportion for females on top since that one is larger:

$$\text{Relative Risk} = \frac{0.70732}{0.70455} = 1.00393$$

Interpreting this, a female is only 1.00393 times more likely to be right-handed than a male is. (Notice the order of rows is flipped here from the left-handed example because of the order of conditional proportions.)

Δ

In case you were wondering, the same techniques work if we have a contingency table that is not 2×2; we just need to isolate the rows and columns in question. Also, as the next example illustrates, the number of rows and columns need not equal each other!

Is it possible to compute relative risk in opposite order, where the smaller conditional proportion is on the numerator instead? The answer is yes, but we have to change our interpretation carefully. By convention, it is just easier to put the larger conditional proportion on the numerator instead so you can quickly see how many times larger it is than the smaller conditional proportion.

EXAMPLE
Here is a 7×2 table. Some college students were asked whether or not they woke up before 10:00 AM on a given morning, and the day of the week and response were recorded. This procedure was repeated for all seven days of the week, and different students were asked every day. To be clear, each student was surveyed exactly once, so nobody is recorded in two different rows. Does the day of the week have an impact on how early a student wakes up? Here are the results.

	Before 10:00 AM	After 10:00 AM	Total
Sunday	33	45	78
Monday	30	40	70
Tuesday	51	48	99
Wednesday	60	39	99
Thursday	58	49	107
Friday	28	51	79
Saturday	11	57	68
Total	271	329	600

Let's answer the following questions:

    A) How many times more likely is a student to sleep in after 10:00 on a Saturday than a Wednesday?
    B) How many times more likely is a student to sleep in after 10:00 on a Friday than a Tuesday?

Solution: For part A, we want to know how many times more likely a student is to sleep in on a Saturday than a Wednesday, so the two rows of interest are Wednesday and Saturday. Let's concentrate on those two rows. It might be helpful to duplicate the two rows on a new chart and ignore the rest of the table to reduce confusion.

	Before 10:00 AM	After 10:00 AM	Total
Wednesday	60	39	99
Saturday	11	57	68
Total	71	96	167

Since we are interested in sleeping in, that is the second column. We first compute the conditional proportions in each row:

The proportion of Wednesday students who sleep in after 10:00 AM is $39/99 = 0.39394$.
The proportion of Saturday students who sleep in after 10:00 AM is $57/68 = 0.83824$.

The relative risk is the larger proportion divided by the smaller proportion:

$$\text{Relative Risk} = \frac{0.83824}{0.39394} = 2.12783$$

Not surprisingly, more people sleep in on Saturdays. Thus, a student is 2.12783 times more likely to sleep past 10:00 AM on a Saturday than on a Wednesday.

We repeat the same steps for part B for Tuesday and Friday. Here are the isolated rows:

	Before 10:00 AM	After 10:00 AM	Total
Tuesday	51	48	99
Friday	28	51	79
Total	79	99	178

We next compute the conditional proportions in each row:

The proportion of Tuesday students who sleep in after 10:00 AM is 48/99 = 0.48485.
The proportion of Friday students who sleep in after 10:00 AM is 51/79 = 0.64557.

The relative risk is the larger proportion divided by the smaller proportion:

$$\text{Relative Risk} = \frac{0.64557}{0.48485} = 1.33149$$

Interpreting this, a student is 1.33149 times more likely to sleep past 10:00 AM on a Friday than on a Tuesday.

Δ

Can we perform a stronger test of association than simply dividing two probabilities? The answer is yes, but it requires techniques we have not yet learned. However, we will see how to conduct such a test in Section 11.2 of these notes. I know you are excited about that!

Chapter 4: Sampling Methods and Collecting Data

While your statistics class obviously concentrates on how to analyze the collected data in appropriate ways, another important component is the manner in which the data are collected in the first place. This chapter explores just how to do that.

Section 4.1: Sampling Methods

It should come as no surprise that a sample needs to be randomly selected and that it should be representative of the population of interest. Similarly, it should make sense that a sample that was not randomly selected or not representative would be a rather lousy one, and therefore any results from it would be questionable.

The question is how do we actually obtain an appropriate sample that is randomly selected and representative of the population. In this chapter, we look at four (plus a non-important fifth) ways to sample from the population.

DEFINITION

The first sampling technique is a **simple random sample**. Here we simply draw a sample of size n from anywhere in the population, and each point has an equal chance of being selected.

This technique is simple to perform; however, we do run the risk of getting a sample that could, by chance, be concentrated on a specific region of the population rather than spread out. The following image shows what a simple random sample might look like if diagrammed. The square is the overall population, and the circles are the sampled points.

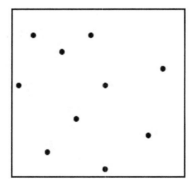

EXAMPLE

We have access to a list of 1000 high school students, and we want to ask a sample of 40 students whether they are planning to go to college. We assign each student a number between 1 and 1000, and then we randomly draw 40 numbers and survey the chosen students. This is a simple random sample because each student is equally likely to be selected for the survey.

$$\Delta$$

The numbers could be chosen by drawing numbers written on slips of paper from a hat, or by using a random number table (discussed later in this chapter), or by computer. The TI-84 will also generate random numbers, and this will be shown later as well.

DEFINITION

The second sampling technique is a **systematic sample**. If we have access to an ordered list, then we can choose a random starting point and a predetermined increment. We then sweep through the list, picking out the subjects by the incremented amount. We stop when we have our required sample size.

This technique is useful when we have an ordered list, such as when the subjects are presorted alphabetically, or by account numbers, etc. If we choose the increment wisely, we will be able to sample subjects from all over the list. The following image shows what a systematic sample might look like if diagrammed.

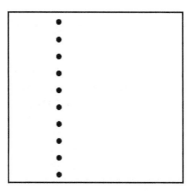

EXAMPLE

Going back to our list of 1000 high school students, now suppose the list is sorted in alphabetical order. We want to pick a random starting number between 1 and 50, and then sample every 50th student after that starting point. By a random method, the number 4 is selected. This means that the 4th, 54th, 104th, 154th, 204th, 254th, etc. students are chosen. The last few are the 804th, 854th, 904th, and 954th (this would generate a total of 20 students). This is a systematic sample because the first student was randomly chosen, and then a predetermined increment chose the subsequent students from an ordered list.

Δ

The next two sampling methods are somewhat more difficult to understand, and sometimes they can get confused. The diagrams will really help distinguish the two. For both techniques, imagine we are going to take a sample of 40 students all over the high school, but this time we are going to take into consideration the grades of the students (9th, 10th, 11th, and 12th grades).

DEFINITION

The third sampling technique is a **stratified sample**. The idea here is to ensure that the sample is truly representative of the population. We first divide the population into different **strata** (plural of **stratum**), which are groups. Then we take a simple random sample from each group and find the average in each of the groups. The last step is to average the averages, as it were.

In an ordinary simple random sample, you take subjects from anywhere in the population. However, in a stratified sample, you take subjects in such a way that they are guaranteed to come from specific sectors of the population, thereby making the sample more representative. From within each group you find the average of that individual group, and then later you find a weighted average of all averages. (This will become clearer in an example in Section 4.3.)

The following diagram illustrates how a stratified sample works. In this diagram there are four groups assumed, and from each group a simple random sample is taken.

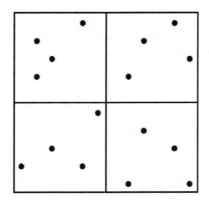

EXAMPLE

We want to take a total sample of 40 students from the high school and ask each one if they plan to go to college. However, we do this in such a way so that ten students are selected from 9th grade, ten from 10th grade, ten from 11th grade, and ten from 12th grade. Doing so might ensure a more representative sample than had we just sampled anywhere from the high school at random.

The ten 9th graders would indicate whether they are going to college, so this would give a proportion. A second, third, and fourth proportions would come from the other grades, and then the four total proportions would be averaged later using a weighted average. This is a stratified sample.

Δ

DEFINITION

The fourth sampling technique is a **cluster sample**. This technique will also strive to get a representative sample with the strata, albeit in a different manner. We first divide the population into different strata. However, this time we randomly choose some of the groups, not all. In the groups we select, we survey every person who falls in that group. We find the group averages, and then the last step is to average the averages.

Keep the following points in mind. With a stratified sample, you consider all groups of the population and sample some subjects per group. In contrast, with a cluster sample, you consider some groups of the population and sample all subjects in the chosen groups.

The following diagram illustrates how a cluster sample works. In this diagram there are four groups assumed, but this time two are selected at random (the top left and bottom right), and from each selected group every subject is surveyed.

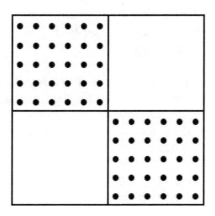

EXAMPLE

Going back to our same example, suppose our 1000 total students can be broken down into 250 students per grade level. We have four grades, and it is decided at random to sample the two grades of sophomores (10th) and seniors (12th). A cluster sample would involve surveying all 250 sophomores and all 250 seniors. We would then find the two averages separately, and then lastly use a weighted average to get the final average.

Δ

DEFINITION

The fifth sampling technique, if that's what you can call it, is a **convenience sample**. This is the laziest sampling method because it is nonrandom. The technique involves sampling people based on how easy it is to obtain the sample rather than making an effort to get a random, representative sample.

EXAMPLE

With the same set of 1000 total students, suppose we want to sample 20, but we just take the first 20 on an alphabetically ordered list. This is convenience sampling because the sample was not randomly chosen. Alternatively, imaging we station ourselves outside the school and selected the first 20 students that happened to walk past. That would be convenience sampling too for the same reason.

Δ

While convenience sampling is no doubt the easiest way to sample, it also gives the least reliable results. The moral of this story is that just like with everything else in life, if you want a good, reliable sample on which to perform a statistical analysis, you have to put forth the effort to get that sample!

EXAMPLE

We want to conduct a survey using University of Florida professors, and they can be divided into the categories of instructor, associate professor, and full professor. Name the type of sampling technique in each of the following situations:

A) We take a sample of 20 professors from each of the three categories.
B) We ignore the three classifications and just randomly sample any 60 professors.
C) It is decided by randomization to work with just instructors and full professors. We then survey everyone falling into either category.
D) We find an alphabetical list of all professors. We decide to start with #3 and pick every 10th professor from there on out, until we have our sample size.
E) We walk into a boardroom meeting and sample the nearest 20 professors.

Solution:
A) Here there are three total strata, or groups. All three are used, but only some professors are chosen. This is stratified sampling.
B) If we take a random sample of any professors, regardless of their classification, then this is a simple random sample. (Note the words "randomly sample" – it is important that they were randomly chosen!)
C) Two groups were selected at random, and then all professors in either group were chosen. This is cluster sampling.
D) Taking a random starting point, and then a fixed increment, from an ordered list is systematic sampling.
E) Surveying the 20 professors who happen to be nearest to us is convenience sampling because this is an easy sample, not a random one. What do you say? Rubbish!

Δ

> **ETYMOLOGY**
>
> The words stratified and convenience come from the Latin *stratum* and *convenire*, which meant "something that has been laid down" and "to agree," respectively. Random derives from the Old High German *rennen* and Old English *rinnan*, both of which meant "to run." Systematic comes to us from the Greek σύστημα, meaning "whole made of several parts." Finally, cluster comes from the Old English *clyster*, which meant "several things growing naturally together."

Section 4.2: Generating Random Numbers

We now have some lists (ordered or otherwise) from which to draw samples. We still need to ensure a random selection from these lists, assuming we are not doing systematic sampling. If done by hand, one technique is to use a random number table, like the one below.

Random Number Table

Row Number	Column Number									
	01 - 05	06 - 10	11 - 15	16 - 20	21 - 25	26 - 30	31 - 35	36 - 40	41 - 45	46 - 50
01	76935	19201	15183	91836	53660	82936	44083	17033	73281	09933
02	27902	67765	46927	29017	92335	39663	40248	66307	29374	17080
03	17314	62881	87434	05297	81092	73230	99257	11001	98328	59154
04	02702	86958	70972	43951	57505	40015	98103	05969	87330	07332
05	83884	86192	32181	56961	50486	99202	77700	54691	05416	61543
06	61577	68488	78624	68404	31760	27970	85372	40582	43935	80729
07	21313	94600	62177	34735	27947	34558	68102	43037	37446	56643
08	83139	16547	17527	57105	79814	97479	01114	11503	39898	59945
09	12455	21647	75622	84045	65442	62063	92554	11190	24626	42994
10	06224	91620	11578	22579	98376	74260	74727	32002	07258	24029
11	09237	53556	76120	85499	28812	57895	61973	50172	83128	46275
12	08881	05035	32154	98091	66271	48579	85955	30065	78327	96509
13	69540	15306	32734	85188	32763	27089	96084	59143	78875	96662
14	87636	34194	96362	62573	52280	15837	71462	72951	99919	47511
15	54296	81223	93896	97834	96953	22068	42407	52655	52330	84587
16	21725	77193	13389	32664	10384	58888	02312	45947	46191	85935
17	27776	58769	29284	11691	99687	84908	48593	20112	52028	22549
18	89325	91063	95310	33877	33698	34306	36397	99616	07202	46422
19	60440	91065	99042	96912	17892	64751	68498	34234	02750	96066
20	06161	22835	48375	15339	46757	98899	68630	61083	36381	35922

Here's how we use one. We first pick a random starting point anywhere on the table (such as pointing a pencil somewhere on the table without looking. We do not have to start at the beginning of a row either). Suppose we choose to start in row 4, column 1. Here is the partial first row:

02702   86958   70972   43951   57505

The gaps between every five digits are just to make it easier to read the table. Suppose for now we have a single-digit number of subjects (here, eight), and we want to assign four of them into a group.

The rule is, we go left to right through the row we selected. Since we have 8 subjects, we can take any single digit between 1 and 8, but we cannot use 9 or 0 (since we do not have a 9th or 0th subject). We also must skip repeating digits. This is much easier to see in an example.

02702   86958   70972   43951   57505

Here is the step-by-step process:

Step 1: Digit 0 is not allowed, so we skip it.
Step 2: Digit 2 is allowed, so we take subject #2. This is the first subject.
Step 3: Digit 7 is allowed, so we take subject #7. This is the second subject.
Step 4: Digit 0 is not allowed, so we skip it.
Step 5: Digit 2 is allowed, but we already chose subject #2, so we skip it.
Step 6: Digit 8 is allowed, so we take subject #8. This is the third subject.
Step 7: Digit 6 is allowed, so we take subject #6. This is the fourth subject.

Now that we have our four subjects $(2, 7, 8, 6)$, we can stop. This means that Group A will consist of subjects $2, 6, 7$, and 8, while Group B will consist of the remaining subjects $1, 3, 4$, and 5.

EXAMPLE

Suppose we have 50 subjects, each having a number 1 through 50, and we want to randomly sample five of them. Let's use the same row on the random number table for illustrative purposes. This time we have a two-digit number of possible subjects (50), so we need to read off the numbers in "couplets," or groups of two. (The digits can be joined across the gaps.) Here is the row again:

02702   86958   70972   43951   57505

Here is the step-by-step process:

Step 1: Digits 02 are allowed, so we take subject #2. This is the first subject.
Step 2: Digits 70 are not allowed, so we skip them.
Step 3: Digits 28 are allowed, so we take subject #28 (this requires joining the 2 across the gap to the 8). This is the second subject.
Step 4: Digits 69 are not allowed, so we skip them.
Step 5: Digits 58 are not allowed, so we skip them.
Step 6: Digits 70 are not allowed, so we skip them.
Step 7: Digits 97 are not allowed, so we skip them.
Step 8: Digits 24 are allowed, so we take subject #24 (this requires joining the 2 across the gap to the 4). This is the third subject.
Step 9: Digits 39 are allowed, so we take subject #39. This is the fourth subject.
Step 10: Digits 51 are not allowed, so we skip them.
Step 11: Digits 57 are not allowed, so we skip them.
Step 12: Digits 50 are allowed, so we take subject #50. This is the fifth subject.

Now that we have our five subjects $(2, 28, 24, 39, 50)$, we can stop. Thus, our sample will consist of subjects $2, 24, 28, 39$, and 50.

Δ

Of course, if you have a TI-84, it is much easier to use it to choose random numbers rather than going through the trouble of a random number table. Here is how we use the graphing calculator.

TI-84 COMMAND: GENERATING RANDOM WHOLE NUMBERS
To generate a specified amount of random whole numbers between a lower bound and an upper bound, inclusive (meaning including the lower and upper bound), press MATH, scroll over to PRB, and choose Option 5: *randInt(*. This command takes three inputs: lower bound, upper bound, and number to sample. In other words, the command is

---

$$randInt(\text{lower bound, upper bound, number to sample})$$

EXAMPLE

Going back to the previous example, given subjects 1 through 50, we want to randomly choose 5 of the subjects. Using the TI-84, we would press $\boxed{\text{MATH}}$, scroll over to PRB, and choose Option 5: randInt(. The command would then be

$$randInt(1, 50, 5)$$

For instance, on one draw we might get 19, 5, 27, 14, and 34. Note that it is possible to get duplicate numbers using this function, in which case simply do another random draw until you have five total numbers that are unique.

Δ

Section 4.3: Example of How to Sample

This section concentrates on a real dataset, from which we shall demonstrate how to use each sampling method and average the results. The dataset consists of the 50 states of the United States (plus the District of Columbia) and how many Electoral College votes each one had in the 2016 election.[1] Each state has an assigned index number between 1 and 51.

Index	State	Votes	Index	State	Votes	Index	State	Votes
1	Alabama	9	18	Kentucky	8	35	North Dakota	3
2	Alaska	3	19	Louisiana	8	36	Ohio	18
3	Arizona	11	20	Maine	4	37	Oklahoma	7
4	Arkansas	6	21	Maryland	10	38	Oregon	7
5	California	55	22	Massachusetts	11	39	Pennsylvannia	20
6	Colorado	9	23	Michigan	16	40	Rhode Island	4
7	Connecticut	7	24	Minnesota	10	41	South Carolina	9
8	Delaware	3	25	Mississippi	6	42	South Dakota	3
9	D.C.	3	26	Missouri	10	43	Tennessee	11
10	Florida	29	27	Montana	3	44	Texas	38
11	Georgia	16	28	Nebraska	5	45	Utah	6
12	Hawaii	4	29	Nevada	6	46	Vermont	3
13	Idaho	4	30	New Hampshire	4	47	Virginia	13
14	Illinois	20	31	New Jersey	14	48	Washington	12
15	Indiana	11	32	New Mexico	5	49	West Virginia	5
16	Iowa	6	33	New York	29	50	Wisconsin	10
17	Kansas	6	34	North Carolina	15	51	Wyoming	3

The goal is to estimate the average number of electoral votes a state has. Now, given all 50 states plus D.C., it can be shown that the population mean number of votes is $\mu = 10.54902$ just by averaging all 51 numbers. However, for the purposes of illustration, suppose we just want to estimate this number by randomly sampling, say, 12 states and computing the average of their votes. Our result will be an estimate of the population mean.

EXAMPLE

The first method is the simple random sample. Here each state has an index number between 1 and 51, and we randomly draw 12 states, note their electoral votes, and average them. Let the sampled index numbers be $1, 6, 8, 22, 25, 27, 29, 30, 33, 36, 41,$ and 48. We turn to the above table and note the chosen states in the following table:

Index	State	Votes	Index	State	Votes	Index	State	Votes
1	Alabama	9	25	Mississippi	6	33	New York	29
6	Colorado	9	27	Montana	3	36	Ohio	18
8	Delaware	3	29	Nevada	6	41	South Carolina	9
22	Massachusetts	11	30	New Hampshire	4	48	Washington	12

The sample mean number of votes is then the average of the twelve votes:

$$\overline{x} = \frac{9 + 9 + 3 + 11 + 6 + 3 + 6 + 4 + 29 + 18 + 9 + 12}{12} = 9.16667$$

The simple random sample of 12 states produced a sample mean of 9.16667 votes.

Δ

EXAMPLE

The second method is the systematic sample. Observe that the list of states is already in alphabetical order. Imagine we decide to randomly choose a number between 1 and 6, pick the corresponding state, and then every fifth state after that, thereby producing a sample of size ten. Suppose the number 5 is selected, so the 5th state on the list is California. We then pick the 10th, 15th, 20th, 25th, 30th, 35th, 40th, 45th, and 50th states, which are shown in the following table:

Index	State	Votes	Index	State	Votes	Index	State	Votes
5	California	55	25	Mississippi	6	45	Utah	6
10	Florida	29	30	New Hampshire	4	50	Wisconsin	10
15	Indiana	11	35	North Dakota	3			
20	Maine	4	40	Rhode Island	4			

The sample mean number of votes is then the average of the ten votes:

$$\overline{x} = \frac{55 + 29 + 11 + 4 + 6 + 4 + 3 + 4 + 6 + 10}{10} = 13.2$$

The systematic sample of 10 states produced a sample mean of 13.2 votes.

Δ

To illustrate the stratified and cluster sampling methods, we need to establish some strata for the states. We can consider geographic regions of the country to do this, namely census regions, of which there are five: Northeast, South, Midwest, West, and Pacific. The following tables divide the states into the appropriate groups. Observe that there is at least one state per group with a large number of electoral votes (at least 20), with the exception of the Pacific region.

Index	South	Votes	Index	Midwest	Votes	Index	West	Votes
1	Alabama	9	1	Illinois	20	1	Arizona	11
2	Arkansas	6	2	Indiana	11	2	California	55
3	Delaware	3	3	Iowa	6	3	Colorado	9
4	D.C.	3	4	Kansas	6	4	Idaho	4
5	Florida	29	5	Michigan	16	5	Montana	3
6	Georgia	16	6	Minnesota	10	6	Nevada	6
7	Kentucky	8	7	Missouri	10	7	New Mexico	5
8	Louisiana	8	8	Nebraska	5	8	Oregon	7
9	Maryland	10	9	North Dakota	3	9	Utah	6
10	Mississippi	6	10	Ohio	18	10	Washington	12
11	North Carolina	15	11	South Dakota	3	11	Wyoming	3
12	Oklahoma	7	12	Wisconsin	10	Index	Northeast	Votes
13	South Carolina	9				1	Connecticut	7
14	Tennessee	11				2	Maine	4
15	Texas	38				3	Massachusetts	11
16	Virginia	13				4	New Hampshire	4
17	West Virginia	5				5	New Jersey	14
Index	Pacific	Votes				6	New York	29
1	Alaska	3				7	Pennsylvannia	20
2	Hawaii	4				8	Rhode Island	4
						9	Vermont	3

Sampling this way would improve representation in our sample by ensuring that we sample at random from all over the country. Otherwise a simple random sample might, by unlucky chance, all come from mostly one specific region, thereby giving unreliable results.

EXAMPLE

It is now time to illustrate the stratified sampling method! The goal here is to take a simple random sample from all five groups. We shall take three states at random from all groups, except for Pacific, where we will sample just one. That means that we need to choose three numbers at random between 1 and 17 for South, three between 1 and 12 for Midwest, and so on, and then randomly choose one of Alaska and Hawaii.

The following table shows the selected states for our example, along with the corresponding averages out of three states per group. Note that for Pacific, since only one state was chosen, the average is just that one state's votes (here 3).

Index	South (17)	Votes	Index	Midwest (12)	Votes	Index	West (11)	Votes
5	Florida	29	4	Kansas	6	1	Arizona	11
12	Oklahoma	7	6	Minnesota	10	7	New Mexico	5
16	Virginia	13	12	Wisconsin	10	10	Washington	12
Avg		16.33333	Avg		8.66667	Avg		9.33333
Index	Northeast (9)	Votes	Index	Pacific (2)	Votes			
1	Connecticut	7	1	Alaska	3			
6	New York	29						
7	Pennsylvannia	20						
Avg		18.66667	Avg		3.00000			

The next step is to work out the overall average. It is tempting to just average the five averages; that is, add them and divide by 5 groups. However, the proper way is to compute a **weighted average** by considering how many total states are in each group. Groups with more states will have more weight.

The way to do this is to note that there are 51 states (counting D.C., even though technically it is not a state) and that the groups have counts of $17, 12, 11, 9$, and 2, all of which add to 51. This means that the South region will have a weight of $17/51$, the Midwest will have weight $12/51$, the West will have $11/51$, the Northeast $9/51$, and the Pacific $2/51$.

This is not as tricky as it may look, because notice that when you add all the fractions, you get $17/51 + 12/51 + 11/51 + 9/51 + 2/51 = 1$, or 100% of the states.

Now we multiply each weight by the corresponding group average to obtain the overall stratified sampling average:

$$\overline{x} = \left(\frac{17}{51} \times 16.33333\right) + \left(\frac{12}{51} \times 8.66667\right) + \left(\frac{11}{51} \times 9.33333\right) + \left(\frac{9}{51} \times 18.66667\right) + \left(\frac{2}{51} \times 3.00000\right)$$
$$= 12.90850$$

The stratified sample of 13 total states produced a sample mean of 12.90850 votes.

Δ

EXAMPLE

And last but not least, we illustrate the cluster sampling method. The goal here is to randomly choose some of the groups and then sample every state within those groups. We shall take two groups at random, and suppose it is decided to go with the South (17 states) and the Northeast (9 states), for a total of 26 states. That means we will find the average of all states for those two groups.

The following table shows the selected groups for our example, along with the corresponding averages out of all states per group.

Index	South	Votes	Index	South	Votes	Index	Northeast	Votes
1	Alabama	9	11	North Carolina	15	1	Connecticut	7
2	Arkansas	6	12	Oklahoma	7	2	Maine	4
3	Delaware	3	13	South Carolina	9	3	Massachusetts	11
4	D.C.	3	14	Tennessee	11	4	New Hampshire	4
5	Florida	29	15	Texas	38	5	New Jersey	14
6	Georgia	16	16	Virginia	13	6	New York	29
7	Kentucky	8	17	West Virginia	5	7	Pennsylvannia	20
8	Louisiana	8	Avg		11.52941	8	Rhode Island	4
9	Maryland	10				9	Vermont	3
10	Mississippi	6				Avg		10.66667

The next step is to work out the overall average. It is tempting to just average the two averages; however, similarly to the stratified method, we instead need to compute a weighted average. Here we take into account how many total states are in both groups.

The way to do this is to note that there are a total of 26 states (counting D.C.) and that the groups have counts of 17 and 9. This means that the South region will have a weight of $17/26$ and the Northeast will have weight 9/26. (The other regions were not selected, so they are left out.) Observe that adding the fractions produces $17/26 + 9/26 = 1$, or 100% of the selected states.

Now we multiply each weight by the corresponding group average to obtain the overall stratified sampling average:

$$\bar{x} = \left(\frac{17}{26} \times 11.52941\right) + \left(\frac{9}{26} \times 10.66667\right) = 11.23077$$

The cluster sample of 26 total states produced a sample mean of 11.23077 votes.

Δ

Section 4.4: Observational Studies versus Experiments

The next topic in this course focuses on designing and setting up observation studies and experiments. We first need to introduce some important terms and concepts, so for now, we take a sojourn from all the equations! To begin, we compare an observational study with an experiment.

DEFINITION

A study is an **observational study** if the subjects cannot be assigned to different groups at random; the groups have already been determined for us. We can observe the groups and look for patterns, but we cannot create our own groups with randomization.

Often a setup can be identified as an observational study when it appears that randomly assigning groups would be impossible or unethical. One consequence of such a study is that while we can pinpoint patterns and correlation, we cannot conclude that one variable causes the other, since there could be lurking variables (cf. correlation from Chapter 3).

EXAMPLE
1) Is there a connection between heart disease and whether a subject is a smoker? You cannot randomly assign some people to be smokers and some not to be – that would be unethical!
2) Are higher SAT scores related to higher college GPAs? We cannot force someone to score high or low on the SAT, and there could be lurking variables such as hours spent studying versus partying.
3) Are sharks in the Pacific Ocean more aggressive than sharks in the Atlantic Ocean? This is a nature question, so we obviously cannot assign sharks to groups based on ocean habitat.

Δ

DEFINITION

A study is said to be an **experiment** or **experimental design** if the subjects can be randomly assigned to groups for the study to be conducted.

Since we can randomly assign subjects to groups ourselves, an experiment can be used to prove causality. That is, by randomly assigning people to groups, any effects that would have come from lurking variables will be reduced greatly, allowing us to make proper conclusions about our variables.

Once again, an experiment can be used to prove that one variable (explanatory) causes the other (response) to turn out specific ways, whereas an observational study cannot; in the latter case, we can look for patterns, but they are not proof of causality.

EXAMPLE

1) Does a new medicine help reduce cholesterol? Given 40 subjects, 20 are randomly assigned to take the new medicine, while the other 20 will take a placebo pill instead.

2) Does the presence of an adorable puppy in a TV advert help increase sales? An advert for the product featuring a puppy (may I suggest a golden retriever!) is randomly assigned to air in 25 states, and a similar advert without the puppy is aired in the other 25 states. The resulting sales for the next month are recorded for both groups.

3) Does a new fertilizer help promote plant growth? A farmer randomly selects five regions of his farm to apply the new fertilizer, and another five regions to give a generic fertilizer, and the heights of the crops are recorded.

Δ

DEFINITION

A **placebo** is a sugar pill that is given in experiments involving a new medicine to the "control group." Usually the subjects do not know which type they are receiving, which we will get to a little later.

ETYMOLOGY

The words observation, experiment, and placebo all have Latin roots. They come from the words *observare*, *experiri*, and *placere*, which meant "to watch," "to try," and "to please,"respectively.

Section 4.5: Observational Studies and Survey Bias

There are three types of observational studies that one can conduct, in the hopes of searching for patterns.

DEFINITION

A **cross-sectional study** is where the opinions of subjects are of interest now, as opposed to a week from now.

EXAMPLE

If we wanted to know who the public currently thinks is going to win the upcoming presidential election, we would do a cross-sectional study, which would tell us the current opinion. Of course, the general opinion could change in the coming weeks.

Δ

DEFINITION

A **prospective study** is where a set of subjects are interviewed, and then some time later, the same subjects are interviewed again for comparisons to be made. (The prefix *pro-* is Latin for forward.)

EXAMPLE

We ask 100 subjects whether or not they are smokers, and then 20 years later, we follow up and see whether these subjects are still alive. Thus, we look into the future with a prospective study.

Δ

DEFINITION

A **retrospective** study is where some subjects with a certain quality of interest are interviewed on personal history, for the hopes of looking for potential connections. (The prefix *retro-* is Latin for backward.)

EXAMPLE
One example is when a food poisoning occurs with some people that attended a party. We can interview people that suffered the poisoning and people that did not, and find out what foods each had eaten.

Δ

DEFINITION
One type of retrospective study is called a **case-control study**, in which subjects who have a response outcome of interest (the cases) and subjects with the other response outcome (the controls) are compared on an explanatory variable.

EXAMPLE
The food poisoning example above is also a case-control study because the controls are people that did not develop food poisoning.

Δ

The next topic to cover involves potential sources of bias in surveys. A carefully constructed and conducted survey will lead to helpful results, but one wrong move and bias is introduced. There are four major types of survey bias that we now look at.

DEFINITION
Sampling design bias occurs when the subjects are not obtained randomly.

Undercoverage is when a survey fails to be representative of the population, or in other words it targets one sector of the population and misses others.

A survey needs to be sent out to a substantial number of subjects for a more accurate estimation. However, there is the danger that only a small number of these people might reply; perhaps the rest forget or are unwilling. **Nonresponse bias** is when a small number of surveys are returned, and this is trouble because while the original sample size might have been representative of the population, the shrunk size probably is not.

Response bias happens when a subject gives an incorrect answer to a survey question, or if the wording of the question is too confusing, or even if the question is "rigged." That is, the researcher could be hoping for people to answer a certain way, so he phrases the question in a positive or negative light.

EXAMPLE
The following are examples of the types of survey bias.
   A) We go to downtown Orlando and survey the first 40 people we see. This is not a random sample and is therefore sampling design bias.
   B) We survey a sample of 50 high school students about their favorite movies, except the survey only goes to freshman. This is undercoverage since other grades were excluded.
   C) We send a survey to 400 people in a specific county asking which candidate they plan to vote for in an upcoming election, but only 34 return the survey. This is nonresponse bias since most surveys were not returned.
   D) A researcher wants to find out what ice cream flavor is most popular in a high school. She personally loves chocolate ice cream and hopes that that flavor is also popular among her school. The question on the survey she sends out is phrased as "Do you prefer ***CHOCOLATE*** ice cream, or some other flavor?" This is response bias since the researcher is clearly trying to "farm" specific responses.

Δ

EXAMPLE
Classify the following situations by the type of survey bias.

A) A company mails a survey to 5000 randomly selected people over the country, inquiring about their household income and work benefits. Two weeks later, only 120 of these surveys are returned.

B) A doctor wants to know what insurance company most patients tend to have. He finds an alphabetical list of his patients, chooses all the people whose last name begins with A, and surveys them.

C) The Minneapolis government wants the public's opinion on whether a new major road through the city should be built. They send out a survey saying, "Do you support the idea of a new interstate through the city, which will reduce traffic on other roads and increase travel time from one part of the city to another?"

D) Prior to the 1948 United States presidential election, all the prediction polls said that Thomas Dewey would beat Harry Truman by a huge margin. On election night, Truman emerged victorious by a landslide. What happened? The vast majority of the polls were conducted by telephone, and back then only the richest Americans owned a phone. These people were more likely to vote for Dewey.

Solution:

A) This is nonresponse bias because a small percentage of the surveys were returned. The researcher must use the few surveys that were completed, which may not be representative of the population like the original sample size probably was.

B) This is sampling design bias because the sampling method is not random, since it involves deliberately taking the first set of patients whose names happen to begin with A.

C) This is response bias because the question is worded in a purposely positive light, presumably in the hopes that people will response "yes."

D) This is undercoverage because most of the telephone calls were to people with a telephone, which covered a small sector of the American population. Most other demographics were therefore ignored. The 1948 election is a classic example of how wrong survey predictions can be if the necessary precautions are not taken!

In fact, some newspapers were already preprinted announcing Truman's predicted defeat. There is a classic photograph from the *Chicago Daily Tribune* showing Truman holding a newspaper announcing his defeat – after he won the election.[2] As you might expect, this was one of the greatest embarrassments in the history of statistics!

Δ

ETYMOLOGY
The word bias has a couple of possible etymological roots. One possibility is that it came from the Greek επικάρσιος, which meant "oblique", and another is that the word arrived in the French language via the Old Provençal *biais*.

Section 4.6: Types of Experiments
There are numerous parts to an experiment, and they all take their own names. First, we have the explanatory and response variables, which we already saw back in Chapter 3.

DEFINITION

The **response variable** is the categorical or quantitative variable of interest. We suspect that it could be influenced by the explanatory variable, and the purpose of the experiment is to test this idea.

The **explanatory variable** is the categorical or quantitative variable that is believed to influence the response variable.

The **experimental units** are the subjects that undergo the experiment.

The **treatments** are conditions, medicines, etc. that are given to the subjects. They can be described as the levels of the explanatory variable.

EXAMPLE

We are growing 10 sets of plants under white light and another set of 10 plants under blue light. It is of interest to see if the light color received causes the plants to grow taller. The plants were randomly assigned to a color.

We believe that the light color could influence how tall the plants grow. This statement tells us that the explanatory variable is light color, while the response variable is the height of the plant (in cm, for instance). The experimental units are the subjects, which here are the 20 plants. The treatments are the levels of the explanatory variable, light color, so the treatments are white light and blue light.

Δ

Due to multiple methods in which an experiment can be conducted, there exist several different types of experimental designs. Let's look at each type.

DEFINITION

In a **completely randomized design**, we have N total independent subjects, and we randomly assign each subject into exactly one group. During the experiment, each subject receives just one treatment, and the results are compared later. Of course, the fact that random assignments took place is important.

EXAMPLE

The plant example above is a completely randomized design because each plant gets just one color of light. No plant receives both colors.

Δ

DEFINITION

In some cases, the subjects across groups may be dependent. If we have two groups, and each person in Group A is somehow related to somebody in Group B, then the groups are dependent. In which case, it would be appropriate to "match up" the dependent subject pairs and compare their individual differences in response variable measurements. This is a **matched pairs** experiment.

How might subjects be dependent across groups? In most cases (and for the purposes of introductory statistics), the same subjects would participate in both groups on different occasions. If the subjects participate in both groups during the course of the experiment, then the two groups are obviously dependent since the same people are in both groups. However, we could also have a study on identical twins. We could assign twin A to one group and twin B to the other, and then test for differences between twin pairs.

DEFINITION

Generally in this class, a matched pairs involves the same people in both groups. If this is the case, then the matched pairs design is also called a **crossover** design. That is, a crossover is a matched pairs in which the same subjects participate in both groups at some point in the experiment. (However, not all matched pairs are crossovers.) Of course, to make a better experiment, the order in which treatments are taken should be randomized.

EXAMPLE

In an experiment, 20 subjects will test the effects of exercise on heart rate. First, 10 people are randomly assigned to engage in three minutes of intense exercise, and then their heart rates are measured immediately following. The other 10 subjects stand still for three minutes, and then their pulses are taken. A little later, everybody switches: those who exercised earlier now stand still for three minutes, and vice versa, and everyone's pulse is taken again.

This is a crossover experiment because at the end, all 20 subjects will have participated in both groups (exercise and no exercise), so the two groups are dependent because they involve the same subjects. For the same reason, this is also a matched pairs experiment due to this dependency.

Δ

Why would we randomize the order in which subjects receive treatments? In some experiments, sometimes the first treatment received can have a "carryover" effect on the second treatment (especially if the treatments are medicines). This effect would be a lurking variable since it was not taken into account. By picking some subjects to have the treatments in reverse order, we eliminate the risk of carryover effects influencing the results.

DEFINITION

If every subject participates in two groups, and their response is recorded in both cases, it may be of interest to instead work with the differences in each person's two scores, and doing analysis on these differences. In such a case, we have a **randomized block design**. This is a type of matched pairs in which we do analysis on differences in peoples' own scores.

Why would we do this? Here is an example: suppose we are testing a new medicine, and we have subjects of a variety of ages. It is possible that younger people may respond differently to the medicine than older people, and if we do a regular average in one group, then the next, all the various age-dependent responses get mixed together. It would be more proper to "block" by person. That is, we instead compute the individual differences between scores, and it is with these differences that the analysis is conducted.

DEFINITION

A **block** in an experiment is referring to the people/subjects participating in the experiment.

Before we do an example, we need to discuss blindness. In an experiment, it is imperative that the subjects do not know which treatment they are receiving at the time they take it. Otherwise the placebo effect may upset results. In case you are not familiar with this term, here is what it means. Sometimes a subject who takes a placebo, but is told or believes it is the real medicine, will in fact respond to the placebo as if it were the medicine. In other words, the patient might experience improved health conditions even though he/she only took the placebo. This is due to the psychological belief that taking the pill will make them feel better rather than from a chemical effect.

Therefore subjects do not know which treatment they receive. However, the researcher may or may not know, depending on the experimental setup.

> **DEFINITION**
> An experiment in which the subjects do not know what they are receiving, but the researcher does, is **single blind**.
>
> An experiment in which the subjects do not know what they are receiving, and neither do the researchers, is **double blind**.

In reality, a double blind experiment is better because it eliminates the temptation for the researcher to "adjust" the results, hoping for a specific outcome.

EXAMPLE

Suppose 30 students taste two different types of cereal: name brand (Group A) and generic brand (Group B). Students taste first one and then the other, and the order in which cereal types are given is random for all students. Without knowing which cereal is which, the students give a rating (1 through 10) on how much they like each cereal. The instructor, who knows which cereal is which, then computes differences with individual ratings and conducts a statistical analysis.

Groups A and B both contain 30 subjects by the end of the experiment, and the same 30 students participate in both groups of cereal tasting. Thus, the two groups are dependent since they contain the same subjects, and therefore this is a crossover experiment (and consequently a matched pairs experiment). Since the instructor records the differences between individual responses, this is also a randomized block design.

The instructor knows which cereal is which, making the experiment single blind. An improvement would be to have another instructor not involved with the exercise determine which cereal goes to which group, hide the key in an envelope, and not tell the main experimenter the decision. Only after the results are collected and fully analyzed is the key revealed.

As an example of how such results would look, suppose the first three students' responses looked like this:

| Group A | 10 | 8 | 3 |
| Group B | 7 | 7 | 1 |

The first two students gave overall high ratings, whereas the third student gave low ratings. Rather than performing a straightforward average for Group A and then Group B, a randomized block design computes the differences with individual ratings (using the students as the blocks), and a statistical analysis is conducted on the differences, the first three of which are shown below:

Group A	10	8	3
Group B	7	7	1
Difference	3	1	2

Δ

Chapter 5 – Probability

In Chapter 5 we set the groundwork for studying and understanding probability, which will come into play in future chapters for statistical testing.

Section 5.1 – Basic Definitions of Probability

We begin with the definition of probability.

DEFINITION

The **probability** of an event is a numerical measure of how likely that event will happen. Probability is always between 0 and 1, inclusive (which means we count the endpoints). The closer the probability is to 1, the more likely the event will occur. The closer the probability is to 0, the less likely the event will happen.

As a formula, the probability of an **outcome**, or a specific event of interest, is equal to the number of times that outcome can happen divided by the total number of possible outcomes.

EXAMPLE

If we want to know the probability of drawing a club from a standard deck of cards, then the outcome of interest is drawing a club. Since there are 13 clubs in a deck of 52 cards, the probability of drawing a club on a single drawing is $13/52 = 0.25$.

Δ

EXAMPLE

Suppose we have an urn full of 8 blue marbles and 10 red marbles, for a total of 18. To compute the probability of drawing a red marble from this urn, the number of times this can happen is 10. Thus, the probability of drawing a red marble is 10/18, or 0.55556.

Δ

ETYMOLOGY

The word probability comes from the Latin *probabilis*, which meant "likely" or "probable."

Suppose we toss a coin 10 times. Assuming the probability of getting heads and tails is 0.50 each, we would expect to see 5 heads and 5 tails in these 10 flips, but this is certainly not always guaranteed to happen. For instance, in a set of 10 tosses, it is not uncommon to observe just 3 tails. This makes a proportion of tails in that sample just 3/10, or 0.30.

However, suppose now we toss the coin a much larger number of times, such as 10,000. Then we may observe, say, 4991 tails, meaning the proportion of tails in this sample is 4991/10000, or 0.4991. This proportion is much closer to the expected proportion of 0.50, and that is because we have a larger sample size. This is not coincidence; in fact, this is the Law of Large Numbers.

DEFINITION

The **Law of Large Numbers** says that if an experiment is repeated a large number of times, the ratio of "successes" to the number of trials will gradually approach the actual probability of the event occurring.

EXAMPLE

The most common letter in the English language is E, which occurs about 12.7% of the time out of all letters (the percentage varies slightly depending which source you consult).[1] Nevertheless, if we were to examine a single sentence, it should come as no surprise that we probably will not see this exact proportion of Es in that sentence. However, if we were to count up the number of times E is used in a large novel, then this constitutes a much larger sample of letters, so E will occur approximately 12.7% of the time in the large sample.

One interesting exception is the novel *A Void*, the English translation of *La Disparition* by Georges Perec, in which the entire nearly 300-page novel refrains from using the letter E.[2] The original version also avoids the letter E as it is also the most common letter in French.[3] What is interesting is that the translation, while maintaining the same letter requirement, is still readable and remains faithful to the original text! (This type of work is called a lipogram, in which specific letters are avoided. This term comes from the Greek λείπω and γράμμα, which meant "to leave out" and "letter.")

Δ

This Law of Large Numbers explains why casinos make money. Some gamblers may be lucky and make money, but most will gamble it straight back. One or two people might win a few thousand dollars and go home with it, but most of the time the casino will win. Put another way, the casino knows that in the long run, it will come out ahead.

Now that we have a basic understanding of what probability is, we next learn how to compute it for specific scenarios. The first step is to write out all possible outcomes.

DEFINITION

The **sample space**, denoted by S, is the set of all possible outcomes of an experiment. The contents of S are often denoted inside curly brackets { }, with outcomes separated by commas.

For one coin toss, you will either get heads or tails, so the sample space has two outcomes: Heads and Tails. We could write the sample space as $\{H, T\}$.

For one roll of a dice, the sample space has six outcomes: $\{1, 2, 3, 4, 5, 6\}$.

EXAMPLE

Suppose we have the thirteen of clubs from a standard deck of cards. The sample space of the thirteen cards would be the numbered cards $(2, 3, ..., 10)$, the jack, the queen, the king, and the ace. The sample space is therefore $\{2, 3, 4, 5, 6, 7, 8, 9, 10, J, Q, K, A\}$.

Δ

DEFINITION

An **event** is any subset of interest from a sample space. Events are denoted with letters.

We typically use letters close to the beginning of the alphabet for this. For example, if we have a standard dice, we want to know the event of rolling an even number. We can let A be the event of rolling an even number, so $A = \{2, 4, 6\}$. If B is the event of rolling an odd number, then $B = \{1, 3, 5\}$. (For some problems, it may be easier to assign letters that stand for specific kinds of events, so for instance we could also define E for an even number or J for drawing a jack from a deck of cards.)

DEFINITION

The **probability of an event A** is the likelihood of the event occurring. It is denoted as $P(A)$ and is read as "The probability of A."

EXAMPLE

Continuing the dice example, our sample space is $S = \{1, 2, 3, 4, 5, 6\}$. The event of rolling an even number is $A = \{2, 4, 6\}$. We can see that three out of the six possible numbers are even, so this means that the probability of rolling an even number is $3/6 = 0.50$. This would be written as

$$P(A) = \frac{3}{6} = 0.50$$

Δ

EXAMPLE

Suppose we toss two coins and count the number of heads. What is the sample space, and what is the probability of tossing exactly one head? Two heads? Zero heads?

Solution: Intuitively, since we have two coins, each of which has a head and a tail side (and both are equally likely), it should make sense that we could get zero heads, one head, or two heads. (We cannot obtain more than two heads since we have just two coins!) However, even though there are three possible outcomes (0, 1, or 2 heads), this does not necessarily mean that each of these three outcomes is equally likely. There are several ways we can figure out this problem, and we illustrate two possibilities.

The first method is to make a two-way table to illustrate the possible combinations of coin tosses.

	Head	Tail
Head	HH	HT
Tail	TH	TT

We can see that the four possible outcomes are HH, HT, TH, and TT.

The second method is to make a tree diagram. We start with the first coin, of which the outcomes are H and T. Then, from each of those outcomes we have two more outcomes for the second coin, also H and T. Our tree diagram would look like this:

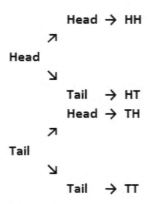

The four possible outcomes are once again HH, HT, TH, and TT. Thus, the sample space is $S = \{HH, HT, TH, TT\}$.

Now that we have the four combinations, we want to know the probability of tossing exactly one head. The two ways this can happen are HT and TH, so define event $A = \{HT, TH\}$. Let's look at our sample space S and event A:

$$S = \{HH, HT, TH, TT\}$$
$$A = \{HT, TH\}$$

The probability of tossing exactly one head is

$$P(A) = \frac{2}{4} = 0.50$$

If we instead want to know the probability of tossing exactly two heads, the only possible outcome is HH. Thus, we can define event $B = \{HH\}$, and so

$$P(B) = \frac{1}{4} = 0.25$$

Lastly, the probability of tossing zero heads would include the event $C = \{TT\}$, so

$$P(C) = \frac{1}{4} = 0.25$$

Δ

In general, there are two types of probabilities. The first is called classical probability, or relative frequency probability.

DEFINITION
Classical Probability, or the **Relative Frequency Probability**, is computed as the fraction of the number of ways an event can happen, divided by the number of possible outcomes. Mathematically, this is written as

$$P(A) = \frac{\text{Number of ways event A can happen}}{\text{Total number of possible outcomes}}$$

This fraction is exactly how we computed the coin toss probabilities in the previous example. When defining this fraction, every time we come across an outcome that has the same characteristic as the event of interest, we call that outcome a "success." Thus, the probability of the event happening is the number of successes divided by the number of possible outcomes. Of course, the word "success" should be interpreted loosely as the event may not always be a good event!

The second type of probability is called subjective probability.

DEFINITION
Subjective probability is a probability that is based on subjective opinion rather than numbers. (This is not usually discussed much in a statistics class.)

EXAMPLE
Suppose during a certain day, a total of 12,345 airplanes had flights. Out of all these flights, 120 of them crossed the International Date Line at some point. (People that fly west across the Date Line go forward a day, thereby literally losing 24 hours of their life. On the other hand, flying east across the Date Line rewards you with going backwards a day, so you would literally be given back the 24 hours you had previously lost!)

If we randomly select one of these flights, what is the probability it crossed the International Date Line?

Solution: We have 12,345 possible flights to pick, so this is the number of possible outcomes. The event of interest A is picking a flight that crosses the International Date Line, of which there are 120 flights. Thus, the probability is

$$P(A) = \frac{120}{12345} = 0.00972$$

Δ

EXAMPLE
If we make a pile of the 13 clubs from a standard deck of cards, what is the probability of randomly picking a face card?

Solution: A face card is a jack, queen, or king. There are 13 possible cards to pick, 3 of which are face cards. If F denotes the event of sampling a face card, then

$$P(F) = \frac{3}{13} = 0.23077$$

Δ

EXAMPLE
A team of astronauts needs to assess the probability that their space shuttle can safely launch on a specified day. However, they cannot compute probability by dividing a number of outcomes by a total number of outcomes. They have to make a subjective decision based on factors such as the weather, personal health, condition of the shuttle, etc.

Δ

Section 5.2 – Properties of Probabilities and Complements
There are two fundamental properties of probabilities that are basic facts and should be easy to recognize:

1) The probability of any event must be between 0 and 1, inclusive. This means that for an event A, $0 \leq P(A) \leq 1$.
2) The total of all the possible probabilities equals 1.

Let's check that these rules are true with the six possible outcomes from rolling a die. Recall that the sample space is $S = \{1, 2, 3, 4, 5, 6\}$. The probability of rolling any individual number is clearly $1/6$, so we have the following:

$$P(1) = \tfrac{1}{6} \qquad P(2) = \tfrac{1}{6} \qquad P(3) = \tfrac{1}{6} \quad P(4) = \tfrac{1}{6} \qquad P(5) = \tfrac{1}{6} \quad P(6) = \tfrac{1}{6}$$

Thus, each individual probability is between 0 and 1, inclusive. It is also easy to see that the sum of all probabilities equals 1:

$$P(1) + P(2) + P(3) + P(4) + P(5) + P(6) = \frac{1}{6} + \frac{1}{6} + \frac{1}{6} + \frac{1}{6} + \frac{1}{6} + \frac{1}{6} = 1$$

EXAMPLE
Here is an example of how to read probability from a contingency table. A university held a blood pressure screening clinic for its professors. The results are summarized in the table below by age group

and blood pressure level.

	Low Blood Pressure	High Blood Pressure	Total
Under 50	68	39	107
Over 50	33	78	111
Total	101	117	218

A) What is the probability that a randomly selected professor from this group is over the age of 50?
B) What is the probability that a randomly selected professor from this group has high blood pressure?
C) Which event is more likely?

Solution: To solve part A, we are randomly selecting a professor from anywhere in this table. There are 218 professors to choose from, so that is the denominator of the fraction. The numerator will be the total number of professors who are over the age of 50, of which there are 111 (we count both low and high blood pressure, as we are only interested in age). Thus, the probability that a professor randomly selected is over 50 is

$$P(\text{Over 50}) = \frac{111}{218} = 0.50917$$

To solve part B, we now want a professor from anywhere in the table that has high blood pressure (regardless of age). The denominator is the total number of professors, which is 218 again. There are 117 professors with high blood pressure. Thus, the probability that a professor randomly selected has high blood pressure is

$$P(\text{High blood pressure}) = \frac{117}{218} = 0.53670$$

As for part C, the more likely outcome is the event with the higher probability. It is therefore more likely to randomly choose a professor with high blood pressure than one who is over 50.

Δ

DEFINITION

The **complement** of an event A is the set of all outcomes in the sample space that are *not* part of event A. It is denoted as A^c, read as "A-complement" or "the complement of A," but some textbooks denote it as $\overline{A}$. The following formula is used to calculate the probability of the complement of A occurring:

$$P(A^c) = 1 - P(A)$$

This should make sense because of the following logic:

1) It is guaranteed that the event will either happen or not happen.
2) It is impossible for the event to both happen and not happen; it will do exactly one of the two.

Thus, $P(A) + P(A^c) = 1$, and therefore $P(A^c) = 1 - P(A)$. The complement formula comes in handy with many probability problems because it often introduces some helpful shortcuts. Here is a Venn diagram of what the complement of A looks like.

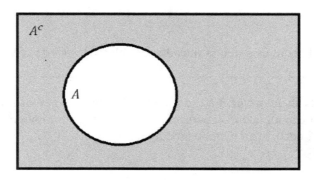

EXAMPLE
With the 13 clubs, let's say event F is drawing a face card. What is the complement of F, and what is the probability of F^c?

Solution: First, $F = \{J, Q, K\}$. The complement of F would be the remaining clubs that are not face cards, so $F^c = \{2, 3, 4, 5, 6, 7, 8, 9, 10, A\}$. There are 10 clubs that are not face cards and 13 possible clubs, so that means that

$$P(F^c) = \frac{10}{13} = 0.76923$$

Note that it is also possible to answer this question by first recognizing that $P(F) = 3/13$, which means that

$$P(F^c) = 1 - \frac{3}{13} = \frac{10}{13}$$

Δ

EXAMPLE
Suppose in a certain town, 58% of the residents have a television in their bedroom. What is the probability that a randomly selected resident of this town does not have a television in his/her bedroom?

Solution: If A denotes the event of having a TV in the bedroom, then $P(A) = 0.58$. Then A^c is the event of not having a TV in the bedroom, so $P(A^c) = 1 - 0.58 = 0.42$.

Δ

EXAMPLE
Suppose we have a classroom with 50 total seats, like the chart below. A shaded square means that someone is in that seat.

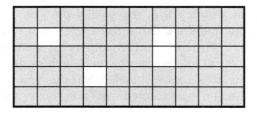

Our goal is to count how many people are present. We could count all full seats, but that would take us quite some time. An alternative is to instead consider the complement, which would involve counting the number of empty seats! There are 4 such seats and 50 total chairs in the room, and so there are $50 - 4 = 46$ empty seats.

Δ

Finally, although not talked about as much in introductory classes, let's briefly discuss odds.

DEFINITION

Given an event A, the **odds in favor of A** are defined to be the number of times A can occur expressed with the number of times A cannot occur. It is usually denoted as two numbers separated by a colon, as in $Y : N$. The probability that A occurs can then be computed as

$$P(A) = \frac{Y}{Y + N}$$

The probability that A does not occur, which is the complement, is then

$$P(A^C) = \frac{N}{Y + N}$$

For instance, when someone announces that a specific horse in a race has odds $1 : 10$ of winning a race, it does not mean a $1/10$ chance of winning. Instead, it means that for every 1 race won, on average the horse loses 10 races. That is a total of 11 races, which means the horse has a $1/11$ chance of winning and therefore a $10/11$ chance of losing.

EXAMPLE

A specific lottery scratch-off card says that your odds of winning are $1 : 5.17$. Find the probability of winning on this card. On another card, it is known that for every 2 cards that are winners, on average there are 13 more cards that are not winners. Find the odds of winning on this second scratch-off card.

Solution: For the first card, we can define $Y = 1$ and $N = 5.17$, so

$$P(\text{Winning}) = \frac{Y}{Y + N} = \frac{1}{1 + 5.17} = 0.16207$$

For the second card, for every $Y = 2$ winning cards, there are $N = 13$ losing cards, which makes 15 total. Thus, the odds of winning on one of these cards are $2 : 13$.

Δ

As a little side note, you may have noticed in situations that involve betting such as playing lotteries, the chances of winning are usually expressed as odds and not as probabilities. This is because many people think they know what odds are, but they get them confused with probability and are tricked into thinking that they have a higher chance of winning than they really do. For instance, with the horse example above, you might see the $1 : 10$ odds and think that it has a $1/10 = 0.10$ chance of winning, but actually the chances are $1/11 = 0.09091$, a bit smaller. The companies want you to look at odds instead of probabilities because odds are harder to interpret correctly, which means the companies will make more money since the majority of people don't always understand the true probabilities of losing. However, now you are in the minority because you have learned what odds really are!

Section 5.3 – And/Or Probabilities and Disjoint Sets

This section concentrates on compound events, which are when two or more events take place simultaneously.

DEFINITION

Given two events A and B, the **probability of A and B** consists of the outcomes that are in both A and B. In other words, this means that both A and B have to occur at the same time. This is written as $P(A \text{ and } B)$, or sometimes as $P(A \cap B)$.

Similarly, the **probability of A or B** consists of the outcomes that are either in A, in B, or in both. In other words, this means that either A occurs and B does not, or B occurs and A does not, or both A and B occur together. Put another way, at least one of A or B occur (possibly both, but that is not necessary). This is written as $P(A \text{ or } B)$, or sometimes as $P(A \cup B)$.

EXAMPLE

Given one roll from a standard dice, what is the probability of rolling a 1 OR a 3? What is the probability of rolling a 1 AND a 3?

Solution: We can solve this easily just by looking at the possibilities. There are 6 possible outcomes of one dice roll. Of these outcomes, the dice can either be a 1 or a 3, which represents two possible "successes." Thus, the probability of rolling either a 1 or a 3 would be

$$P(1 \text{ or } 3) = \frac{2}{6} = 0.33333$$

As for the probability of rolling both a 1 and a 3 on the same roll, we can quickly see that this is impossible since exactly one number should emerge from one roll. Thus,

$$P(1 \text{ and } 3) = \frac{0}{6} = 0$$

Δ

Here is a Venn diagram of what $P(A \text{ or } B)$ would look like. The shaded region means that the events of interest can occur in A only (left), or both A and B (middle), or B only (right).

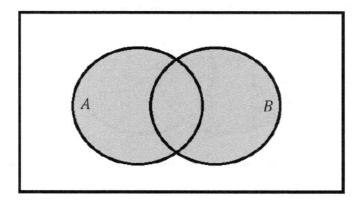

Here is a Venn diagram of what $P(A \text{ and } B)$ would look like. The shaded region in the middle means that the events of interest can only occur in both A and B. Put another way, if the event is in A but not B, or vice versa, it does not count.

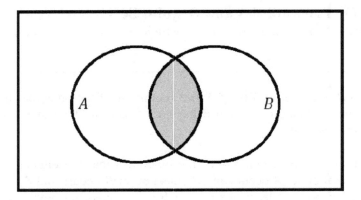

Incidentally, in 1880 English mathematician John Venn introduced Venn diagrams in his publication *On the Diagrammatic and Mechanical Representation of Propositions and Reasonings*.[4] He was born in Kingston upon Hull, a town in Yorkshire that happens to be less than 50 miles from Scarborough, where my family is from!

PROBABILITY OF *A* OR *B*

Given two events *A* and *B* along with their probabilities, we can compute the probability of *A* or *B* using the following formula:

$$P(A \text{ or } B) = P(A) + P(B) - P(A \text{ and } B)$$

This formula should make sense if we study the following Venn diagrams. We first look at the probability of *A* (first diagram, light gray area) and then add in the probability of *B* (second diagram, dark gray and light gray areas). However, in doing so, we have counted the middle area (*A* and *B*) twice (second diagram, dark gray area). We therefore must compensate and subtract the probability of *A* and *B* to avoid double-counting it (third diagram, where the light gray area represents the now correctly counted probability).

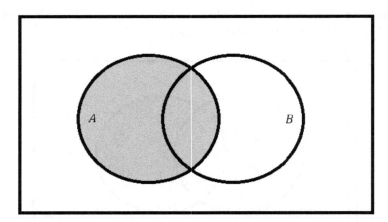

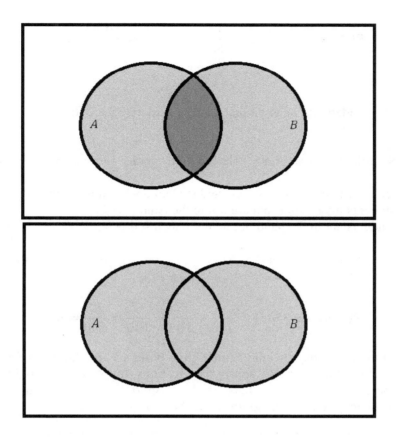

EXAMPLE

Given a standard deck of cards, what is the probability of randomly drawing a card that is a diamond and an ace? How about the probability of randomly drawing a card that is a diamond or an ace?

Solution: To find P(Diamond and Ace), we recognize that there are 52 cards total in the deck, so 52 will be the denominator. The numerator is the number of cards that are both diamonds and aces. There is only one such card, the Ace of Diamonds, and so

$$P(\text{Diamond and Ace}) = \frac{1}{52} = 0.01923$$

To find P(Diamond or Ace), we can use two different approaches. First, we again know that the denominator will be 52. The numerator is the total number of cards that are either a diamond or an ace or both. There are 13 diamonds and 4 aces, except one of the aces is also a diamond, so we only count 3 more aces. Thus, the numerator is $13 + 3 = 16$, making the answer

$$P(\text{Diamond or Ace}) = \frac{16}{52} = 0.30769$$

The second method uses the formula we have just learned. First, we can find the probability of drawing a diamond, followed by the probability of drawing an ace. With 13 diamonds and 4 aces, that means that P(Diamond) $= 13/52$ and P(Ace) $= 4/52$. We already worked out that P(Diamond and Ace) $= 1/52$. Thus, the probability of drawing a card that is a diamond or an ace is

$$P(\text{Diamond or Ace}) = \frac{13}{52} + \frac{4}{52} - \frac{1}{52} = \frac{16}{52} = 0.30769$$

Δ

EXAMPLE

A school has 100 ninth-graders. It is known that 51 play a sport, 32 are in the band, and 12 participate in both activities.

A) Find the probability that a randomly selected ninth-grader participates in at least one of these two activities.
B) Find the probability that a randomly selected student does neither of these activities.
C) How many students play a sport but are not in the band?
D) How many students are in the band but do not play a sport?

Solution: For part A, we have $P(\text{Sport}) = 51/100$, $P(\text{Band}) = 32/100$, and $P(\text{Sport and Band}) = 12/100$. Using the formula,

$$P(\text{Sport or Band}) = \frac{51}{100} + \frac{32}{100} - \frac{12}{100} = \frac{71}{100} = 0.71$$

To answer the remaining questions, it would be helpful to build a Venn diagram of all possible situations and indicate the number of students in the appropriate sections. Intuitively, it should make sense that we have four possible outcomes for an individual student: Sport Only, Band Only, Sport and Band, or Neither. Let's start in the middle of the diagram: 12 do both activities.

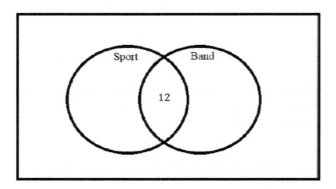

Next, 51 students play a sport, but this includes 12 that are also in the band. It therefore follows that $51 - 12 = 39$ play a sport but are not in the band.

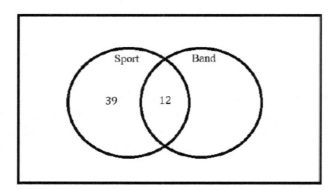

There are 32 students that are in the band, but this includes 12 that also play a sport. It therefore follows that $32 - 12 = 20$ are in the band but do not play a sport.

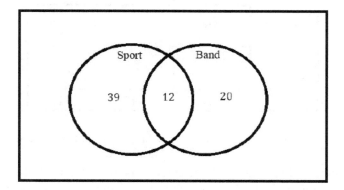

Finally, there are 100 students total. We have discovered that 39 play a sport only, 20 are in the band only, and 12 do both. This means that the number of students who do neither activity would be $100 - 39 - 20 - 12 = 100 - 71 = 29$.

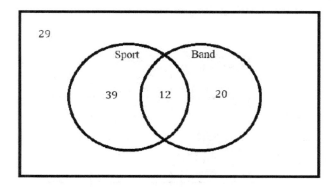

With 29 students who do neither activity, this means that for part B,

$$P(\text{Neither Sport nor Band}) = \frac{29}{100} = 0.29$$

To answer the remaining questions, 39 students play a sport but are not in the band, and 20 students are in the band but do not play a sport.

Δ

We can also compute AND and OR probabilities of two events given a contingency table. The easiest way to do this is to look at each individual cell and ask whether those cells satisfy both/at least one of the attributes of interest.

In particular, with a table with two rows and two columns (not counting the row and column with totals), you will find that one cell is used for an AND probability, whereas three cells are taken for an OR probability.

EXAMPLE
Here is the blood pressure chart again.

	Low Blood Pressure	High Blood Pressure	Total
Under 50	68	39	107
Over 50	33	78	111
Total	101	117	218

A) If a person is selected at random, what is the probability that the person is under 50 and has low blood pressure?
B) What is the probability that a randomly selected person is under 50 or has low blood pressure? In other words, they could be under 50 only, or have low blood pressure only, or have both traits.
C) Find the probability that someone selected at random is over 50 or has high blood pressure.
D) Find the probability that someone selected at random is over 50 and has high blood pressure.

Solution: Since this is a two-way table, we can easily find where in the table the traits of interest fall. Parts A and B deal with the events of being under 50 and having low blood pressure. The table is shown again with those areas in dark gray.

	Low Blood Pressure	High Blood Pressure	Total
Under 50	68	39	107
Over 50	33	78	111
Total	101	117	218

The 68 represents the "AND," where professors have both traits and the dark gray row and column overlap. This means that

$$P(\text{Under 50 and Low Blood Pressure}) = \frac{68}{218} = 0.31193$$

The 68, 39, and 33 together represent the "OR," where professors have at least one trait or both traits in a dark gray cell. This means that

$$P(\text{Under 50 or Low Blood Pressure}) = \frac{68}{218} + \frac{39}{218} + \frac{33}{218} = \frac{140}{218} = 0.64220$$

Next, parts C and D deal with the events of being over 50 and having high blood pressure. The table is shown again with those areas in dark gray.

	Low Blood Pressure	High Blood Pressure	Total
Under 50	68	39	107
Over 50	33	78	111
Total	101	117	218

The 78 represents the "AND," where professors have both traits and the dark gray row and column overlap. Thus,

$$P(\text{Over 50 and High Blood Pressure}) = \frac{78}{218} = 0.35780$$

The 39, 33, and 78 together represent the "OR," where professors have at least one trait or both traits in a dark gray cell. Thus,

$$P(\text{Over 50 or High Blood Pressure}) = \frac{39}{218} + \frac{33}{218} + \frac{78}{218} = \frac{150}{218} = 0.68807$$

Δ

One other useful topic concerns events that cannot occur together.

DEFINITION

Two events A and B are **disjoint**, or **mutually exclusive**, if it is impossible for them to occur at the same time. In other words, $P(A \text{ and } B) = 0$. Consequently, if A and B are disjoint, the formula for $P(A \text{ or } B)$ simplifies to

$$P(A \text{ or } B) = P(A) + P(B)$$

Here is a Venn diagram of what two disjoint sets would look like. Notice they do not overlap.

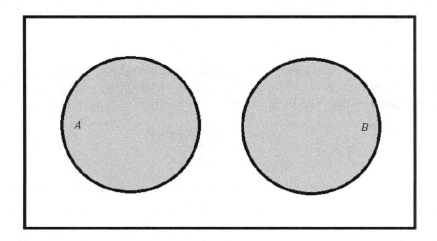

EXAMPLE

A piggybank is known to contain eight pennies, three nickels, two dimes, and five quarters. You reach inside and randomly pick one coin.

    A) Find the probability of choosing a coin that is both a nickel and a quarter.
    B) Find the probability of choosing a coin that is either a nickel or a quarter.
    C) Find the probability of choosing a coin whose value is a multiple of 5 cents.

Solution: First note that we are drawing exactly one coin, so let N and Q denote the events of drawing a coin that is a nickel and a coin that is a quarter, respectively. For part A, it is impossible for a coin to be both a nickel and a quarter, so $P(N \text{ and } Q) = 0$. These are disjoint events.

For part B, we need to use the formula we learned earlier, $P(N \text{ or } Q) = P(N) + P(Q) - P(N \text{ and } Q)$, except since N and Q are disjoint, the formula simplifies to

$$P(N \text{ or } Q) = P(N) + P(Q)$$

Since there are $8 + 3 + 2 + 5 = 18$ total coins, of which we have 3 nickels and 5 quarters,

$$P(N \text{ or } Q) = P(N) + P(Q) = \frac{3}{18} + \frac{5}{18} = \frac{8}{18} = 0.44444$$

For part C, the penny (1 cent) is the only coin whose value is not a multiple of 5 (the nickel, dime, and quarter are worth 5, 10, and 25 cents, respectively). There are 8 pennies, so there are $18 - 8 = 10$ coins that are not pennies (using the idea of the complement), which means

$$P(\text{multiple of } 5) = 1 - P(\text{penny}) = 1 - \frac{8}{18} = \frac{10}{18} = 0.55556$$

Δ

Section 5.4 – Conditional Probability

Up until now we have been working with "straightforward probabilities." We have been able to solve most of these simply by thinking of how many total outcomes there are, and then how many outcomes of interest, or successes, can occur, and dividing the two. There is another type called conditional probability that we will study in this section.

DEFINITION

Given two events A and B, the **probability of A given B** is the probability that A occurs, given that B has already occurred. This is written as $P(A \mid B)$ and is read "the probability of A given B." This situation is known as **conditional probability**. The formula for the probability of A given B is

$$P(A \mid B) = \frac{P(A \text{ and } B)}{P(B)}$$

However, in most cases we will not need this formula since we can usually build the probability fraction by figuring out the denominator, followed by the numerator.

What this means is that the denominator of the probability fraction is no longer the total number of possible outcomes. We are told that a specific event has already happened, and so given that event, we want to know the probability of a further event happening.

For instance, if you roll a dice and it is known that an even number was rolled, what is the probability that you rolled a 2?

Previously we would have said that the sample space was $S = \{1, 2, 3, 4, 5, 6\}$ and that the denominator of the probability fraction was 6. However, this time we know that the number rolled was even. That means that now $S = \{2, 4, 6\}$, which means the denominator is in fact 3. Of these three numbers, there is only one way to roll a 2, and so we would write

$$P(\text{Rolling a 2} \mid \text{Even Number}) = \frac{1}{3} = 0.33333$$

We should also give an example of using the formula in the box above (although in most cases, I would recommend just counting how many possible events are in the denominator, followed by how many possible events are in the numerator). Repeating the dice example, we would set up

$$P\big((\text{Rolling a 2} \mid \text{Even Number}\big) = \frac{P(\text{Rolling a 2 and Even Number})}{P(\text{Even Number})}$$

For the denominator, three of the six possible numbers are even, so $P(\text{Even Number}) = 3/6 = 1/2$. For the numerator, notice that the events "rolling a 2" and "even number" can be rewritten simply as "rolling a 2" since rolling that number results in an even number anyway, so $P(\text{Rolling a 2 and Even Number}) = P(\text{Rolling a 2}) = 1/6$. Thus,

$$P\big((\text{Rolling a 2} \mid \text{Even Number}\big) = \frac{1/6}{1/2} = \frac{1}{6} \times \frac{2}{1} = \frac{1}{3} = 0.33333$$

We arrive at the same answer, albeit in a more complicated approach. For these conditional probability questions, please use whichever approach is easiest for you!

As another example, suppose you have a standard deck of cards and randomly draw a card. Given that the card is a heart, what is the probability that it is a 5 or a jack?

To solve this, we are told that the selected card is a heart, of which there are 13. That means that the denominator is 13. Of these thirteen cards, we want either a 5 or a jack, so there are two possible cards. That means that

$$P(\text{5 or Jack} \mid \text{Heart}) = \frac{2}{13} = 0.15385$$

Forgive this little diversion, but we need an English grammar lesson. An independent clause is a sentence (meaning it has a subject and a verb) that can stand alone as its own complete sentence. A subordinate clause also has a subject and a verb, but when standing alone it is a fragment. Only when it is paired with an independent clause do the two come together as a complete sentence.

EXAMPLE
The sentence "The chef will cook the pizza" is an independent clause because it has a subject (the chef), a verb (will cook), and it can stand alone as its own sentence.

Now consider the sentence "When the toppings are ready, the chef will cook the pizza." The statement "the chef will cook the pizza" is the meat of the sentence (pun intended!) as that is the independent clause. However, the statement "When the toppings are ready" is a fragment because it cannot stand alone as a complete sentence. It is therefore a subordinate clause.

$$\Delta$$

What does this have to do with probability? Given a probability question, we can determine whether it is a straightforward probability or a conditional probability by analyzing the grammatical components of the sentence.

The question "What is the probability of randomly drawing a card that is a heart?" is an independent clause because the entire statement stands alone as its own sentence. Thus, it is a straightforward probability question (not conditional), so we would consider all 52 cards in the denominator. There are 13 hearts, so the answer is 13/52.

On the other hand, consider the question "If a randomly selected card is a heart, what is the probability that it is a jack?" The main part of the sentence, "what is the probability that it is a jack," is the independent clause, but "if a randomly selected card is a heart" is a subordinate clause because it is a fragment if left alone. This tells us that the entire question is for a conditional probability.

Of course, if the word "given" is used in the question, you know right away that it is a conditional probability! However, you will not always see the word "given" due to the marvelous flexibility of the English language. Consider these variations:

"Given that the randomly selected card is a heart, …"
"If the randomly selected card is a heart, …"
"Assuming that the randomly selected card is a heart, …"
"If we are told that the randomly selected card is a heart, …"

EXAMPLE
We have an urn full of marbles of the following colors: 20 red, 16 blue, 17 green, and 8 yellow. We reach inside the urn and randomly select a marble.

A) What is the probability of drawing a primary color? (Red, yellow, blue)
B) What is the probability the marble drawn is not red?
C) If the marble drawn was a primary color, what is the probability it was blue or yellow?

Solution: To solve part A, this is a straightforward probability question (the sentence is an independent clause). There are 61 marbles inside the urn, so 61 will be the denominator. There are $20 + 8 + 16 = 44$ marbles that are a primary color, and so the answer is

$$P(\text{Primary Color}) = \frac{44}{61} = 0.72131$$

Part B is also a straightforward probability because the sentence is another independent clause. Again, 61 is the denominator. There are $16 + 17 + 8 = 41$ marbles that are a color other than red, and so the answer is

$$P(\text{Not Red}) = \frac{41}{61} = 0.67213$$

Note that we can also answer the question by using the complement formula by noting that there are 20

118

red marbles:

$$P(\text{Not Red}) = 1 - P(\text{Red}) = 1 - \frac{20}{61} = \frac{41}{61} = 0.67213$$

For part C, observe that even though the word "given" is not used, the probability is now conditional. We are told that the marble was a primary color, of which there are 44, which is the denominator. Of these 44 marbles, $16 + 8 = 24$ are either blue or yellow. That means that

$$P(\text{Blue or Yellow} \mid \text{Primary Color}) = \frac{24}{44} = 0.54545$$

Note that one way we could spot the conditional part of this question is that "If the marble drawn was a primary color" is a subordinate clause. That would give us a clue that the denominator will be something other than the grand total of 61 marbles. (As a side note, it is disturbingly ironic that the only occasions in life when urns are mentioned seem to be with cremation and probability!)

Δ

EXAMPLE

The following chart contains all the currently allowed two-letter words that can be played in Scrabble ... a whopping 124![5] Suppose we randomly select a word from this list.

Two-Letter Words Allowed in Scrabble															
AA	AB	AD	AE	AG	AH	AI	AL	AM	AN	AR	AS	AT	AW	AX	AY
BA	BE	BI	BO	BY	CH	DA	DE	DI	DO	EA	ED	EE	EF	EH	EL
EM	EN	ER	ES	ET	EX	FA	FE	FY	GI	GO	GU	HA	HE	HI	HM
HO	ID	IF	IN	IO	IS	IT	JA	JO	KA	KI	KO	KY	LA	LI	LO
MA	ME	MI	MM	MO	MU	MY	NA	NE	NO	NU	NY	OB	OD	OE	OF
OH	OI	OM	ON	OO	OP	OR	OS	OU	OW	OX	OY	PA	PE	PI	PO
QI	RE	SH	SI	SO	ST	TA	TE	TI	TO	UG	UH	UM	UN	UP	UR
	US	UT	WE	WO	XI	XU	YA	YE	YO	YU	ZA	ZO			

A) What is the probability of selecting a word whose first letter is A?
B) If the word selected began with A, what is the probability that the second letter is a vowel? (Y does not count!)
C) Given that the chosen word begins with E, what is the probability that the second letter is in the first half of the alphabet? (A, B, ..., L, M)

Solution: Part A is a straightforward probability question. There are 124 words, of which 16 begin with A. Thus,

$$P(\text{First letter is A}) = \frac{16}{124} = 0.1290$$

To solve part B, observe that we are only concerning ourselves with the words beginning with A, of which there are 16. This means that the denominator is no longer 124, but is now 16. Of these 16 words, there are 3 where the second letter is a vowel: AA, AE, and AI. This means that

$$P(\text{Second letter is a vowel} \mid \text{First letter is A}) = \frac{3}{16} = 0.1875$$

As for part C, the first part of the sentence "Given that the chosen word begins with E" indicates that this is another conditional probability. We are only focusing on the words that begin with E, of which there are 12. Of these 12, how many have a second letter that is in the first half of the alphabet? There are 7: EA, ED, EE, EF, EH, EL, and EM. That means that

$$P(\text{Second letter is in first half of alphabet} \mid \text{First letter is E}) = \frac{7}{12} = 0.58333$$

Δ

We now turn to finding conditional probabilities in a contingency table. If you recall from the end of Chapter 3, we were computing conditional probabilities for contingency tables. Those were literally conditional probabilities.

Consider the following contingency table. Here we are looking at a sample of two different types of batteries (AA versus C) and investigating how many of them are working and how many are faulty. This is often done as part of a quality control check.

	Not Working	Working	Total
Type AA	60	700	760
Type C	40	660	700
Total	100	1360	1460

In Chapter 3, we would have said, "What proportion of the AA batteries are working?" Now, we can also phrase it as "Given that a battery selected is AA, what is the probability it is working?" Another choice of words would be: "If the battery drawn from the sample is AA, what is the probability it is working?"

To answer the question, we know that we are dealing with AA only (and not all 1460 batteries), and so we are only considering the 760 qualifying batteries. We look in that row only and then note that 700 of the AAs are in good condition. Hence, the answer is

$$P(\text{Working Battery} \mid \text{AA}) = \frac{700}{760} = 0.92015$$

What question would we be answering if we had instead computed 1360/1460? First, 1460 is the grand total, so the question is straightforward and not conditional. The 1360 figure represents all the working batteries. Thus, the proportion 1360/1460 represents the probability that a randomly selected battery is working.

EXAMPLE
Let's do some more with the battery table.

	Not Working	Working	Total
Type AA	60	700	760
Type C	40	660	700
Total	100	1360	1460

A) What is the probability of randomly selecting a C battery?
B) If the battery drawn is a C, what is the probability it is not working?
C) Given that the battery sampled is faulty, what is the probability it was an AA type?
D) What situation would be indicated by the probability 660/1360?

Solution: Part A is a straightforward probability because we only want the proportion of C batteries. There are 1460 total batteries, 700 of which are C. The answer is

$$P(C) = \frac{700}{1460} = 0.47945$$

For part B, we are only concerned with the C batteries, of which there are 700. Of these 700, there are 660 that are working (in that same row of the table). This means that

$$P(\text{Working} \mid C) = \frac{660}{700} = 0.94286$$

For part C, we are told that the chosen battery is faulty, or not working. This is conditional, and there are 100 batteries that are not working. Of these 100, 60 are AA, and so

$$P(AA \mid \text{Not Working}) = \frac{60}{100} = 0.60$$

As for part D, we need to work out the corresponding question that has an answer of 660/1360. First, the denominator is not 1460, which tells us that the probability is conditional. The 1360 figure represents all the working batteries, so we are given that the randomly sampled battery is working. That means we should stay in the "working" column of the table, which leads us to the 660 figure, the C batteries in that column.

The 660/1360 probability is therefore the answer to this question: "If the selected battery is working, what is the probability it is a C battery?" In notation,

$$P(C \mid \text{Working}) = \frac{660}{1360} = 0.48529$$

Δ

Section 5.5 – Independent Events
This section introduces the concept of independent events.

DEFINITION

Two events *A* and *B* are said to be **independent** if the chances of one event occurring have no impact on whether or not the other event occurs. In other words, perhaps both, one, or neither of the events will happen, but one has no effect on the other.

Two events are **dependent** if they are not independent.

For instance, consider the following events:

A = Getting a tail on a coin toss.

B = Getting a tail on a different coin toss.

The outcome of one coin toss has no impact on what happens on another coin toss, so A and B are independent events. On the other hand, consider the next two events:

C = Studying for eight hours for an exam.
D = Getting an A on the exam.

Clearly, the more you study for an exam, the more likely you will get a high score on the exam. This means that C and D are related and therefore dependent.

DEFINITION

If two events A and B are independent, then the probability of both A and B occurring at the same time can be computed using the following formula known as the **multiplication rule**:

$$P(A \text{ and } B) = P(A) \times P(B)$$

In other words, the multiplication rule can be used only if the two events are known to be independent. It does not work if the events are dependent.

EXAMPLE

We have two drawers, one of which contains 5 pairs of black socks and 6 pairs of white socks. The other drawer contains 2 red hats, 4 blue hats, and 3 black hats. Assume we are not looking when we reach into the drawers.

A) Find the probability of drawing a black pair of socks and a black hat.
B) Find the probability of drawing a white pair of socks and a red hat.

Solution: For both parts, since we are not looking when we make draws, the choice of sock color has no effect on the choice of hat color. Thus, sock color and hat color are independent of each other, so we can use the formula we just learned. Note that there are 11 pairs of socks and 9 hats total. For part A,

$$P(\text{Black Socks and Black Hat}) = P(\text{Black Socks}) \times P(\text{Black Hat})$$
$$= \frac{5}{11} \times \frac{3}{9}$$
$$= \frac{15}{99} = 0.15152$$

For part B,

$$P(\text{White Socks and Red Hat}) = P(\text{White Socks}) \times P(\text{Red Hat})$$
$$= \frac{6}{11} \times \frac{2}{9}$$
$$= \frac{12}{99} = 0.12121$$

Δ

EXAMPLE
Here is the blood pressure chart – again!

	Low Blood Pressure	High Blood Pressure	Total
Under 50	68	39	107
Over 50	33	78	111
Total	101	117	218

A) Find the probability that a randomly selected professor is under 50.
B) Find the probability that a randomly selected professor has low blood pressure.
C) Find the probability that a randomly selected professor is under 50 and has low blood pressure.
D) Are the events "under 50" and "having low blood pressure" independent?

Solution: For part A, this is simply the number of professors under 50 divided by the total:

$$P(\text{Under 50}) = \frac{107}{218} = 0.49083$$

Part B is similar, only with professors with low blood pressure:

$$P(\text{Low Blood Pressure}) = \frac{101}{218} = 0.46330$$

For part C, we now concern ourselves with professors who are under 50 and have low blood pressure, of which there are 68 in the table:

$$P(\text{Under 50 and Low Blood Pressure}) = \frac{68}{218} = 0.31193$$

Lastly, part D asks whether "under 50" and "having low blood pressure" are independent events. To answer that, we need to see if the multiplication rule can be used, or in other words if the following equation is true:

$$P(\text{Under 50 and Low Blood Pressure}) = P(\text{Under 50}){\times}P(\text{Low Blood Pressure})$$

We have all three probabilities from above, so let's see if the equation works:

$$P(\text{Under 50 and Low Blood Pressure}) = 0.31193$$
$$P(\text{Under 50}){\times}P(\text{Low Blood Pressure}) = 0.46330{\times}0.31193$$
$$= 0.22740$$

This tells us that the probability $P(\text{Under 50 and Low Blood Pressure})$ does not equal $P(\text{Under 50}){\times}P(\text{Low Blood Pressure})$, which means that the two events cannot be independent.

$$\Delta$$

This example shows us that if two events are dependent, then the multiplication rule cannot be used. It only works if the events are independent. (As a side note, if the formula $P(A \text{ and } B) = P(A){\times}P(B)$ is true, it does not necessarily prove that A and B are independent. However, if the formula is not true, then A and B are definitely not independent.)

This last interesting example uses all the important probability concepts.

EXAMPLE
Easter Sunday is a movable holiday, which means it changes dates every year. Easter can fall on one of thirty-five different dates from March 22 through April 25, and statisticians have calculated the following probabilities that Easter occurs on any of these individual days. These probabilities are shown in the following table.[6]

Date	Prob.	Date	Prob.	Date	Prob.	Date	Prob.	Date	Prob.
Mar 22	0.00483	Mar 29	0.03383	Apr 5	0.03383	Apr 12	0.03383	Apr 19	0.03867
Mar 23	0.00950	Mar 30	0.03325	Apr 6	0.03325	Apr 13	0.03325	Apr 20	0.03325
Mar 24	0.01425	Mar 31	0.03325	Apr 7	0.03325	Apr 14	0.03325	Apr 21	0.02850
Mar 25	0.01933	Apr 1	0.03383	Apr 8	0.03383	Apr 15	0.03383	Apr 22	0.02417
Mar 26	0.02333	Apr 2	0.03267	Apr 9	0.03267	Apr 16	0.03267	Apr 23	0.01867
Mar 27	0.02900	Apr 3	0.03383	Apr 10	0.03383	Apr 17	0.03383	Apr 24	0.01450
Mar 28	0.03267	Apr 4	0.03267	Apr 11	0.03267	Apr 18	0.03463	Apr 25	0.00737

A) Find the probability that for a randomly selected year, Easter falls in March.
B) For a randomly selected year, if Easter is known to fall in March, find the probability that it occurs on March 22.
C) Suppose Easter is considered early if it falls within the first possible week (March 22 though March 28) and late if it falls within the last possible week (April 19 through April 25). For a randomly selected year, find the probability that Easter occurs early and late.
D) For a randomly selected year, find the probability that Easter occurs early or late.
E) For two randomly selected years, find the probability that Easter is late in both years.
F) For three randomly selected years, find the probability that Easter is in April for all three years.

Solution: This problem is oozing statistics from every pore! For part A, the probability that Easter falls in March for a random year is simply equal to the sum of the probabilities for each of the ten possible dates of March 22 through March 31:

$$P(\text{March}) = P(\text{March 22}) + P(\text{March 23}) + \cdots + P(\text{March 31})$$
$$= 0.00483 + 0.00950 + 0.01425 + 0.01933 + 0.02333 + 0.02900 + 0.03267 + 0.03383$$
$$+ 0.03325 + 0.03325$$
$$= 0.23324$$

Thus, the probability that Easter falls in March is slightly less than one-fourth.

For part B, this is a conditional probability because Easter is given to be in March, so we are only concerned with the ten March dates. Due to the problem giving probabilities and not counts, we have no choice but to use the conditional probability formula, the one mentioned briefly earlier:

$$P(A \mid B) = \frac{P(A \text{ and } B)}{P(B)}$$

Here we want the probability that Easter falls on March 22 given that it falls in March. Using the above formula,

$$P(\text{March 22} \mid \text{March}) = \frac{P(\text{March 22 and March})}{P(\text{March})}$$

Notice that the event "March 22 and March" is the same event as "March 22" since this date is obviously in March, and so

$$P(\text{March 22} \mid \text{March}) = \frac{P(\text{March 22})}{P(\text{March})} = \frac{0.00483}{0.23324} = 0.02071$$

In part C, let E and L denote the events that Easter is early and that Easter is late, respectively. Then $\square(E \text{ and } L)$ would be the event that in a given year, Easter is both early and late. This is impossible since Easter cannot be both early and late at once (so E and L are disjoint), so $P(E \text{ and } L) = 0$.

Next, we want the probability that Easter falls early or late, so now we need $P(E \text{ or } L)$ for part D. Since E and L are disjoint, we have $P(E \text{ or } L) = P(E) + P(L)$, so we just need to add up the probabilities for the individual dates that are considered early and late.

$$
\begin{aligned}
P(E) &= P(\text{March 22}) + P(\text{March 23}) + \cdots + P(\text{March 27}) + P(\text{March 28}) \\
&= 0.00483 + 0.00950 + 0.01425 + 0.01933 + 0.02333 + 0.02900 + 0.03267 \\
&= 0.13291
\end{aligned}
$$

$$
\begin{aligned}
P(L) &= P(\text{April 19}) + P(\text{April 20}) + \cdots + P(\text{April 24}) + P(\text{April 25}) \\
&= 0.03867 + 0.03325 + 0.02850 + 0.02417 + 0.01867 + 0.01450 + 0.00737 \\
&= 0.16513
\end{aligned}
$$

Using these definitions of early and late, the probability that Easter is early is 0.13291, while the probability that Easter is late is 0.16513. Thus, the probability that in a given year Easter is early or late is

$$P(E \text{ or } L) = P(E) + P(L) = 0.13291 + 0.16513 = 0.29804$$

Part E asks for the probability that in two randomly chosen years, Easter is late in both years. Denote these events as L_1 and L_2. Since the years are randomly chosen, the two events are independent, so we can multiply them using our work from part D:

$$P(L_1 \text{ and } L_2) = P(L_1) \times P(L_2) = 0.16513 \times 0.16513 = 0.02727$$

Finally, part F asks for the probability that in three randomly chosen years, Easter is in April in all three years. We first need the probability that Easter falls in April for one year, and this is the complement of the event of occurring in March (from part A):

$$P(\text{April}) = 1 - P(\text{March}) = 1 - 0.23324 = 0.76676$$

Now let A_1, A_2, and A_3 denote the events of Easter occurring in April in three randomly selected years. Again, these events are independent, so we can multiply them:

$$P(A_1 \text{ and } A_2 \text{ and } A_3) = P(A_1) \times P(A_2) \times P(A_3)$$

$$= 0.76676 \times 0.76676 \times 0.76676$$
$$= 0.45079$$

If you have ever wondered how Easter is determined, in simplified terms you find the date of the first full moon (called the Paschal Full Moon) that occurs on or after March 21. Easter is then the first Sunday that occurs after this date. Should this full moon fall on a Sunday, Easter would be the following Sunday.

Δ

Section 5.6 – Factorials and Combinations*

In Chapter 6, we will be dealing with a specific type of discrete distribution called the binomial distribution. Before studying it, it would be helpful to cover factorials and combinations. Chances are (pun intended!) you have seen this material before in an algebra class, but we will go over it again. We start with the factorial. (Note that your statistics class may or may not cover the material in this section; if not, feel free to skip it.)

DEFINITION

The **factorial** of a whole number n is the product of all whole numbers from 1 up to that number n. It is written as $n!$ (pronounced "n factorial" – so 3! is not pronounced as "THREE!!!"), and it can be interpreted as follows. Given n unique items, $n!$ is the number of ways these items can be ordered.

The formula for the factorial is

$$n! = n \times (n-1) \times (n-2) \times \cdots \times 2 \times 1$$

By convention, we say that $0! = 1$ and $1! = 1$.

EXAMPLE

We have four different photos that we want to arrange in a photo frame with four open spaces. How many ways can we arrange them? What about if we were arranging six different photos in a photo frame with six open spaces?

Solution: First, we need to work out in how many ways we can arrange four unique photos. This is a factorial, so

$$4! = 4 \times 3 \times 2 \times 1 = 24$$

If we are instead arranging six unique photos, then the answer is

$$6! = 6 \times 5 \times 4 \times 3 \times 2 \times 1 = 720$$

There are 24 ways to arrange four unique photos, but the number escalates to 720 ways to arrange six unique photos.

Δ

The reason we keep saying "four unique items" and other variations is because the factorial formula changes a little when some of the items repeat themselves. It is perhaps easier to see how this works with some examples rather than write out an explicit formula.

EXAMPLE

Find the number of ways to arrange the letters of the word GRAPE, the word BANANA, and the words ABRA CADABRA.

Solution: The word GRAPE has five letters, each of which is unique, and so there are $5! = 5 \times 4 \times 3 \times 2 \times 1 = 120$ ways of arranging the letters. (A few examples are GRAPE, AEGPR, and PEARG.)

The word BANANA has six letters, so at first glance you might expect the answer to be $6! = 6 \times 5 \times 4 \times 3 \times 2 \times 1 = 720$ arrangements. However, this is not the case because A appears three times and N appears twice. What we have to do is divide 6! by 3! (for the three As) and also by 2! (for the two Ns).

The logic here is that three As can be arranged $3! = 3 \times 2 \times 1 = 6$ ways, but since they are the same letter, all six arrangements of three As are the same: AAA. That means that we divide by 6. Similarly, with two Ns, there are $2! = 2 \times 1 = 2$ ways to arrange two Ns, but they are the same: NN and NN. That means that we also divide by 2.

Also, B appears just once. We do not need to adjust for that, but nevertheless to explain it mathematically, there is $1! = 1$ way to arrange it, so we literally divide by 1 (although dividing by 1 does not affect anything).

Here is the formula we are using:

$$\frac{(\text{number of letters of BANANA})!}{(\text{number of Bs})! \, (\text{number of As})! \, (\text{number of Ns})!}$$

Let's put in the numbers we know:

$$\frac{6!}{1! \, 3! \, 2!}$$

Rather than use a calculator, we can use the definition of a factorial and cancel out some numbers (and use the fact that multiplying by 1 has no effect):

$$\frac{6!}{1! \, 3! \, 2!} = \frac{6 \times 5 \times 4 \times 3 \times 2 \times 1}{(1) \times (3 \times 2 \times 1) \times (2 \times 1)}$$
$$= \frac{6 \times 5 \times 4 \times \cancel{3 \times 2 \times 1}}{(1) \times (\cancel{3 \times 2 \times 1}) \times (2 \times 1)}$$
$$= \frac{6 \times 5 \times 4}{2}$$
$$= \frac{6 \times 5 \times 2 \times 2}{2}$$
$$= \frac{6 \times 5 \times 2 \times \cancel{2}}{\cancel{2}}$$
$$= 6 \times 5 \times 2$$
$$= 60$$

After all that work, there are 60 ways to uniquely arrange the letters of BANANA.

Let's do another example with this rearranging technique and create some magic with the letters of ABRA CADABRA: how many unique arrangements are there?

First, there are 11 total letters to include five As, two Bs, two Rs, one C, and one D. Here is the starting formula:

$$\frac{(\text{number of letters of ABRA CADABRA})!}{(\text{number of As})!\,(\text{number of Bs})!\,(\text{number of Rs})!\,(\text{number of Cs})!\,(\text{number of Ds})!}$$

Rather than panic at the thought of computing 11!, we can just creatively cancel out some numbers:

$$\frac{11!}{5!\,2!\,2!\,1!\,1!} = \frac{11\times10\times9\times8\times7\times6\times5\times4\times3\times2\times1}{(5\times4\times3\times2\times1)\times(2\times1)\times(2\times1)\times(1)\times(1)}$$

$$= \frac{11\times10\times9\times8\times7\times6\times\cancel{5\times4\times3\times2\times1}}{(\cancel{5\times4\times3\times2\times1})\times(2\times1)\times(2\times1)\times(1)\times(1)}$$

$$= \frac{11\times10\times9\times8\times7\times6}{2\times2}$$

$$= \frac{11\times10\times9\times(2\times2\times2)\times7\times6}{2\times2}$$

$$= \frac{11\times10\times9\times(\cancel{2\times2}\times2)\times7\times6}{\cancel{2\times2}}$$

$$= 11\times10\times9\times2\times7\times6$$

$$= 83160$$

There are 83,160 possible ways to arrange the letters of ABRA CADABRA. (Had we computed 11! in the first step, we would have seen that it was equal to 39,916,800.)

Δ

The other major topic in this section to discuss is the combination of n items k at a time.

DEFINITION

The **combination** of n items k at a time is the number of possible unique ways (meaning that order does not matter) we can choose k items from a group of n items, where $0 \leq k \leq n$. Mathematically, it is denoted as

$$\binom{n}{k}$$

This is read as "the combination of n items k at a time." It is computed with the formula

$$\binom{n}{k} = \frac{n!}{(n-k)!\,k!}$$

For example, if we have the four letters A, B, C, and D, and we want to find how many ways we can choose two letters, then $n = 4$ and $k = 2$. The answer is

$$\binom{4}{2} = \frac{4!}{(4-2)!\,2!} = \frac{4!}{2!\,2!} = \frac{4\times3\times2\times1}{(2\times1)\times(2\times1)} = \frac{(\cancel{2\times2})\times3\times2\times1}{\cancel{2\times2}} = 3\times2\times1$$
$$= 6$$

Thus, given the four letters A, B, C, and D, there are 6 ways we can choose two of them at a time where order does not matter. Those 6 combinations are as follows: AB, AC, AD, BC, BD, and CD. (Note that since order does not matter, we count AB and BA as the same combination. If we did want order to matter, we would instead be dealing with a **permutation**, which we are not usually concerned with in this class.)

EXAMPLE

Given a class of twelve students, you are going to choose four of those students to participate in a competition. How many possible combinations of four students are there?

Solution: Here $n = 12$ and $k = 4$, so we use the combination formula:

$$\binom{12}{4} = \frac{12!}{(12-4)!\,4!} = \frac{12!}{8!\,4!}$$

At this point, a little handy shortcut would be handy to learn. It would be a bit of a hassle to write out 12! as the product of all numbers from 12 down to 1. Observe that $12! = 12 \times 11!$ just by the definition of the factorial formula. This can be seen as follows:

$$\begin{aligned} 12! &= 12 \times 11 \times 10 \times 9 \times 8 \times 7 \times 6 \times 5 \times 4 \times 3 \times 2 \times 1 \\ &= 12 \times (11 \times 10 \times 9 \times 8 \times 7 \times 6 \times 5 \times 4 \times 3 \times 2 \times 1) \\ &= 12 \times 11! \end{aligned}$$

But why stop there? It is also true that $12! = 12 \times 11 \times 10!$ just by retracing the parentheses:

$$\begin{aligned} 12! &= 12 \times 11 \times 10 \times 9 \times 8 \times 7 \times 6 \times 5 \times 4 \times 3 \times 2 \times 1 \\ &= 12 \times 11 \times (10 \times 9 \times 8 \times 7 \times 6 \times 5 \times 4 \times 3 \times 2 \times 1) \\ &= 12 \times 11 \times 10! \end{aligned}$$

Going back to the combination formula, observe that there is an 8! in the denominator. It would be nice to cancel it out with something in the numerator to avoid a lot of handwriting. The good news is that we can use the definition of the factorial to do just that. We simply write 12! so that it has 8! as part of it:

$$\begin{aligned} 12! &= 12 \times 11 \times 10 \times 9 \times 8 \times 7 \times 6 \times 5 \times 4 \times 3 \times 2 \times 1 \\ &= 12 \times 11 \times 10 \times 9 \times (8 \times 7 \times 6 \times 5 \times 4 \times 3 \times 2 \times 1) \\ &= 12 \times 11 \times 10 \times 9 \times 8! \end{aligned}$$

Let's use this in the combination:

$$\binom{12}{4} = \frac{12!}{8! \times 4!} = \frac{12 \times 11 \times 10 \times 9 \times \cancel{8!}}{\cancel{8!} \times 4!} = \frac{12 \times 11 \times 10 \times 9}{4!}$$

This is a lot simpler to compute! Let's simplify it:

$$\begin{aligned} \frac{12 \times 11 \times 10 \times 9}{4!} &= \frac{12 \times 11 \times 10 \times 9}{4 \times 3 \times 2 \times 1} = \frac{(4 \times 3) \times 11 \times (5 \times 2) \times 9}{4 \times 3 \times 2 \times 1} \\ &= \frac{(\cancel{4 \times 3}) \times 11 \times (5 \times \cancel{2}) \times 9}{\cancel{4 \times 3 \times 2} \times 1} \\ &= 11 \times 5 \times 9 \\ &= 495 \end{aligned}$$

Given 12 total students, there are 495 possible ways to choose any 4 of the students, where order does not matter.

Δ

EXAMPLE

Let's find simple forms for $\binom{n}{0}$, $\binom{n}{1}$, and $\binom{n}{n}$.

Solution: Using the combination formula,

$$\binom{n}{0} = \frac{n!}{(n-0)!\,0!} = \frac{n!}{n!} = 1$$

$$\binom{n}{1} = \frac{n!}{(n-1)!\,1!} = \frac{n!}{(n-1)!} = \frac{n(n-1)!}{(n-1)!} = n$$

$$\binom{n}{n} = \frac{n!}{(n-n)!\,n!} = \frac{n!}{0!\,n!} = 1$$

These are useful shortcut formulas that come in handy when we get to the binomial distribution in Chapter 6.

Δ

The above examples have been computed by hand, but now we see how the graphing calculator can be used.

TI-84 COMMAND: FACTORIALS AND COMBINATIONS

To compute a factorial, first type the number for which you wish to find the factorial. Next, press $\boxed{\text{MATH}}$, scroll right to the PRB menu, and then select Option 4: !. Doing so will bring you back to the home screen, and you will see a ! next to your number. Press $\boxed{\text{ENTER}}$, and the result will be the factorial of your number.

To compute the combination of n things k at a time, first type the number n. Next, press $\boxed{\text{MATH}}$, scroll right to the PRB menu, and then select Option 3: nCr. Doing so will bring you back to the home screen, and you will see nCr next to your number. Now type the number k, press $\boxed{\text{ENTER}}$, and the result will be the combination of n things k at a time. (In these notes we are using k instead of r for the notation, but the command uses the letter r although it represents the same thing.)

EXAMPLE

To compute 6! like we did in an earlier example, type 6, select the ! on the TI-84, and the calculator will give you 720.

To compute $\binom{12}{4}$ like we did in an earlier example, type 12, select the nCr on the TI-84, then type 4, and the calculator will give you 495.

Δ

Section 5.7 – The Monty Hall Problem*

We conclude Chapter 5 with a famous probability problem that is frequently taught at some point in mathematics or statistics because it is a fun yet frustrating mindbender. It is loosely based on the American game show *Let's Make A Deal* and is named after Monty Hall (not Python!), one of the original hosts of the TV show. Here we paraphrase the problem and give some background before walking you through a simplified explanation of the answer.

The problem goes like this. You are on a game show and are faced with three closed doors labeled Door 1, Door 2, and Door 3. The host tells you that behind one of the doors is a car, and behind the other two doors are goats. The host (who always knows what is behind each door) asks you to select one of the doors in the hopes that you win the grand prize, the car. However, instead of opening your door, the host opens one of the other two doors, revealing a goat. He then asks you if you want to keep the door you chose or switch to the other remaining closed door. Is it to your advantage to switch doors? (For instance, you select Door 1, so the host opens Door 2 to show a goat. You then need to either keep your original Door 1 or switch to Door 3.)

Think about this problem for a moment. The answer is either "it is advantageous to switch doors," "it is advantageous to keep your first door," or "it doesn't matter what you do." You might intuitively think that with one wrong door being eliminated, you would then have a 50:50 chance of winning the car, in which case it doesn't matter whether you switch doors. In other words, once the host reduces the doors to two, one car and one goat, the probability of your door having the car is 1/2 and the probability of the other door having the car is 1/2, or so it appears. Is it really that simple?

Unfortunately there is a lot more to this classical brainteaser than you would expect. To begin, Marilyn vos Savant, an American author and magazine columnist who was listed in the *Guinness Book of Records* as having the highest recorded IQ, was asked this question in her "Ask Marilyn" column in *Parade* magazine, a September 1990 issue.[7] She provided her own answer, which was that the contestant should switch doors since doing so resulted in a 2/3 probability of winning the car (and not 1/2 as one would expect). Her answer was consistent with the original answer published by Steve Selvin in a 1975 volume of the *American Statistician*.[8,9]

After Savant published her answer, *Parade* received about ten thousand letters from readers claiming that Savant was wrong, quite a lot of which were from mathematicians and scientists.[10,11] However, despite this backlash, Savant's answer was in fact correct, and in 1992 she published a follow-up column in *Parade* further explaining her point.[12]

Now, how do we solve this problem? First, let's carefully go through the main pointers and assumptions for the Monty Hall problem.

1) There are three closed doors, one of them containing a car and the other two containing goats.
2) The host knows what is behind each door.
3) When you pick a door, the host always opens a door that you did not select. This door always reveals one of the goats and never the car.
4) The host always gives you the option to keep your original door or switch to the remaining closed door.
5) We also need to assume that you in fact want to win the car instead of a goat!

Although this problem can be solved using probability formulas, we instead go through it just by verbally talking through the possibilities. Let's assume that Doors 1 and 2 have goats and Door 3 has the car. There are three possibilities that can happen from this assignment, and in each case we are going to switch doors. (The actual assignment of doors does not matter, so we can illustrate what is going on assuming that Door 3 had the car.)

The first possibility is that you choose Door 1. The host would have to open Door 2 and show a goat, so now you either keep Door 1 or switch to Door 3. If you switch to Door 3, you win the car.

The second possibility is choosing Door 2. The host would then open Door 1 to show a goat, and now you either stay with Door 2 or switch to Door 3. If you switch to Door 3, you win the car.

The third possibility is that you select Door 3. The host would open either of Doors 1 and 2 (it does not matter which one), showing a goat. You now decide whether to keep Door 3 or switch to the remaining closed door. If you switch to the remaining door, you win a goat.

Now, looking at these three possible scenarios where we switch doors, it is clear that in two of them we win the car and in only one scenario we don't win the car. Thus, if we always switch doors, we expect to win the car 2/3 of the time, not 1/2! The following diagram summarizes what we just explained (for the last scenario, where the host could open either of Doors 1 or 2, assume he opens Door 1).

	Door 1 Goat	Door 2 Goat	Door 3 Car
Pick Door 1	Keep Door 1 Lose	Door Opened	Switch to Door 3 Win
Pick Door 2	Door Opened	Keep Door 2 Lose	Switch to Door 3 Win
Pick Door 3	Door Opened	Switch to Door 2 Lose	Keep Door 3 Win

Why is the answer not 1/2 as expected? Although the host is reducing the number of closed doors to two, that does not mean that both remaining doors have a 1/2 probability of containing the car. We have to stick with the original probabilities of winning from the original three doors before any are opened.

In the beginning, if you pick any door, it has a 1/3 chance of having the car. There is therefore a 2/3 chance that the car is behind one of the remaining two doors. We can summarize the situation as follows:

A) The car is behind the door you picked. This happens with probability 1/3.
B) The car is behind one of the other two doors. This happens with probability 2/3.

When the host opens one of the remaining doors, if you keep your original door, you still have a 1/3 chance of winning the car. That means that the remaining closed door now has a 2/3 chance of having the car because the statement "the car is behind one of the other two doors" reduces to "the car is behind the remaining closed door." The 2/3 probability is now concentrated on that one door rather than being spread over two doors. We can now update our situation after one of the doors has been opened:

A) The car is behind the door you picked. This happens with probability 1/3.
B) The car is behind the remaining closed door. This happens with probability 2/3.

It is therefore in your best interest to switch doors since the probability of winning the car is greater if you switch!

Another way to look at this puzzle is to instead suppose you have a large number of doors, say 100. One of the doors has a car and the other 99 have goats. Suppose you pick Door 1, and so you only have a 1/100 chance of being correct. That means that the probability that one of the remaining doors has the car is 99/100. The host would then open 98 of the other doors, each time showing goats, and assume he keeps Door 61 closed. If you keep Door 1, you still have a 1/100 chance of being correct, but if you switch to Door 61, you have a 99/100 chance of winning the car.

If you are still not convinced, an experiment or computer simulation will give the same results. One thing you could do is deal three playing cards face down to a friend, two clubs and one heart, where you know which card is the heart. Your friend picks a card, but instead of flipping it over, you flip over one of the remaining cards, showing a club. Have your friend switch cards, at which point you reveal it and record whether your friend switched to a card that was the heart or one of the clubs. Now repeat this procedure several times and record the outcome each time. You will find that the more trials you perform, the more likely that switching cards results in wins close to 2/3 of the time.

Thus, if you are lucky enough to be on such a game show and are faced with the above situation, contrary to intuition, the best thing for you to do is to switch doors to have a better chance of winning the car. If you instead trust your intuition, there is a high chance of you taking home one of those mischievous goats!

Chapter 6 – Probability Distributions

This chapter introduces us to probability distributions and their characteristics. We also learn how to use the binomial distribution and the normal distribution.

Section 6.1 – Summarizing Possible Outcomes and Probabilities

We kick off this chapter with a brief discussion of random variables.

DEFINITION

A **random variable** is a quantity that can take on specific numerical values for each possible outcome of a situation. A **discrete random variable** is a variable that can only take a countable number of possible values, usually whole numbers only. A **continuous random variable** is a variable that can take on an infinite number of possible, uncountable number of values with any number of decimals.

For instance, let X be the time (in minutes) taken to complete a 5K race. X is a random variable that can equal any positive value, and it is continuous because the time could be 30 minutes, or it could be 26.865 minutes, or 24.12345 minutes, or other decimal values.

As another example, let X be the number of spades you are holding in a five-card poker hand. Since X can be 0, 1, 2, 3, 4, or 5 only, this is a discrete random variable (so you cannot have 3.6189 spades in a hand!).

Given a random variable X, we can construct a probability distribution to represent the probabilities at the specific values that X can take.

DEFINITION

A **probability distribution** of a discrete random variable is a table, a graph, or a mathematical equation that shows all possible values the random variable could be, along with their corresponding probabilities.

DISCRETE PROBABILITY DISTRIBUTION REQUIREMENTS

There are two basic requirements for a discrete probability distribution to be valid:

Requirement 1: Each individual probability is between 0 and 1, inclusive.
Requirement 2: The sum of all possible probabilities is 1.

EXAMPLE

Suppose we roll a fair dice, which means that all six sides have equal probability of occurring. Let X denote the number of dots showing on one roll.

Outcome	1	2	3	4	5	6
Probability	1/6	1/6	1/6	1/6	1/6	1/6

This is a discrete random variable because X can take on the whole numbers 1, 2, 3, 4, 5, or 6, and nothing else. To check whether it is a valid probability distribution, observe that all probabilities are 1/6, which is between 0 and 1, inclusive. In addition, if we add them all together, the total sum is 1:

$$P(1) + P(2) + P(3) + P(4) + P(5) + P(6) = \frac{1}{6} + \frac{1}{6} + \frac{1}{6} + \frac{1}{6} + \frac{1}{6} + \frac{1}{6} = 1$$

Thus, this is a valid probability distribution.

Δ

EXAMPLE

Suppose in a certain town, it is known that the number of living grandparents a person has follows the probability distribution in the table below. The number of living grandparents, X, can only be 0, 1, 2, 3, or 4, so it is a discrete probability distribution (you cannot have a decimal number of grandparents alive!)

X	P(X)
0	0.05
1	0.12
2	0.15
3	0.36
4	

    A) Find the missing probability of having all four grandparents alive.
    B) What is the probability of having at least two grandparents alive?
    C) What is the probability of having more than two grandparents alive?

Solution: The first job is to find the missing probability, $P(4)$. This is easy since all five probabilities have to add to 1, so we just need to solve for $P(4)$:

$$P(0) + P(1) + P(2) + P(3) + P(4) = 1$$
$$0.05 + 0.12 + 0.15 + 0.36 + P(4) = 1$$
$$0.68 + P(4) = 1$$
$$P(4) = 1 - 0.68$$
$$P(4) = 0.32$$

Thus, the probability of having four grandparents alive is 0.32.

For part B, we want the probability of at least two grandparents. The phrase "at least two" means two or more, so here that would be 2, 3, or 4. Thus,

$$P(\text{at least } 2) = P(2) + P(3) + P(4)$$
$$= 0.15 + 0.36 + 0.32$$
$$= 0.83$$

In contrast, for part C, we want the probability of more than two grandparents. The phrase "more than two" does not include the number two (unlike the phrase "at least"), so here that would be 3 or 4. Thus,

$$P(\text{more than } 2) = P(3) + P(4)$$
$$= 0.36 + 0.32$$
$$= 0.68$$

Δ

When computing a probability, be careful to note the exact wording of what it is asking for. Misread, and you could run the risk of getting a wrong answer, and we cannot have that, can we? Reference the following summary table, where X is the variable and a is a number of interest. This table works for discrete distributions. (Note that thanks to the flexibility of the English language, the entries in the left column could be phrased differently.)

Phrase	Notation	Example Numbers
X is less than a	$P(X < a)$	..., $a - 2, a - 1$
X is at most a	$P(X \leq a)$	..., $a - 2, a - 1, a$
X is exactly a	$P(X = a)$	a
X is at least a	$P(X \geq a)$	$a, a + 1, a + 2, ...$
X is more than a	$P(X > a)$	$a + 1, a + 2, ...$

Section 6.2 – Expected Value of a Discrete Distribution

We can go further than just compute probabilities; we can also find the mean of a discrete probability distribution. It is computed as the following formula.

DEFINITION

The mean of a random variable is the average value that results from the possible outcomes and their probabilities. Also called the **expected value**, this is the value that, on average, you would expect to obtain from the possible values. It can and likely will be a decimal answer, but there is nothing wrong with that – remember, it is only an average! (It would actually be incorrect to round to the nearest whole number.)

To compute the expected value, if the possible outcomes are $x_1, x_2, ..., x_n$ with corresponding probabilities $P(x_1), P(x_2), ..., P(x_n)$, the mean is

$$\text{Mean} = \sum x_i \times P(x_i) = \left(x_1 \times P(x_1)\right) + \left(x_2 \times P(x_2)\right) + \cdots + \left(x_n \times P(x_n)\right)$$

In higher statistics, the notation $E(X)$ is used to represent the mean.

What you do is multiply each possible value by its probability and then add up the results. This is literally a weighted value.

To be clear, the mean of a random variable is the long-run average outcome of the experiment. In this sense, as the number of trials of the experiment increases, the average result of the experiment gets closer to the mean of the random variable. Put another way, if you sampled a number from the distribution, say, a thousand times and averaged the results, you will find that the average would be very close to the expected value.

Perhaps some examples are in order!

EXAMPLE

Going back to the grandparents distribution, here is the table again:

X	P(X)
0	0.05
1	0.12
2	0.15
3	0.36
4	0.32

We need to find the expected number of grandparents alive a person has in this community. In this first example, we will make a third column which is equal to each value X times its probability $P(X)$.

X	P(X)	X×P(X)
0	0.05	0 x 0.05 = 0
1	0.12	1 x 0.12 = 0.12
2	0.15	2 x 0.15 = 0.30
3	0.36	3 x 0.36 = 1.08
4	0.32	4 x 0.32 = 1.28

The expected value is then found by adding up everything in the third column:

$$\text{Mean} = \sum x_i \times P(x_i) = 0 + 0.12 + 0.30 + 1.08 + 1.28 = 2.78$$

If we are careful with calculations, we can also type the whole thing into our graphing calculator and compute it in one fell swoop:

$$\begin{aligned} \text{Mean} &= (0 \times 0.05) + (1 \times 0.12) + (2 \times 0.15) + (3 \times 0.36) + (4 \times 0.32) \\ &= 0 + 0.12 + 0.30 + 1.08 + 1.28 \\ &= 2.78 \end{aligned}$$

To interpret this answer, if you randomly sample someone from this community, you can expect the number of living grandparents they have, on average, to be 2.78. (Again, it is acceptable to get a decimal answer – this is only an average!) Another way to think of it is that if we sample a large number of people from this community and average the number of living grandparents each, that average will be approximately 2.78. This is the Law of Large Numbers in action.

Δ

EXAMPLE
And now for a mindbender! In a certain game, we have to select one of three cards, each a different color, at random from an envelope. If we choose the green card, we win $100. If we pick the yellow card, we win nothing, and if we choose the red card, we lose $250. Assume that we are equally likely to pick any of the cards.

    A) Set up a probability table to illustrate the possible win/loss outcomes.
    B) On one play, how much do we expect to win or lose?
    C) Given this answer, is it a good idea for us to risk playing this game?

D) Now suppose we play this game 100 times. In the long run, how much money do we expect to win or lose?

Solution: First, let's set up a table that shows the three possible outcomes. Let X denote the amount of money we win. The only possible win amounts are $100, $0, and −$250 (the last one is negative because it is a loss). Each is equally likely, so with three outcomes, the probability is 1/3 each. We can go ahead and fill in the third column if we want to compute the expected value that way.

X	$P(X)$	$X \times P(X)$
100	1/3	100 x 1/3 = 33.33333
0	1/3	0 x 1/3 = 0
-250	1/3	-250 x 1/3 = -83.33333

For part B, we just compute the expected value by adding up the contents of the third column, or by computing the whole sum at once:

$$\text{Mean} = \left(100 \times \frac{1}{3}\right) + \left(0 \times \frac{1}{3}\right) + \left(-250 \times \frac{1}{3}\right)$$
$$= 33.33333 + 0 - 83.33333$$
$$= -50$$

Note that we subtract 83.33333 due to the negative sign. The expected value is −$50, and this means that on one play, you expect to lose $50 on average. The negative sign represents a loss. To answer part C, since your expected outcome is to lose $50 rather than gain anything, it is not a good idea to risk playing this game. (Even though −$50 is not one of the three possible outcomes, again this is only an average.)

For part D, if we play the game 100 times, how much do we expect to gain or lose? To answer that, if we expect to lose $50 for one play, then on average we expect to lose $50×100 = $5000 for one hundred plays. Again, not a good game to risk playing!

Δ

EXAMPLE
Suppose we purchase a raffle ticket for $5. A total of 100 tickets were purchased altogether, and only one will win $100; the others win nothing. <u>Including the cost of the ticket,</u> fill in the table with the possible amounts won, and compute the expected amount you will win. (Hint: you are computing the expected profit.)

Solution: Observe that there are two possible outcomes: we either win $100 or we win nothing. However, here is where it gets tricky – we have to take into account the cost of the ticket!

Suppose our ticket is a winner. Although we won $100, we also had to pay $5, which means that our profit was in fact $95. (Recall from basic economics that revenue minus cost equals profit.) On the other hand, if our ticket is a loser, we won nothing, and on top of that we paid $5. That means that our profit was −$5, which represents a loss.

Next, it is known that 1 out of 100 tickets is a winner, so the probability is $1/100 = 0.01$. That means that the probability of losing is $99/100 = 0.99$. Now we can fill in the table:

X	P(X)	X×P(X)
95	0.01	95 x 0.01 = 0.95
-5	0.99	-5 x 0.99 = -4.95

The expected value, or here the expected profit, is then

$$\text{Mean} = \left(95 \times \frac{1}{100}\right) + \left(-5 \times \frac{99}{100}\right) = -4$$

If we buy one of these tickets, on average we expect to lose $4. Again, the negative sign represents a loss.

Δ

EXAMPLE

If we pick a year at random and count how many Friday 13ths are in that year, it turns out there will be 1, 2, or 3 such days. (In other words, every year has to have at least one Friday 13th but no more than three, which is bad news for people who have triskaidekaphobia!) Examining the modern Gregorian calendar, which goes in a 400-year cycle (why?), it can be shown that the probabilities that a randomly chosen year has one, two, or three Friday 13ths are as follows. For instance, 42.75% of all years feature exactly one Friday 13th.

# Friday 13ths	P(X)
1	0.4275
2	0.4250
3	0.1475

A) Find the probability that a year selected at random has more than two Friday 13ths.
B) Find the probability that a year selected at random has at least two Friday 13ths.
C) In a given year, how many Friday 13ths do we expect to see?

Solution: For part A, the event "more than two Friday 13ths" does not include two, so the only allowed outcome is three. Thus, the probability is just 0.1475.

For part B, the event "at least two Friday 13ths" includes two and three, so the probability is 0.425 + 0.1475 = 0.5725.

Part C involves getting our new friend, the expected value. Let's compute that third column:

# Friday 13ths	P(X)	X×P(X)
1	0.4275	1 x 0.4275 = 0.4275
2	0.4250	2 x 0.4250 = 0.85
3	0.1475	3 x 0.1475 = 0.4425

The mean is computed as

$$\begin{aligned} \text{Mean} &= (1 \times 0.4275) + (2 \times 0.4250) + (3 \times 0.1475) \\ &= 0.4275 + 0.85 + 0.4425 \\ &= 1.72 \end{aligned}$$

In a given year, we expect, on average, to see 1.72 Friday 13ths. (To answer the other question posed earlier, the Gregorian calendar, introduced by Pope Gregory XIII in 1582, says that years divisible by 4 are leap years, meaning they have a February 29th, except turn-of-the-century years are not leap years unless they are also divisible by 400. Thus, the years 1800 and 1900 were not leap years, but 2000 was and 2100 will not be. The Gregorian calendar therefore goes in a 400-year cycle instead of a 4-year one, assuming it is not changed anytime soon.[1])

Δ

You will have noticed by now that the allowed numbers we see are whole numbers, yet the expected value/mean is almost always a decimal. That is perfectly acceptable, since the mean is simply an average of what we see over a long run of time. In other words, the expected value is the long-run average of all trials (cf. the Law of Large Numbers).

Section 6.3 – Standard Deviation of a Discrete Distribution*

The standard deviation of a discrete distribution has a formula that is an extension of the expected value formula. It is a bit more complicated in the sense that it has more steps, and in fact not every introductory statistics class will teach this formula. If that describes your class, or if you simply do not fancy the look of this section, you may go ahead and skip it.

DEFINITION

If the possible outcomes are $x_1, x_2, \ldots, x_n$ with probabilities $P(x_1), P(x_2), \ldots, P(x_n)$, the standard deviation of a discrete distribution is

$$\text{St. Dev.} = \sqrt{\sum x_i^2 \times P(x_i) - (\text{Mean})^2}$$
$$= \sqrt{\left(x_1^2 \times P(x_1)\right) + \left(x_2^2 \times P(x_2)\right) + \cdots + \left(x_n^2 \times P(x_n)\right) - (\text{Mean})^2}$$

In higher statistics classes, the summation part is sometimes denoted as $E(X^2)$. Using this notation, we can write it in a simpler form:

$$\text{St. Dev.} = \sqrt{E(X^2) - (\text{Mean})^2} = \sqrt{E(X^2) - \left(E(X)\right)^2}$$

The standard deviation is computed in the following steps:

1) Compute the sum $E(X^2) = \left(x_1^2 \times P(x_1)\right) + \left(x_2^2 \times P(x_2)\right) + \cdots + \left(x_n^2 \times P(x_n)\right)$.
2) Subtract the mean squared.
3) Take the square root of the result.

EXAMPLE

Once again, consider the grandparents distribution, which we showed earlier has a mean of 2.78. Here is the table again:

X	P(X)
0	0.05
1	0.12
2	0.15
3	0.36
4	0.32

We need to find the standard deviation of the number of grandparents alive a person has in this community. In this first example, we will make a third column which is equal to the square of each value, X^2, times its probability $P(X)$.

X	P(X)	$X^2 \times P(X)$
0	0.05	$0^2 \times 0.05 = 0$
1	0.12	$1^2 \times 0.12 = 0.12$
2	0.15	$2^2 \times 0.15 = 0.60$
3	0.36	$3^2 \times 0.36 = 3.24$
4	0.32	$4^2 \times 0.32 = 5.12$

The first step is to add up the squared values times their probabilities:

$$\begin{aligned}
E(X^2) &= (0^2 \times 0.05) + (1^2 \times 0.12) + (2^2 \times 0.15) + (3^2 \times 0.36) + (4^2 \times 0.32) \\
&= (0 \times 0.05) + (1 \times 0.12) + (4 \times 0.15) + (9 \times 0.36) + (16 \times 0.32) \\
&= 0 + 0.12 + 0.60 + 3.24 + 5.12 \\
&= 9.08
\end{aligned}$$

The second step is to subtract the mean squared:

$$\begin{aligned}
E(X^2) - (\text{Mean})^2 &= 9.08 - 2.78^2 \\
&= 9.08 - 7.7284 \\
&= 1.3516
\end{aligned}$$

The third and final step is to take the square root:

$$\begin{aligned}
\text{St. Dev.} &= \sqrt{E(X^2) - (\text{Mean})^2} \\
&= \sqrt{1.3516} \\
&= 1.16258
\end{aligned}$$

To summarize, the mean of this distribution is 2.78, and the standard deviation is 1.16258.

Δ

EXAMPLE
Consider the Friday 13th distribution, which we showed earlier has a mean of 1.72. Here is the table again:

# Friday 13ths	P(X)
1	0.4275
2	0.4250
3	0.1475

We need to find the standard deviation of the number of Friday 13ths in a year. In this second example, we will make a third column which is equal to the square of each value, X^2, times its probability $P(X)$.

# Friday 13ths	P(X)	$X^2 \times P(X)$
1	0.4275	$1^2 \times 0.4275 = 0.4275$
2	0.4250	$2^2 \times 0.4250 = 1.7$
3	0.1475	$3^2 \times 0.1475 = 1.3275$

The first step is to add up the squared values times their probabilities:

$$\begin{aligned} E(X^2) &= (1^2 \times 0.4275) + (2^2 \times 0.425) + (3^2 \times 0.1475) \\ &= (1 \times 0.4275) + (4 \times 0.425) + (9 \times 0.1475) \\ &= 0.4275 + 1.7 + 1.3275 \\ &= 3.455 \end{aligned}$$

The second step is to subtract the mean squared:

$$\begin{aligned} E(X^2) - (\text{Mean})^2 &= 3.455 - 1.72^2 \\ &= 3.455 - 2.9584 \\ &= 0.4966 \end{aligned}$$

The third and final step is to take the square root:

$$\begin{aligned} \text{St. Dev.} &= \sqrt{E(X^2) - (\text{Mean})^2} \\ &= \sqrt{0.4966} \\ &= 0.70470 \end{aligned}$$

To summarize, the mean of this distribution is 1.72, and the standard deviation is 0.70470.

Δ

Section 6.4 – Properties of the Binomial Distribution

In Chapter 5, we saw how combinations and factorials worked. Now that we have seen the basic definitions of a probability distribution, it is time to get acquainted with a specific one. There are multiple approaches to learning this distribution, but we first start with the formula and working out specific examples by hand. Later we will see how the TI-84 handles the dirty work.

Here is the situation. There are a total of n subjects, each of which has a specified probability p of having a specific attribute of interest, independent of the other subjects. If a subject has that attribute, that is considered a "success," and it is a "failure" otherwise. The question of interest is this: what is the probability that out of these n subjects, there are x successes, and consequently $n - x$ failures?

Enter the binomial distribution.

DEFINITION

Suppose there are n independent subjects, each of which has the same probability p of having a quality of interest (a success). This is a **binomial distribution** with n subjects and probability of success p, denoted as $Bin(n, p)$. The probability of having exactly x successes out of n subjects is given by the following formula:

$$P(X = x) = \binom{n}{x} p^x (1 - p)^{n-x}$$

Here x can take on the values $0, 1, \ldots, n$.

ETYMOLOGY

The word binomial comes from the Latin *bi* (having two) and the ancient Greek νόμος (part), so it literally means "having two parts." The binomial distribution gets its name from the fact that each subject has two possible outcomes: success or failure. (If there were three possible outcomes, it would be a trinomial distribution.)

Note that the binomial distribution is a proper probability distribution since each probability is between 0 and 1, and it can be shown that all possible probabilities sum to 1 (although we will not show that here).

To warm up, let's first find the probability of 0 successes, followed by n successes. Given n subjects and 0 successes, each of which has probability p of success, we use the formula:

$$P(X = 0) = \binom{n}{0} p^0 (1 - p)^{n-0} = 1 \times 1 \times (1 - p)^n$$
$$= (1 - p)^n$$

This should actually make sense because the probability of a failure is $(1 - p)$. The probability of having two subjects and both being failures is $(1 - p)(1 - p) = (1 - p)^2$. As an extension, the probability of all n subjects being failures is $(1 - p)$ multiplied by itself n times, or $(1 - p)^n$.

Next, here is the probability of n successes out of n subjects:

$$P(X = n) = \binom{n}{n} p^n (1 - p)^{n-n} = 1 \times p^n \times 1$$
$$= p^n$$

Again, this should make sense because if there are n subjects and each and every one was a success, the probability is p multiplied by itself n times, or p^n. But now what if you want to find the probability of having, say, exactly 3 successes and therefore $n - 3$ failures? This is where the binomial distribution is needed.

EXAMPLE

Let's now do an example with actual numbers. You have an 80% track record of scoring on a given shot in basketball. During a game, you make two free throws. Let X be the number of shots you make that successfully go through the net. Find the probability of scoring zero, one, and two times.

Solution: We first solve this problem using basic counting skills, and then afterwards we go back and solve it using the binomial formula. First, there are two free throws, so $n = 2$. The probability of scoring on one shot is 0.80, so $p = 0.80$. Let X equal the number of successful shots, so X can be 0, 1, or 2. Free throws are independent, and each shot has two possible outcomes: a score or not a score (a miss). This is a binomial problem!

Intuitively, there are four possible outcomes of two shots under these circumstances:

1) First shot is a miss; second shot is a miss (Miss, Miss)
2) First shot is a miss; second shot is a score (Miss, Score)
3) First shot is a score; second shot is a miss (Score, Miss)
4) First shot is a score; second shot is a score (Score, Score)

Let's find the probability of each of these outcomes, keeping in mind that the probability of scoring on one shot is 0.80, and therefore the probability of missing is 0.20.

1) For (Miss, Miss), the probability is $0.20 \times 0.20 = 0.04$.
2) For (Miss, Score), the probability is $0.20 \times 0.80 = 0.16$.
3) For (Score, Miss), the probability is $0.80 \times 0.20 = 0.16$.
4) For (Score, Score), the probability is $0.80 \times 0.80 = 0.64$.

The event "zero scores" is the (Miss, Miss) scenario, and that occurs with probability 0.04. Similarly, the event "two scores" is the (Score, Score) scenario, and that occurs with probability 0.64.

However, the event "one score" is the (Miss, Score) and also the (Score, Miss) scenario, so the joint probability is found by adding the probabilities:

$$(0.20 \times 0.80) + (0.80 \times 0.20) = 2(0.80)(0.20) = 0.32$$

This is because there are two different ways of scoring exactly one time. Thus, we have the following probabilities:

$$P(X = 0) = (0.20)^2 \qquad = 0.04$$
$$P(X = 1) = 2(0.80)(0.20) = 0.32$$
$$P(X = 2) = (0.80)^2 \qquad = 0.64$$

Let's now find the probabilities again, only this time using the binomial distribution formula with $n = 2$ and $p = 0.80$. (Note that the first set of parentheses, the one with the 2 and the x, is not a fraction; it is the combination symbol!)

$$P(X = x) = \binom{2}{x}(0.80)^x(1 - 0.20)^{2-x} = \binom{2}{x}(0.80)^x(0.20)^{2-x}$$

The probability of scoring zero times out of two throws is

$$P(X = 0) = \binom{2}{0}(0.80)^0(0.20)^{2-0} = 1 \times 1 \times (0.20)^2 = 0.04$$

The probability of scoring exactly once out of two throws is

$$P(X = 1) = \binom{2}{1}(0.80)^1(0.20)^{2-1} = 2\times0.80\times0.20 = 0.32$$

The probability of scoring two times out of two throws is

$$P(X = 2) = \binom{2}{2}(0.80)^2(0.20)^{2-2} = 1\times(0.80)^2\times1 = 0.64$$

These probabilities match what we calculated by hand earlier.

Δ

EXAMPLE

On a certain beach, it is known that 30% of the seashells that wash up on the sand are sand dollars. You walk on the beach one day, close your eyes, and pick up five seashells at random without looking. Find the following probabilities:

A) Picking no sand dollars.
B) Picking at least one sand dollar.
C) Picking exactly three sand dollars.
D) Picking exactly five sand dollars.
E) Picking less than five sand dollars.

Solution: First, let's check that this is indeed a binomial distribution. There are $n = 5$ subjects, the seashells, each of which is independent of the others. Each seashell has a probability $p = 0.30$ of being a sand dollar, and each seashell has two possible outcomes: success (a sand dollar) or failure (not a sand dollar). Lastly, the data are discrete because the number of sand dollars in our sample can only be 0, 1, 2, 3, 4, or 5, and nothing else. This is indeed a binomial distribution. The formula to use takes the form

$$P(X = x) = \binom{5}{x}(0.30)^x(1 - 0.30)^{5-x} = \binom{5}{x}(0.30)^x(0.70)^{5-x}$$

For part A, the probability of picking no sand dollars is

$$P(X = 0) = \binom{5}{0}(0.30)^0(0.70)^{5-0} = 1\times1\times(0.70)^5 = 0.16807$$

Part B is where things start to get interesting. We want the probability of picking at least one sand dollar. Going back to the fact that X can be 0, 1, 2, 3, 4, or 5 only, "at least one" means 1 or greater. This encompasses the numbers 1, 2, 3, 4, and 5 – or in other words, all possibilities other than 0. That means that "at least 1" is the complement of 0 – and we have a shortcut formula we can use for that!

To be clear, the following chart might be useful:

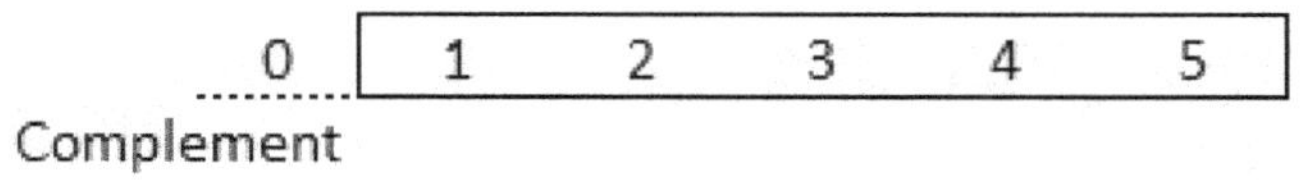

0	1	2	3	4	5
Complement					

This means that the answer is

$$P(X \geq 1) = 1 - P(X = 0) = 1 - 0.16807 = 0.83193$$

For part C, we get to compute one of the probabilities right in the middle:

$$P(X = 3) = \binom{5}{3}(0.30)^3(0.70)^{5-3} = \binom{5}{3}(0.30)^3(0.70)^2$$

Let's start with the combination:

$$\binom{5}{3} = \frac{5!}{(5-3)!\,3!} = \frac{5!}{2!\,3!} = \frac{5\times4\times\cancel{3!}}{2\times1\times\cancel{3!}} = \frac{5\times(2\times2)}{\cancel{2}} = 10$$

The probability is

$$P(X = 3) = 10(0.30)^3(0.70)^2 = 0.1323$$

For part D, the probability of picking five sand dollars is

$$P(X = 5) = \binom{5}{5}(0.30)^5(0.70)^{5-5} = 1\times(0.30)^5\times1 = 0.00243$$

Finally, in part E we need the probability of picking less than five sand dollars. Going back to the fact that X can be 0, 1, 2, 3, 4, or 5 only, "less than five" means 4 or less. This encompasses the numbers 0, 1, 2, 3, and 4…or in other words, all possibilities other than 5. That means that "less than 5" is the complement of 5, so we can use the shortcut formula again! Here is a similar chart to what we saw earlier:

0	1	2	3	4	5
					Complement

This means that the answer is

$$P(X < 5) = 1 - P(X = 5) = 1 - 0.00243 = 0.99757$$

Δ

The previous problem involved making tables to illustrate the possible numbers and which ones we needed to consider for the problem at hand. This is a very handy technique to learn for these binomial probability problems, especially when we start using the graphing calculator! Let's practice some more making those binomial tables.

EXAMPLE
A certain town is known to be home to 54% females and 46% males. You are going to select 12 people at random for a jury, and let X be the number of females on the chosen jury. Without actually finding the probabilities, draw a table illustrating the following outcomes.

    A) The jury contains exactly six females.
    B) The jury contains seven or fewer females.
    C) The jury contains less than three females.
    D) The jury contains more than ten females.
    E) The jury contains at least three females.

Solution: These problems all require recognizing that X can take the values 0, 1, 2, and so on up through 12. We then simply circle the allowed numbers per scenario. In part A, the only allowed number is 6.

0   1   2   3   4   5 $\boxed{6}$ 7   8   9   10   11   12

In part B, we want seven or fewer. Following the table, this means the numbers 7 and less, so all numbers 0, 1, and so on through and including 7.

$\boxed{0 \quad 1 \quad 2 \quad 3 \quad 4 \quad 5 \quad 6 \quad 7}$ 8   9   10   11   12

Part C asks for less than three. This means the numbers less than 3 *but not including* 3, or in other words 0, 1, and 2.

$\boxed{0 \quad 1 \quad 2}$ 3   4   5   6   7   8   9   10   11   12

For part D, more than ten means the numbers greater than 10 *but not including* 10. Here that is just 11 and 12.

0   1   2   3   4   5   6   7   8   9   10 $\boxed{11 \quad 12}$

Finally, part E wants at least three. That means the numbers above 3, including 3:

0   1   2 $\boxed{3 \quad 4 \quad 5 \quad 6 \quad 7 \quad 8 \quad 9 \quad 10 \quad 11 \quad 12}$

Δ

The next topic concerns the mean and standard deviation of the binomial distribution.

MEAN AND STANDARD DEVIATION OF THE BINOMIAL DISTRIBUTION

Suppose there are n independent subjects, each of which has the same probability p of having a quality of interest (a success). As we have seen, this is a binomial distribution with n subjects and probability of success p. The mean (or expected value) and the standard deviation of the binomial distribution are given by the following formulas:

$$\text{Mean} = np$$
$$\text{Standard Deviation} = \sqrt{np(1-p)}$$

You might also see the standard deviation given as $\sqrt{npq}$, where $q = 1 - p$, the probability of an individual failure.

EXAMPLE

In the previous example, a certain town is known to be home to 54% females and 46% males. You are going to select 12 people at random for a jury, and let X be the number of females on the chosen jury.

Find the expected number of females on a jury, as well as the standard deviation of the number of females.

Solution: This is a binomial situation because there are $n = 12$ independent subjects, each of which has probability $p = 0.54$ of being female. Thus, the mean of this binomial distribution is

$$\text{Mean} = np = 12 \times 0.54 = 6.48$$

The standard deviation is

$$
\begin{aligned}
\text{Standard Deviation} &= \sqrt{np(1-p)} \\
&= \sqrt{12 \times 0.54 \times (1 - 0.54)} \\
&= \sqrt{12 \times 0.54 \times 0.46} \\
&= \sqrt{2.9808} \\
&= 1.72650
\end{aligned}
$$

Δ

Another good topic is the shape of the binomial distribution. Suppose $n = 8$ and $p = 0.50$, then the possible values that the number of successes X can take is $0, 1, 2, \ldots, 8$. The following graph shows what this distribution looks like, where the height of each bar represents the probability (for instance, $P(X = 4) = 0.27344$). This distribution is clearly symmetric, and this happens when $p = 0.50$.

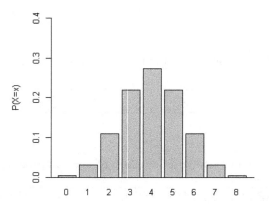

Next, suppose $n = 8$ and $p = 0.30$. The following graph shows what this distribution looks like (for instance, $P(X = 2) = 0.29648$), and it is clearly skewed right. This happens when $p < 0.50$.

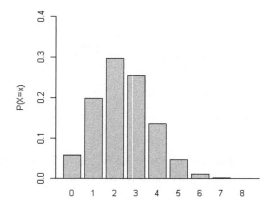

Lastly, suppose $n = 8$ and $p = 0.70$. The following graph shows what this distribution looks like (for instance, $P(X = 2) = 0.01000$), and it is clearly skewed left. This happens when $p > 0.50$.

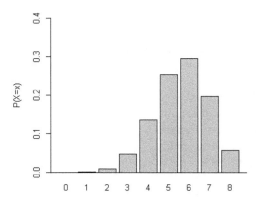

SHAPE OF THE BINOMIAL DISTRIBUTION

Suppose there are n independent subjects, each of which has the same probability p of having a quality of interest (a success). As we have seen, this is a binomial distribution with n subjects and probability of success p.

If $p < 0.50$, then the distribution is skewed right.
If $p = 0.50$, then the distribution is symmetric.
If $p > 0.50$, then the distribution is skewed left.

Section 6.5 – Examples of Using the Binomial Distribution

In this section we see how to use the TI-84 to find binomial probabilities. Your instructor might have you find these probabilities using online calculators, statistical software, or tables, in which case refer to your instructor's directions for how to do that.

TI-84 COMMAND: FINDING PROBABILITIES ON THE BINOMIAL DISTRIBUTION

To find the binomial probability of exactly x successes out of n subjects, each with probability p of success, press 2nd, VARS, and choose Option A: $binompdf($. The command is

$$binompdf(n, p, x)$$

To find the binomial probability of at most x successes out of n subjects, each with probability p of success, press 2nd, VARS, and choose Option B: $binomcdf($. The command is

$$binomcdf(n, p, x)$$

Notice that both commands use n, p, and x, in that order, and the way to remember that is that the letters are in alphabetical order. Also, use $binompdf(\ )$ for exactly x out of n successes, but use $binomcdf(\ )$ for at most x out of n. This includes 0, 1, and so on up to and including x.

The problem with using $binomcdf(\ )$ is that it cannot be used directly when you need to find "at least x" or "greater than x" (or even "less than x"). In those instances, you need to draw a sketch of the "allowed" numbers and then figure out a way to use $binomcdf($) correctly. This will often involve subtracting something from 1.

EXAMPLE
Let's return to the jury problem again. A certain town is known to be home to 54% females and 46% males. You are going to select 12 people at random for a jury, and let X be the number of females on the chosen jury. Find the following probabilities:

    A) The jury contains exactly six females.
    B) The jury contains seven or fewer females.
    C) The jury contains less than three females.
    D) The jury contains more than ten females.
    E) The jury contains at least three females.

Solution: First, recognize that $n = 12$ and $p = 0.54$. For part A, our sketch was the following:

$$0 \quad 1 \quad 2 \quad 3 \quad 4 \quad 5 \quad \boxed{6} \quad 7 \quad 8 \quad 9 \quad 10 \quad 11 \quad 12$$

Since only one number is involved, we can compute $P(X = 6)$ using the $binompdf($) function:

$$P(X = 6) = binompdf(12, 0.54, 6) = 0.21706$$

In part B, we want seven or fewer. Our sketch was the following, encompassing all numbers 0, 1, and so on through and including 7.

$$\boxed{0 \quad 1 \quad 2 \quad 3 \quad 4 \quad 5 \quad 6 \quad 7} \quad 8 \quad 9 \quad 10 \quad 11 \quad 12$$

Since we need all numbers up to and including 7, we can use the $binomcdf($) function directly:

$$P(X \leq 7) = binomcdf(12, 0.54, 7) = 0.71980$$

Part C asks for less than three. This means the numbers less than 3 <u>but not including</u> 3, or in other words 0, 1, and 2.

$$\boxed{0 \quad 1 \quad 2} \quad 3 \quad 4 \quad 5 \quad 6 \quad 7 \quad 8 \quad 9 \quad 10 \quad 11 \quad 12$$

Another way to state this is the numbers up to and including 2. In other words, $P(X < 3) = P(X \leq 2)$, and so now we can use the $binomcdf($) function:

$$P(X < 3) = P(X \leq 2) = binomcdf(12, 0.54, 2) = 0.00952$$

Parts D and E get tricky because now we need to be creative. For part D, more than ten means the numbers greater than 10 <u>but not including</u> 10. Here that is just 11 and 12.

| 0 | 1 | 2 | 3 | 4 | 5 | 6 | 7 | 8 | 9 | 10 | 11 | 12 |

Complement

The problem is that the $binomcdf(\quad)$ function only gives the probability below and including x. What do we do? Using our sketch, recognize that the complement of "11 and 12" is "$0, 1, ..., 10$," or in other words all numbers up to and including 10. Using the complement formula, that means

$$P(X > 10) = 1 - P(X \leq 10)$$

Thus,

$$
\begin{aligned}
P(X > 10) &= 1 - P(X \leq 10) \\
&= 1 - binomcdf(12, 0.54, 10) \\
&= 1 - 0.99310 \\
&= 0.00690
\end{aligned}
$$

Finally, part E wants at least three. That means the numbers above 3, including 3:

| 0 | 1 | 2 | 3 | 4 | 5 | 6 | 7 | 8 | 9 | 10 | 11 | 12 |

Complement

Again, since the region of interest is "3 and above," the complement is "$0, 1, 2$", or in other words all numbers up to and including 2. Using the complement formula, that means

$$P(X \geq 3) = 1 - P(X \leq 2)$$

And so we can compute

$$
\begin{aligned}
P(X \geq 3) &= 1 - P(X \leq 2) \\
&= 1 - binomcdf(12, 0.54, 2) \\
&= 1 - 0.00952 \\
&= 0.99048
\end{aligned}
$$

By the way, the shape of this binomial distribution is skewed left since $p > 0.50$.

Δ

This previous example shows how critical it is to make sketches of the numbers of interest before going to the TI-84. You want to see very clearly which numbers are needed and which numbers are not, and in some cases you will need to subtract from 1.

EXAMPLE
A grocery store is known to sell cartons in which an individual egg is broken with probability 0.08. You randomly select an 18-egg carton, and let X be the number of broken eggs inside.

A) Find the probability that the carton contains no broken eggs.
B) Find the probability that the carton contains at least one broken egg.
C) Find the probability that the carton contains more than 2 broken eggs.
D) Find the expected number of broken eggs inside the carton, as well as the standard deviation.

E) What shape is this distribution?

F) Find the probability that the carton contains between 3 and 6 broken eggs, inclusive.

Solution: First, this is a binomial distribution because there are $n = 18$ eggs that are assumed to be randomly chosen and therefore independent. Each egg has probability $p = 0.03$ of already being broken.

For part A, the probability of an egg not being broken is $1 - 0.08 = 0.92$, and therefore the probability of all 18 eggs not being broken is $(0.92)^{18} = 0.22294$. You can also use the *binompdf* ( ) function with $x = 0$ broken eggs:

$$binompdf(18, 0.08, 0) = 0.22294$$

For part B, the event "at least one egg is broken" is the complement of "no eggs are broken." This can be seen by recognizing that "at least one" includes the numbers $1, 2, 3, \dots, 18$, and so this is the complement of the remaining number 0:

0	1	2	3	4	5	6	7	8	9	10	11	12	13	14	15	16	17	18

Complement

Using the previous answer, we have

$$P(X \geq 1) = 1 - P(X = 0) = 1 - 0.22294 = 0.77706$$

Part C asks for more than 2 broken eggs. "More than 2" means "3 or more," and so our sketch looks like this:

0	1	2	3	4	5	6	7	8	9	10	11	12	13	14	15	16	17	18

Complement

To use the *binomcdf* ( ) function, we will need to instead find the complement, which is $0, 1, 2$.

$$P(X \leq 2) = binomcdf(18, 0.08, 2) = 0.82980$$

Thus, the probability of having more than 2 broken eggs is

$$P(X > 2) = P(X \geq 3) = 1 - P(X \leq 2)$$
$$= 1 - 0.82980$$
$$= 0.17020$$

For part D, the expected number of broken eggs inside this carton is the mean, which is

$$\text{Mean} = np = 18 \times 0.18 = 1.44$$

The standard deviation is

$$\text{Standard Deviation} = \sqrt{np(1 - p)}$$
$$= \sqrt{18 \times 0.08 \times (1 - 0.08)}$$
$$= \sqrt{18 \times 0.08 \times 0.92}$$
$$= \sqrt{1.3248}$$

$$= 1.15100$$

Next, since $p < 0.50$, part E is that this binomial distribution is skewed right. Lastly, part F requires us to be a little creative. Let's look at a sketch of what we need, which is between 3 and 6, inclusive (meaning we include 3 and 6).

0	1	2	3	4	5	6	7	8	9	10	11	12	13	14	15	16	17	18

The problem is exactly how do we find the probability for these four numbers and nowhere else. There are at least two different ways we could solve for it. The first is to recognize that if we were to include the probability of 0, 1, and 2, we would have all numbers up to and including 6. In other words,

$$P(X \leq 6) = P(X \leq 2) + P(3, 4, 5, 6)$$

It therefore follows that

$$P(3, 4, 5, 6) = P(X \leq 6) - P(X \leq 2)$$

We already have $P(X \leq 2) = 0.82980$ from part C, and using the TI-84 again,

$$P(X \leq 6) = binomcdf(18, 0.08, 6) = 0.99970$$

Thus,

$$P(3, 4, 5, 6) = P(X \leq 6) - P(X \leq 2)$$
$$= 0.99970 - 0.82980$$
$$= 0.16990$$

If you did not like this approach, the second way to solve this problem is to simply find the individual probabilities at 3, 4, 5, and 6, and then add them:

$$P(X = 3) = binompdf(18, 0.08, 3) = 0.11961$$
$$P(X = 4) = binompdf(18, 0.08, 4) = 0.03900$$
$$P(X = 5) = binompdf(18, 0.08, 5) = 0.00950$$
$$P(X = 6) = binompdf(18, 0.08, 6) = 0.00179$$

The answer is then

$$P(3, 4, 5, 6) = 0.11961 + 0.03900 + 0.00950 + 0.00179$$
$$= 0.16990$$

Δ

Section 6.6 – Properties of the Normal Distribution
In the remainder of this chapter we discuss one of the most important continuous probability distributions of them all, the normal distribution. Back in Chapter 1, we were first introduced to the concept of a bell-shaped histogram, with an example shown below.

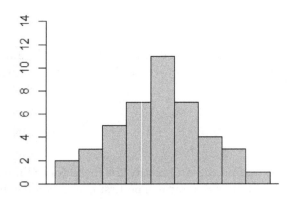

In Chapter 2, we transitioned this bell-curve to a smooth-looking curve when we looked at the Empirical Rule.

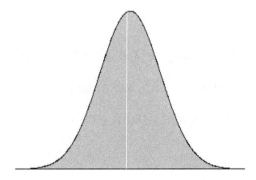

Although we have sparingly used the word normal up to this point, we now formally make your acquaintance with it.

DEFINITION

The **normal distribution** is a continuous probability distribution. It is characterized by a smooth bell-curve function that is symmetric, so the mean equals the median. Thus, the normal distribution is the formal name for the bell-curve. By convention, the mean and standard deviation of the normal distribution are denoted as μ and σ, respectively.

A commonly used special case is called the **standard normal distribution**, which is just a normal distribution with mean 0 and standard deviation 1. Z-scores and their associated probabilities are computed from this curve.

By convention, if you work with a standard normal distribution, a data point is denoted as Z since it is a Z-score. If you work with any other normal distribution, a data point is denoted as X.

For instance, the heights of men in a specific country could follow a normal distribution with mean 69 inches and standard deviation 3.2 inches. There might be some men with unusually short heights and unusually tall heights, but most heights will fall around and on either side of the mean of 69, in an approximately symmetric fashion. This distribution would be continuous because a height could be 67 inches, or 67.1 inches, or 67.1215 inches, or any other combination of decimal values.

There are three very important properties of the normal distribution that you need to know about.

154

PROPERTIES OF THE NORMAL DISTRIBUTION
Property 1: The area under the normal distribution curve represents a specific probability.
Property 2: The total area under the curve for the normal distribution is 1.
Property 3: The normal curve is symmetric.

Let's discuss these points further.

Property 1: The area under the normal distribution curve is literally a probability, so it is necessarily between 0 and 1. For instance, in the following sketch, the shaded region between A and B represents the probability that a variable X falls between A and B, or $P(A \leq X \leq B)$. (Thus, when we say "the area under the curve," we are referring to the probability.)

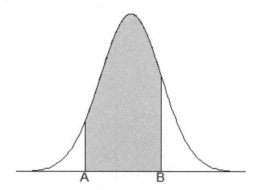

As an example, suppose the mean male height in a specific country is normally distributed with mean 69 inches and standard deviation 3.2 inches. The probability of randomly choosing a male whose height is between 70 and 73 inches, or $P(70 \leq X \leq 73)$, is represented by the shaded region in the following sketch:

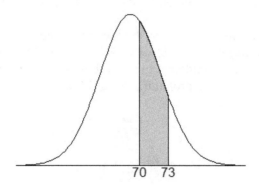

If we compute the probability here, it turns out to be 0.27168 (we will see later how to obtain this answer; for now, just take my word for it). In practical terms, this means that the probability that a male has a height between 70 and 73 inches is 0.27168, or 27.168%. Graphically, the area of the gray region on the above sketch is 0.27168. In other words, the area of the gray region and the probability are the same number.

Property 2: The entire area from the left side of the normal distribution to the right side is 1, as seen in the gray portion of the curve below.

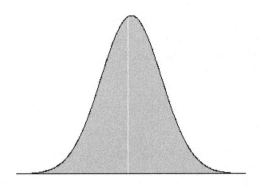

Consequently, we can use this property to answer some normal probability questions. For example, suppose we "cut" the normal curve into two pieces, and we are told that the left area (white) is 0.70. The goal is to find the area of the right (gray) region. Since the total area under the curve is 1, the right region must have area 0.30.

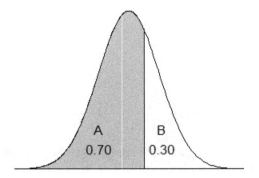

This can easily be solved if we call the areas of the two regions in the above sketch A and B. We necessarily have $A + B = 1$, and if we are given $0.70 + B = 1$, then $B = 1 - 0.70 = 0.30$.

As an extension, suppose we cut the normal distribution into three pieces with areas A, B, and C. Let's say we know the left region (white) has probability 0.20 and the right region (light gray) has probability 0.30. The goal is to find the area of the middle region (dark gray). Since we know the probabilities of two of the three regions, the middle must have probability/area 0.50.

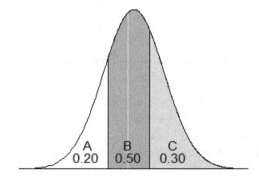

This can be solved by noting that $A + B + C = 1$. Since $A = 0.20$ and $C = 0.30$, then $B = 1 - 0.20 - 0.30 = 0.50$.

Of course, we could keep extending this idea. If we feel the need to cut the normal curve into one hundred regions, and we know the areas of ninety-nine of them, we can easily find the one hundredth by simple subtraction!

Property 3: The fact that the normal curve is symmetric comes into play when finding probabilities. For instance, consider the following sketch of the standard normal distribution (so it has mean 0 and standard deviation 1). The Z-scores -1 and 1 are shown on the graph, cutting it into three regions. The goal is to find the area of the middle region (gray). This is equivalent to finding the probability $P(-1 \leq Z \leq 1)$.

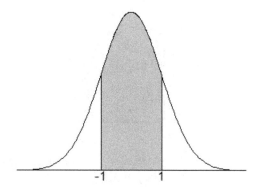

The symmetric property says that since $Z = -1$ and $Z = 1$ are the same distance away from the mean 0, the area below $Z = -1$ (left region, white) is the same as the area above $Z = 1$ (right region, white). This is a crucial property to understand!

Now let's find the middle region's probability if we are told that the right region above $Z = 1$ has area 0.158655. We label that on the sketch:

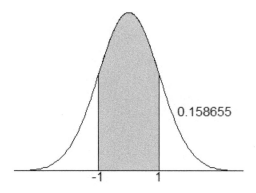

By symmetry, the left region below $Z = -1$ also has probability 0.158655:

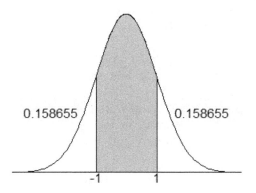

Thus, the middle region (between $Z = -1$ and $Z = 1$) has a probability that can be found by subtraction from 1:

$$1 - 0.158655 - 0.158655 = 0.68269$$

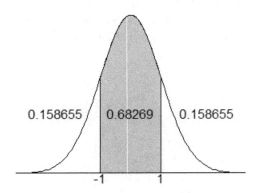

What this means is that the probability between $Z = -1$ and $Z = 1$ is 0.68269, or 68.269% of the standard normal curve. Put another way, if a population is normally distributed, then we can expect 68.269% of observations to be within one standard deviation of the mean, on both sides. Does this sound familiar? Recall the Empirical Rule, which told us that about 68% fall within one standard deviation of the mean. The above example simply makes this percentage more precise! (One reason we are pursuing these calculations is so that we don't have to rely on using the Empirical Rule every time; we can now find the probability around any Z-score.)

Another consequence of the above properties is that the probability to the left of the mean μ is 0.50, which is the same as the probability to the right of μ.

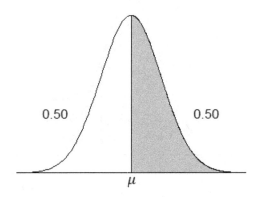

Generally, there are two types of problems concerning the normal distribution, and the strategies (and TI-84 commands) need to be adjusted accordingly.

Problem 1: Given the Z-score or data point X, find a probability associated with Z or X.
Problem 2: Given the probability, find a Z-score or data point X associated with the probability.

The examples shown over the previous few pages all illustrated Problem 1 since the goal in those examples was to find probabilities. However, we can also go in reverse to get a Problem 2 scenario. For instance, let's twist the previous example slightly and say that the probability above an unknown Z is 0.158655.

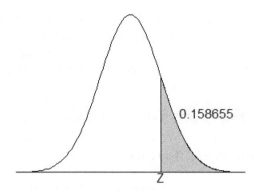

The goal now is to find the Z that cuts the standard normal curve in such a way that it gives probability 0.158655 above Z. From the previous example, we already know that the answer is $Z = 1$. In general, there is a TI-84 command that will help us figure out the Z-score given a probability, but we will get to that later.

Get comfortable with all the properties and topics in this section, as they are about to come into play not only for the rest of this chapter, but also the rest of this book!

The final part of this section is not necessary to understand, but we are including it for those of you that have taken a calculus class. When we find the probability between A and B on the normal distribution, we are finding the integral of the normal distribution function from A to B since the integral represents the area under the curve. If $f(x)$ denotes the normal distribution, then the mathematical way to represent the probability would be

$$P(A \leq X \leq B) = \int_A^B f(x)dx$$

The function that represents the normal distribution is

$$f(x) = \frac{1}{\sigma\sqrt{2\pi}} \exp\left\{-\frac{(x-\mu)^2}{2\sigma^2}\right\}, -\infty < x < \infty$$

For the standard normal distribution, the function reduces to

$$f(x) = \frac{1}{\sqrt{2\pi}} \exp\left\{-\frac{x^2}{2}\right\}, -\infty < x < \infty$$

If you did not understand the notation here, no need to worry – we will not use it again in these notes!

Section 6.7 – Finding Normal Probabilities and Z-Scores
Now that we have seen the important properties of the normal distribution, the next step is to learn exactly how to compute probabilities on the normal curve. For now, we will just work with the standard normal distribution, but the ideas extend in simple ways when the mean and standard deviation are different values.

In these notes, we concentrate on using the TI-84 to find these probabilities. Depending on the nature of your course and instructor, you might be asked to find probabilities using a standard normal table, a graphing calculator, Excel, online calculators, or certain software programs. If you need to find the probabilities using a method other than the TI-84, refer to your class notes to see how to compute them. (See Appendix C for a standard normal table.)

TI-84 COMMAND: FIND PROBABILITIES ON THE NORMAL DISTRIBUTION

To find the probability between a lower limit and an upper limit on the normal distribution, press $\boxed{\text{2nd}}$, $\boxed{\text{VARS}}$, and choose Option 2: $normalcdf($. The command is

$$normalcdf(\text{lower limit}, \text{upper limit}, \text{mean}, \text{sd})$$

If there is no lower limit, use -999999, and if there is no upper limit, use 999999. If you are using the standard normal distribution, which has mean 0 and standard deviation 1, then you may leave off the mean and standard deviation in the command, as in the following:

$$normalcdf(\text{lower limit}, \text{upper limit})$$

The reason why we use a big number for the lower or upper limit if none is specified is because the normal distribution technically spreads over all possible values (in mathematical terms, we say that the domain is negative infinity to positive infinity). If there is no upper limit, we need to use some huge number as a substitute. You can use 999999, or some other similar choice such as 99999999, 10^{10}, etc.

A word of advice: when you see a normal distribution problem, the very first thing you should do is draw a sketch of a bell-curve labeling exactly what you are given and what it is you need to find. If you neglect to draw a sketch, you are practically guaranteed to get confused later in the problem. So, with these problems, "Step Zero" is to draw a sketch. May I introduce a new saying here:

"When in doubt, draw it out!"

EXAMPLE

Use the TI-84 to find the following probabilities: $P(Z \geq 0.5)$, $P(-2 \leq Z \leq 1.3)$, and $P(Z \leq 1.75)$.

Solution: To find $P(Z \geq 0.5)$, let's first sketch it. We want the area above (to the right of) $Z = 0.5$, the gray region.

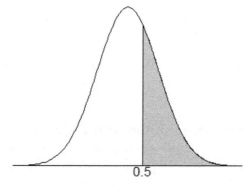

This sketch tells us that the lower limit is $Z = 0.5$ and the upper limit is a large number, so we can use 999999. Thus, we use the TI-84 command as follows:

$$normalcdf(0.5, 999999) = 0.30854$$

The answer is that the gray area represents the probability above $Z = 0.5$, and this probability is 0.30854. Put another way, 30.854% of the standard normal curve is above $Z = 0.5$ (and so the remaining 69.146% of the curve is below $Z = 0.5$).

Next, let's sketch the area for $P(-2 \leq Z \leq 1.3)$. We can easily see that the lower limit is $Z = -2$ and the upper limit is $Z = 1.3$.

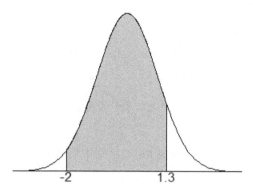

Using the TI-84,

$$normalcdf(-2, 1.3) = 0.88045$$

This means that on the standard normal distribution, the probability between $Z = -2$ and $Z = 1.3$ is 0.88045. Finally, for $P(Z \leq 1.75)$, we need the probability below (to the left of) $Z = 1.75$, the gray region.

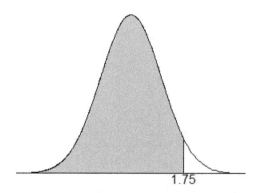

This sketch tells us that the lower limit is a large negative number and the upper limit is $Z = 1.75$, so we can use -999999 for the lower limit. Thus, we use the TI-84 command as follows:

$$normalcdf(-999999, 1.75) = 0.95994$$

The gray area represents the probability below $Z = 1.75$, and this probability is 0.95994.

$$\Delta$$

The previous example shows how to find probabilities given Z-scores. We can also use the TI-84 to find a Z-score associated with a given probability.

TI-84 COMMAND: FIND Z-SCORES ON THE NORMAL DISTRIBUTION

To find the Z-score (or data point) that gives a specified probability on the normal distribution, press 2nd , VARS , and choose Option 3: $invNorm($. The command is

$$invNorm(\text{probability to the left}, \text{mean}, \text{sd})$$

Note that with the specified probability, the TI-84 will give you the Z-score (cr data point) that gives that probability below it (not above). If you are using the standard normal distribution, which has mean 0 and standard deviation 1, then you may leave off the mean and standard deviation in the command, as in the following:

$$invNorm(\text{probability to the left})$$

This concept can be a little confusing at first, so we launch straight into an example.

EXAMPLE

Answer the following questions relating to the standard normal distribution.

    A) What Z-score has probability 0.30 below it?
    B) Find the Z-score such that the probability above Z is equal to 0.40.
    C) Find the Z-scores such that the probability between $-Z$ and Z is 0.50.

Solution: Part A is the most straightforward application. Our sketch reveals that we need to find Z so that the probability below (to the left of) Z is 0.30.

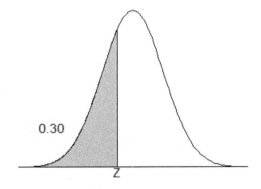

The probability is already a "left-tail" probability, so we can just use the TI-84 directly:

$$invNorm(0.30) = -0.52440$$

What this means is that if we choose $Z = -0.52440$, then the probability below this Z is equal to 0.30. In other words, 30% of the standard normal curve falls below $Z = -0.52440$ (and consequently 70% falls above it). The sketch is updated to reflect this fact.

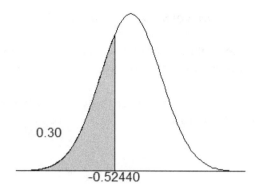

Caution: a probability, of course, must be between 0 and 1. However, a Z-score can be positive or negative. If you get a negative Z-score as your answer, don't panic – it is possible to have one! It just means that you are below the mean rather than above it. On the other hand, if you get a negative probability as your answer, you have definitely gone wrong somewhere!

For part B, our sketch reveals that we need to find Z so that the probability above (to the right of) Z is 0.40.

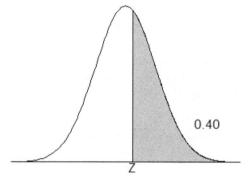

It is tempting to go ahead and use the TI-84 with the function $invNorm(0.40)$ to get the answer. However, this is not correct as that function gives you the Z-score with 0.40 to the left of it. We want the Z-score with 0.40 to the right! The $invNorm(\ \ )$ function requires the left-tail probability. Looking back at our sketch, we instead need to find the probability *below* Z given that the probability *above* Z is 0.40. Remember that the total probability under the curve is 1, which means that the left-tail probability is $1 - 0.40 = 0.60$.

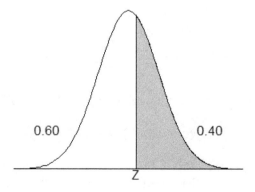

Now we can use the TI-84 in the correct fashion:

$$invNorm(0.60) = 0.25335$$

If we choose $Z = 0.25335$, then the probability below this Z is equal to 0.60 (and at the same time, the probability above Z is 0.40, which is what we were originally trying to answer).

For part C, we need the Z-scores such that the probability between $-Z$ and Z is 0.50. The following sketch illustrates what we are trying to find.

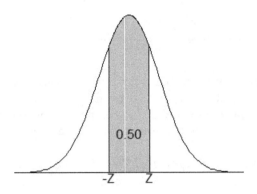

This problem looks a little tricky until you start dissecting what we are given, and how we can use it to uncover other missing pieces. For a start, if probability 0.50 is in the middle of the curve, then $1 - 0.50 = 0.50$ is left over to spread in the two remaining pieces (lower left and upper right). Next, notice that $-Z$ and Z are the same distance away from the mean 0. That means that the area below $-Z$ (the left tail) and the area above Z (the right tail) are the same. So

$$\text{left tail area} = \frac{0.50}{2} = 0.25 = \text{right tail area}$$

The updated sketch is

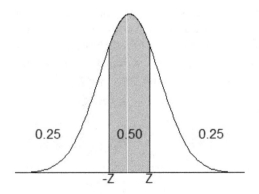

We quickly see that the easiest next step is to find $-Z$ with probability 0.25 to the left:

$$invNorm(0.25) = -0.67449$$

There are two possible ways to get the other Z on the right side of the mean 0. The first method is the easier one, and that is to just recognize that due to symmetry, if the left Z-score is -0.67449, then the right Z-score must be 0.67449.

If you are not convinced, try the second method, which is to find the Z-score that gives the area of the left tail (0.25) plus the area of the middle (0.50) below it, a combined 0.75 probability. Then we can compute

$$invNorm(0.75) = 0.67449$$

Either way, we have shown that on a standard normal distribution, probability 0.50 is between the Z-scores -0.67449 and 0.67449.

Δ

Section 6.8 – Examples of Using the Normal Distribution

In this final section of Chapter 6, we present a nice sampling of examples of how to use the normal distribution in practice. Previously we had just been working with the standard normal distribution with mean 0 and standard deviation 1. Now we can extend the idea to other normal distributions with different means and standard deviations.

EXAMPLE

The daily high temperature on a certain island in the summer follows a normal distribution with mean 98°F and standard deviation 4.4°F.

A) Find the probability that a randomly selected daily high temperature is 102° or higher.
B) Find the probability that a randomly selected daily high temperature is 86° or lower.
C) Is either temperature unusual?
D) Find the Z-score for a daily high temperature of 102°, and find the probability above that Z-score.

Solution: For part A, we simply draw a sketch of the situation to get an idea of which way to use the TI-84. We are given a data point (temperature) and asked to find a probability. A temperature of 102° or higher means we shade to the right of 102.

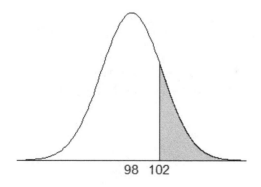

Remember that since the mean and standard deviation are different, we need to include them in the command. The lower limit is 102, and the upper limit is 999999.

$$normalcdf(102, 999999, 98, 4.4) = 0.18165$$

Similarly, for part B we draw a sketch. A temperature of 86° or lower means we shade to the left of 86.

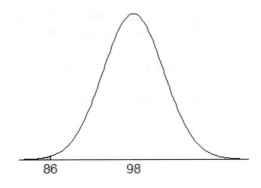

The lower limit is -999999, and the upper limit is 86.

$$normalcdf(-999999, 86, 98, 4.4) = 0.00319$$

For part C, we have discovered that the probability of having a high temperature greater than 102° is 0.18165, and the probability of having a high temperature less than 86° is only 0.00319. Remember that the higher the probability, the greater the likelihood that the said event will occur.

Is it feasible for the high temperature to be greater than 102°? Yes, it is – to put the probability of 0.18165 in perspective, the probability of rolling a 1 on a standard dice is 0.16667. It is certainly not too unusual to roll a 1, and the probability of 0.18165 is a little higher. In contrast, the probability of the high temperature being lower than 86° is only 0.00319, which is very low and therefore an unusual occurrence. In other words, it is extremely unlikely that the daily high temperature observed on this island in summer would be 86° or less. (Later in these notes, we will study actual thresholds that will indicate exactly what it means to be "unusual," but here it is clear what the answer is.)

As for part D, we need to find the Z-score for 102° and then find the probability above that Z-score. Let's do it:

$$Z = \frac{x - \mu}{\sigma} = \frac{102 - 98}{4.4} = \frac{4}{4.4} = 0.90909$$

Remember that since we computed the Z-score, it now follows a standard normal distribution with mean 0 and standard deviation 1. So now we can find the probability above our Z (after drawing your sketch, of course).

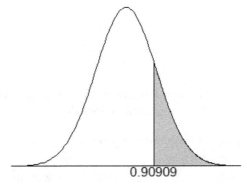

The probability is

$$normalcdf(0.90909, 999999) = 0.18165$$

Aha – it is the same probability as from part A! This is not a coincidence – this will always be the case. Let's go over that again – here are the two sketches from parts A and D again.

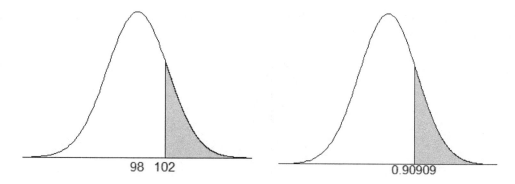

When we find the probability above (or below) a data point on a normal distribution, then we standardize it (meaning we convert it to a Z-score), the probability above (or below) that Z-score will match what it was with the data point.

Δ

DEFINITION

Suppose a data point x is from a normal distribution with mean μ and standard deviation σ. We can **standardize** the data point x, which means convert it to a Z-score:

$$Z = \frac{x - \mu}{\sigma}$$

The Z will also be from a normal distribution but the standard one, with mean 0 and standard deviation 1. Thus, standardizing a data point just means converting it to a Z-score, and converting its normal distribution to a standard normal distribution. That means that any probabilities found from x will be the same as those found from Z.

One more note about the previous problem. You will notice that for the upper limit, which was technically infinity, we used 999999 in the TI-84. That number choice was made simply to illustrate that the upper limit in the graphing calculator is an enormous number, so we can just find the probability above 102°. I am not suggesting that the temperature on the island could reach 999,999°F (by comparison, the highest temperature ever recorded on Earth was 134°F, observed on July 10, 1913 in Death Valley, California[2])!

Similarly, to find the probability below 86°, we used −999999 as the lower limit. Again, this just indicates an infinite lower bound to allow for the computation to take place. This is not to say that the temperature could reach −999,999°F (by comparison, absolute zero is around −459.67°F, and as you probably know, this temperature has never been recorded anywhere in the universe)!

EXAMPLE
The height of ten-year-old children in a certain state follows a normal distribution with mean 54 inches and standard deviation 3.5 inches.

A) Find the probability that a randomly chosen ten-year-old has a height between 51 and 55 inches.

B) What height would correspond to the 90th percentile in this population?

C) A roller coaster in this state has a height requirement of at least 4 feet for passengers. If a ten-year-old child is randomly selected, what is the probability that he/she will not be allowed on the roller coaster?

Solution: Part A is straightforward when we draw our sketch (the mean of 54 is not written simply because the height 55 is too close visually):

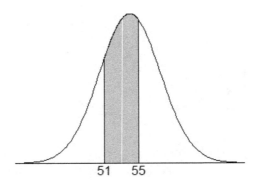

We quickly see that the lower limit is 51 and the upper limit is 55. Since we need to find a probability, we once again use the *normalcdf*( ) function:

$$normalcdf(51, 55, 54, 3.5) = 0.41677$$

Part B is a little different because we turn back to percentiles. Recall from Chapter 2 that the 90th percentile is the data point such that 90% of the observations fall below (to the left of) that point. On a normal distribution, this would look like the following:

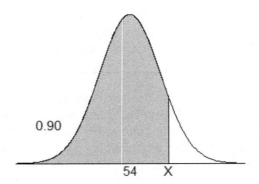

This means that given the probability of 0.90, we want the data value X so that probability 0.90 falls to the left of X. That means we need to use the *invNorm*( ) function because now we start off with a probability instead.

$$invNorm(0.90, 54, 3.5) = 58.48543$$

The answer is that a ten-year-old with a height of 58.48543 inches would be at the 90th percentile, meaning that 90% of all ten-year-olds in this state would have a height at or below this measurement (and the remaining 10% would be taller).

Part C is an example of a real-life application of the normal distribution. Suppose among this population a roller coaster has a height requirement of at least 4 feet (which is 48 inches). That means that anyone who is shorter than 48 inches cannot ride the roller coaster for safety reasons. If we randomly choose a ten-year-old in this population, what is the probability that they will not be allowed on the ride? That means we are interested in the event a ten-year-old is 48 inches or shorter, which translates to the following sketch:

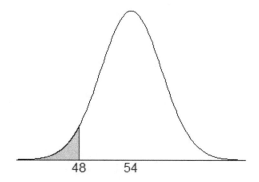

We are given a data point and need a probability, so we use $normalcdf(\ )$ with lower limit -999999 and upper limit 48:

$$normalcdf(-999999, 48, 54, 3.5) = 0.04324$$

This means that there is a 0.04324 probability that a ten-year-old selected at random would fail the height requirement for this roller coaster.

Δ

EXAMPLE
If you watched us cut the normal curve into two and then three pieces in the earlier sections and for some strange reason wanted more pieces to be cut, then this problem is for you! In a specific geology class, test scores are normally distributed with mean 72 and standard deviation 12. The instructor sets the grades in such a way so that the top 8% receive an A, the next 10% a B, the next 12% a C, the next 7% a D, and the remaining grades get an F. Find all the grade cutoffs (and round to two decimals).

Solution: This is a great example of why sketches are so important! Here we are cutting the normal curve into *five* pieces. But don't worry – the same rules apply in that the sum of all five pieces must still be equal to 1. For a start, we need to find the percentage of grades that fail, as that is the one percentage that is missing:

$$100\% - 8\% - 10\% - 12\% - 7\% = 63\%$$

Translating everything onto a sketch and arranging the pieces from left to right, we have the following, where the letter grade cutoffs to be found are denoted as F|D, D|C, C|B, and B|A (this will hopefully make it clear which letter grade is on either side of each boundary). For instance, the region to the right of B|A is a grade A (the 8%), while the next region is a grade B (the next 10%), and so on, with the leftmost region below F|D is a failing grade. Note that we zoomed in on the normal curve since the cutoffs are very close together.

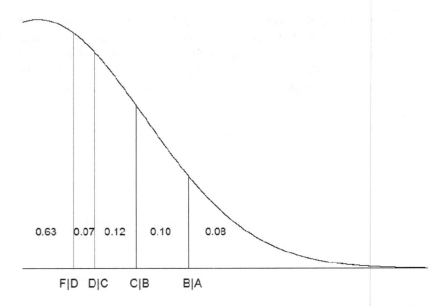

Probably the most straightforward way to solve this problem is to start from the left side and work our way to the right, if only because the *invNorm(   )* function requires left-tail probabilities. That means we first need to find the point F|D, the cutoff below which is a fail, and we know that represents probability 0.63.

$$invNorm(0.63, 72, 12) = 75.98224 \rightarrow 75.98$$

This means that any score below 75.98 is a fail, while scores above 75.98 are a pass of some sort. (One reason we are rounding to two decimals rather than one decimal or a whole number is to make the grade boundary easier to see – after all, most grades are whole numbers!) Let's update the sketch:

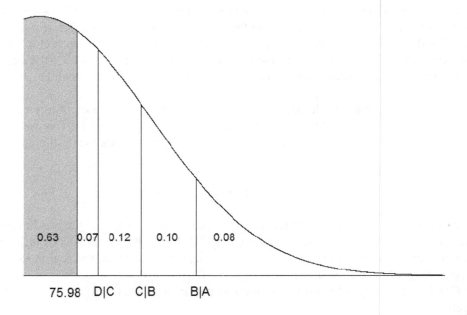

The next step is to find the D|C, below which we have a grade D or worse, and above which at least a grade C. Observe that the total probability in the two leftmost regions is $0.63 + 0.07 = 0.70$, so now we need to find the 70th percentile:

$$invNorm(0.70, 72, 12) = 78.29281 \rightarrow 78.29$$

Thus, grades below 75.98 are an F, while grades between 75.98 and 78.29 are a D.

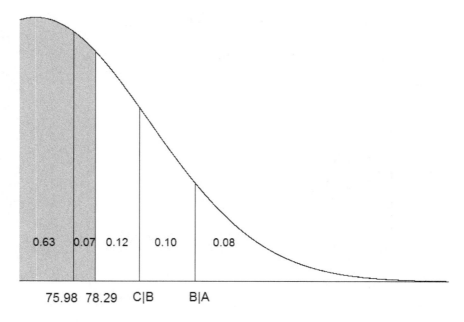

Next, we go for the C|B cutoff, below which we have a grade C or worse, and above which at least grade B. The total probability in the three leftmost regions is $0.63 + 0.07 + 0.12 = 0.82$, so we now find the 82nd percentile:

$$invNorm(0.82, 72, 12) = 82.98438 \rightarrow 82.98$$

Thus, grades between 75.98 and 78.29 are a D, while grades between 78.29 and 82.98 are a C.

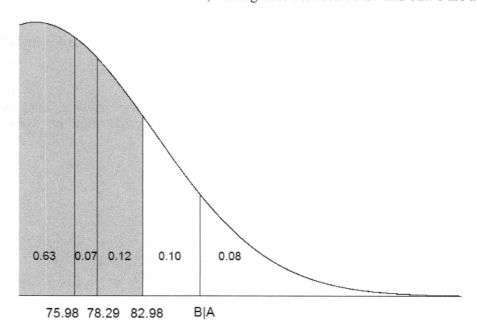

Lastly, we go for the B|A cutoff, below which we have a grade B or worse, and above which grade A. The total probability in the four leftmost regions is $0.63 + 0.07 + 0.12 + 0.10 = 0.92$, so we now find the 92nd percentile:

$$invNorm(0.92, 72, 12) = 88.86086 \rightarrow 88.86$$

Here is the complete and final sketch of the grade cutoffs.

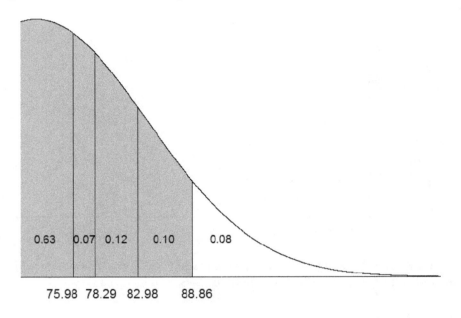

To recap, here are the results. A grade below 75.98 is an F, a grade between 75.98 and 78.29 is a D, a grade between 78.29 and 82.98 is a C, a grade between 82.98 and 88.86 is a B, while a grade above 88.86 is an A.

Δ

We have some more examples coming your way that are mindbenders, but they will hopefully be helpful if you come across anything similar in your homework!

EXAMPLE
A population follows a normal distribution with mean μ and standard deviation σ. Find the probability that an observation falls in the dark gray region (above $\mu + 0.53\sigma$). Also find the probability that an observation falls in the light gray region (between μ and $\mu + 0.53\sigma$).

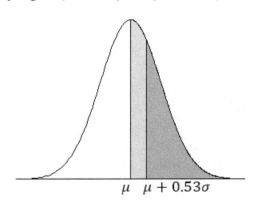

Solution: This question seems very tricky since no numbers are given for μ and σ. However, think back to the Empirical Rule: when we found the value that was 2 deviations above the mean, we computed $\mu + 2\sigma$. In other words, we went 2 deviations to the right of the mean, which corresponds to a Z-score of $Z = 2$.

The same idea is used here: we are 0.53 standard deviations above the mean, so $Z = 0.53$. That means we can translate this scenario to a standard normal distribution with mean 0 and standard deviation 1, as in the following sketch:

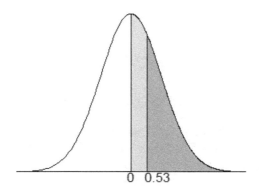

Now we can use familiar techniques. For the dark gray region on the right side, the lower limit is 0.53 and the upper limit is 999999, so the area of the right region is

$$normalcdf(0.53, 999999) = 0.29806$$

As for the light gray region in the middle, observe that the lower limit is 0 and the upper limit is 0.53, so the area of the middle region is

$$normalcdf(0, 0.53) = 0.20194$$

An alternative way to find the middle area is to recognize that the left side of the normal curve (below 0) has area 0.50 by symmetry, and so since the left and right regions have probabilities 0.29806 and 0.50, respectively, we can compute

$$1 - 0.29806 - 0.50 = 0.20194$$

Δ

EXAMPLE
Answer the following questions for a normal distribution.

    A) Find the probability that an observation falls within 2.58 standard deviations of the mean.
    B) Find the Z-score such that 43% of the curve falls within Z standard deviations of the mean.

Solution: For part A, remember that when we say an observation is within 2.58 standard deviations of the mean, the Z-score is between -2.58 and 2.58 (so going out on both sides of the mean 0). Thus, we can find the probability between -2.58 and 2.58 on the standard normal distribution, as in the following sketch:

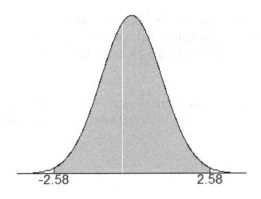

The answer is

$$normalcdf(-2.58, 2.58) = 0.99012$$

Next, for part B we want to find the Z-score value such that 43% of the standard normal distribution lies within Z standard deviations of the mean. That means that the probability between $-Z$ and Z is 0.43, as in the middle region of the following sketch:

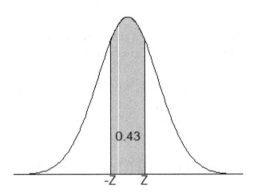

Since $-Z$ and Z are the same distance away from the mean of 0, that tells us that the area of the left region and the area of the right region are the same due to symmetry. Since 0.43 is in the middle, that means that $1 - 0.43 = 0.57$ is left over, and half of that is in both the left and right sides. Thus, both the remaining regions have probability $0.57/2 = 0.285$. Our updated sketch looks like this:

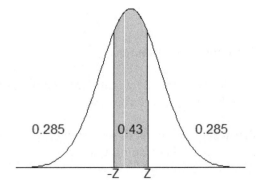

Now we can find the Z-score cutoff that gives probability 0.285 to the left using the *invNorm( )* function:

$$invNorm(0.285) = -0.56805$$

By symmetry, the upper Z-score is $Z = 0.56805$. To answer the question, 43% of the standard normal curve lies between $Z = -0.56805$ and $Z = 0.56805$.

$$\Delta$$

EXAMPLE

The lengths of stalagmites in a certain cave in India are normally distributed with a mean of 3.9 feet and a standard deviation of 0.6 feet.

    A) What stalagmite length is the 98th percentile?
    B) How many standard deviations above the mean is the 98th percentile?
    C) What is the percentile for a stalagmite length of 3.1 feet?
    D) Find the lower quartile, upper quartile, and IQR.

Solution: For parts A and B, the 98th percentile is the stalagmite length such that 98% of all stalagmite lengths fall below it, as in the following diagram:

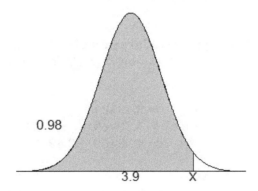

This is a straightforward application of the $invNorm(\quad)$ function:

$$invNorm(0.98, 3.9, 0.6) = 5.13225$$

To find how many standard deviations above the mean this percentile is, we standardize it and turn it into a Z-score:

$$Z = \frac{X - \mu}{\sigma} = \frac{5.13225 - 3.9}{0.6} = 2.05375$$

Thus, the 98th percentile is a length of 5.13225 feet, and it is 2.05375 standard deviations above the mean (above because it is positive).

Parts C and D draw upon information we learned back in Chapter 2. First, to find the percentile for a stalagmite with length 3.1 feet, that means that we find the probability to the left of 3.1, then convert it to a percentile. Here is our sketch:

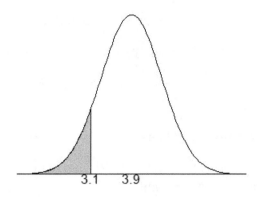

The lower limit is -999999, and the upper limit is 3.1.

$$normalcdf(-999999, 3.1, 3.9, 0.6) = 0.09121$$

However, a percentile is a whole-number percentage, and so this probability as a percentage is 9.121%. Rounded to the nearest whole number, the percentile is 9, or put another way the 9th percentile is a stalagmite with length 3.1 feet.

Finally, we need to compute the lower quartile (25th percentile), the upper quartile (75th percentile), and the interquartile range (upper quartile minus lower quartile). Using the same percentile techniques from the $invNorm(\quad)$ function, we have

$$invNorm(0.25, 3.9, 0.6) = 3.49531$$
$$invNorm(0.75, 3.9, 0.6) = 4.30469$$
$$IQR = 4.30469 - 3.49531 = 0.80938$$

Δ

As you can see, the first step with these normal problems is to make sketches before jumping to the TI-84. Only then will you be able to see visually what you know, what you need to find, and any tricks you may need to deploy. Realize that in at least some cases there could be more than one way to solve the problem, and your job is to choose the method that makes the most sense to you.

The reason we have spent a lot of time on these problems is that you need to be rock-solid confident with how to solve them. Almost all the remaining chapters in this book at some point draw upon the techniques you have learned in these past three sections, so you need to be comfortable with them now. And don't forget…

"When in doubt, draw it out!"

Chapter 7 – Sampling Distributions

In this chapter we focus on two new distributions that are extensions of what we learned in Chapter 6: the Sampling Distribution of the Sample Mean, and the Sampling Distribution of the Sample Proportion. These sound complicated from the names alone, but we will see that with some slight and careful extensions of what we already know, they are actually easier than they look.

Section 7.1 – The Basic Concepts of Sampling Distributions

Before we get to sampling distributions, let's review what we learned in Chapter 6. We learned how to find probabilities like the following. Test scores are normally distributed with a population mean of 78 and a population standard deviation of 6. What is the probability that a randomly selected student scored higher than 85?

To answer this question, we would use the $normalcdf(\quad)$ function on the TI-84. The key here is to realize that the question wants the probability for **just one student**. Our sketch reveals that the lower limit is 85 and the upper limit is 999999.

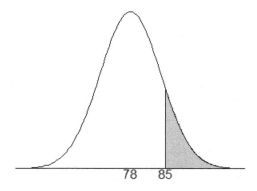

The answer would be

$$normalcdf(85,99999,78,6) = 0.12167$$

Now let's generalize this question to the following situation. Test scores are normally distributed with a population mean of 78 and a population standard deviation of 6. A random sample of nine students is computed. What is the probability that **the average test score of these nine students** is higher than 85?

This means that we are not concerned with just one student, but instead the average of nine students. It turns out that we can compute such a probability with the normal distribution as well, provided that certain conditions are met. We can do this with the graphing calculator, but instead of looking at the distribution of the individual values (like we looked at before), we need the distribution of the possible sample means we could get from samples of a specific size. To help, we need to create a curve of all the possible sample means we could get.

As an example, let's say that the population we are interested in is all freshmen at a specific college. We are interested in the average number of siblings per freshman (so for each individual, it could be 0, 1, 2, etc.).

Imagine that the population average number of siblings per freshman was known to be $\mu = 1.901$ (for example, from a college census). For now, let's assume that the average number of siblings is normally distributed. This is a population mean because it describes the whole population of freshmen at this college.

Now suppose we took a random sample of 5 freshmen, asked them how many siblings they had, and averaged the values of those 5 people. Here is our sample:

Person #	1	2	3	4	5
Siblings	0	1	3	2	2

The average from these 5 people would be a sample mean because it is just for these 5 people, not everyone in the class. In this case, the sample mean is $\bar{x} = 1.6$.

Let's do it one more time for 5 more people (a new random sample of the same size):

Person #	1	2	3	4	5
Siblings	4	1	2	3	2

In this new sample, the sample average is now $\bar{x} = 2.4$.

Sometimes we will get a sample mean below the population mean (first survey), sometimes we will get a sample mean above the population mean (second survey), and occasionally we might get a sample mean exactly equal to the population mean.

Here is the idea: imagine we repeated this procedure by sampling a bunch of freshmen in groups of 5, found the average number of siblings per sample, and we did this over and over again a large number of times, so that we have many combinations of 5 people. Now we record all these sample means and graph them to look at their pattern. This distribution is called the **Sampling Distribution of the Sample Means**.

DEFINITION
The **sampling distribution of the sample means (or averages)** is the distribution that describes the possible values that sample means of a specified sample size n can take, along with their corresponding probabilities. Under certain conditions, the sampling distribution of the sample means is normally distributed.

To be clear, the population mean μ stays the same, but the sample mean $\bar{x}$ changes from sample to sample.

As an illustration, suppose we took 100 total samples, each of size 5, and recorded the 100 sample averages. The first ten are 1.8, 3.8, 2.8, 1.2, 2.6, 1.8, 1.2, 1.2, 2.0, and 1.6 (I shall spare you the list of ninety remaining averages!). Now let's consider all sample averages we found and plot them on a graph:

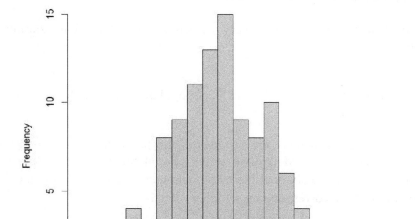

Sampling Distribution of the Sample Mean of Number of Siblings

This is a graph of all 100 sample means we found. Recall that we assumed the number of siblings an individual has was normally distributed and that the population mean was $\mu = 1.901$. What can you say about the above graph?

It too seems to have an approximately normal distribution, and furthermore, the center of the graph appears to be 1.901 as well. The above graph is the **sampling distribution of <u>sample averages</u>**, since it is a plot of the 100 different samples we took. As we shall see soon, it turns out that the sampling distribution will be approximately normal under certain conditions, and it will have the same mean as the population.

To find probabilities involving these sample means, like the probability that a sample of five people will have an average of more than 2 siblings per person, we will have to use the *normalcdf* ( ) function on the TI-84. To pull this off, we need to know three things:

1) What is the mean, the overall average of all the possible sample means?
2) What is the standard deviation, the spread of all the values for all the possible sample means?
3) What is the shape of the distribution of these sample means? To use the *normalcdf* ( ) function, they need to be normally distributed.

We will talk about these three things and how to calculate these probabilities very soon.

Section 7.2 – The Sampling Distribution of the Sample Means
Here is the general idea behind obtaining the sampling distribution of the sample means.

1) Obtain a simple random sample of size n.
2) Compute the sample mean $\overline{x}$.

3) Assuming that we are sampling from a finite population, repeat steps 1 and 2 until all simple random samples of size n have been obtained.

This is easy to do with a finite population with very few values. Let's look at an example to make sure we get the hang of the idea.

EXAMPLE
Draw all possible samples of size $n = 2$ from the population $\{2, 4, 6, 8\}$. Construct the sampling distribution of the sample mean.

Solution: To do this, recognize that there are 4 values in the population, from which we are choosing samples of size 2. (In general, you would hardly ever see a population this tiny! This is just for illustrative purposes!) It turns out that there are six possible combinations of values (recall that $\binom{4}{2} = 6$), so we can just list them all and compute the corresponding sample averages:

$$\{2, 4\} \rightarrow \bar{x} = 3$$
$$\{2, 6\} \rightarrow \bar{x} = 4$$
$$\{2, 8\} \rightarrow \bar{x} = 5$$
$$\{4, 6\} \rightarrow \bar{x} = 5$$
$$\{4, 8\} \rightarrow \bar{x} = 6$$
$$\{6, 8\} \rightarrow \bar{x} = 7$$

To obtain the population mean, we compute it from the original four points $\{2, 4, 6, 8\}$. It turns out to be $\mu = 5$ (a Greek letter because it is for the population). The following is a graph of what this distribution looks like. Although a bit of a stretch, one could perhaps argue that it looks approximately normal.

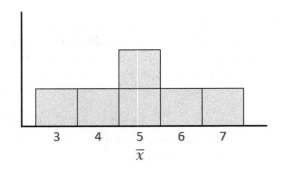

What is the probability that we would get a sample mean of 5 from a sample of size 2 from this population? In this particular example, we can get the exact answer. There are six combinations, two of which have a sample mean of 5. Thus, the probability is $2/6 = 0.33333$.

Δ

Of course, in reality we will not have all the values from a population because most populations we look at are too large. Thus, to find probabilities involving sample means, we need to know what the distribution looks like. We need to know the mean, the standard deviation, and the shape.

First, recall from earlier chapters that the population mean is μ, while the population standard deviation is σ. To answer these questions, these values will actually be told to us. (In practice, these values are usually unknown, as we shall see in subsequent chapters, but in this chapter they will be given.)

First Characteristic: The Mean
The average of all possible sample means we could get will always be equal to the overall population mean itself. In other words, the mean of the sampling distribution is μ.

In the previous example, we showed that the population mean was $\mu = 5$. To find the mean of the sampling distribution of sample averages, we just take all possible values and average them, so we find the average of the six values 3, 4, 5, 5, 6, and 7. That average is also 5, which matches $\mu = 5$.

Second Characteristic: The Standard Deviation
When we are talking about the spread, or standard deviation, of a sampling distribution, we call it by the new name **standard error**. This term can get a bit confusing at first, but just think of the standard error as a type of standard deviation. It measures the spread of a sample statistic like the sample mean. It just places a value on the spread of all the possible sample mean values.

DEFINITION
The **standard error** is simply the standard deviation of the sampling distribution of the sample means. Given a sample of size n, the formula is

$$\text{standard error} = \frac{\sigma}{\sqrt{n}}$$

Why is the standard error equal to this formula? Individual values in a population are going to be all over the place. Some will be high, some will be low, and their population standard deviation is equal to σ.

However, sample means are not as spread out. Yes, we might have some high values and we might have some low values in a sample, but for the most part these values are going to average out close to the mean. Thus, the standard error or spread is going to be quite a bit smaller than σ; it is actually $\sigma/\sqrt{n}$. (A nifty bit of calculus will establish this formula, but we shall not explore that road!)

Third Characteristic: The Shape of the Distribution
To find these probabilities associated with sample means, we need to ensure that the distribution of these sample means is in fact bell-shaped or normal, otherwise we cannot use the $normalcdf(\ )$ function. To check for this, we need for at least one of the following statements to be true. They can both be true, but we only require one:

1) If the population is normally distributed, then the sampling distribution of the sample mean is normally distributed as well, regardless of sample size.
2) If the sample size is large enough (usually we say n greater than 30), the sampling distribution of the sample mean is approximately normal, regardless of the distribution of the population. (This is the **Central Limit Theorem**.)

DEFINITION
The **Central Limit Theorem** says that given a sampling distribution of sample means, if the sample size used is large enough ($n > 30$), then the shape of the sampling distribution of sample means is approximately normal. It does not matter whether the original population was normal, skewed, bi-modal, or unknown – the sampling distribution of sample means will be approximately normal provided $n > 30$!

Caution: Some textbooks might suggest using other minimum numbers such as 20 or 40. In these notes, we will use 30.

There has been a lot of information here, so let's summarize the key points.

SUMMARY: SAMPLING DISTRIBUTION OF SAMPLE MEANS

Consider a population of values with mean μ and standard deviation σ. Now suppose we select a random sample of size n and compute $\overline{x}$, with the goal of describing the sampling distribution of the sample mean. The following statements are true:

Statement 1: The mean of the sampling distribution is μ.

Statement 2: The standard deviation of the sampling distribution is $\frac{\sigma}{\sqrt{n}}$. This is called the **standard error**.

Statement 3: The shape of the sampling distribution is approximately normal if …

      a) The population from which we sampled is known to be normal, or …

      b) The sample size is large enough, $n > 30$ (**Central Limit Theorem**).

      c) If both those statements are false, then no conclusion can be made about the sampling distribution's shape.

MNEMONIC

The **Central Limit Theorem** may sometimes be abbreviated as CLT. That is TLC spelled backwards!

Based on all these points we have talked about, we can now find probabilities involving sample means using the $normalcdf($ $)$ function on the TI-84. We can do this keeping the three points in mind:

1) The sampling distribution of the sample mean should be normal. Check to see if the population is known to be normal, or if not, whether the sample size is greater than 30.
2) The mean is still the same, the population mean μ.
3) The standard deviation is now the standard error, $\sigma/\sqrt{n}$.

That means that to compute probabilities, we do the following.

TI-84 COMMAND: SAMPLING DISTRIBUTION OF SAMPLE MEANS

These are the same instructions you saw in Chapter 6. To find the probability between a lower limit and an upper limit on the normal distribution, press $\boxed{\text{2nd}}$, $\boxed{\text{VARS}}$, and choose Option 2: $normalcdf($. The command is

$$normalcdf(\text{lower limit, upper limit, mean, sd})$$

If there is no lower limit, use -999999, and if there is no upper limit, use 999999. Using the required formulas, that means we type

$$normalcdf\left(\text{lower limit, upper limit}, \mu, \frac{\sigma}{\sqrt{n}}\right)$$

We use this new standard deviation (called the standard error) in the computations because sample means are not as spread out as much as individual data values, so the new standard deviation is $\sigma/\sqrt{n}$ rather than just σ.

Why do we suddenly divide by the square root of n when we didn't before? Here is the answer. In previous probability questions, you had situations such as "Find the probability that a person scores higher than X," or some variation. If you think about it, you literally had a sample of size $n = 1$, one individual. In this case, the standard error was

$$\frac{\sigma}{\sqrt{n}} = \frac{\sigma}{\sqrt{1}} = \sigma$$

Thus, the standard error happened to reduce to σ, which is precisely what we used in the previous chapter. So the answer is that you actually did use the standard error formula and just didn't realize it at the time, simply because n was equal to 1!

EXAMPLE

Suppose a single value is selected from a normal population with mean $\mu = 5$ and standard deviation $\sigma = 1$. Find the probability that that one value is greater than 5.8. Next, suppose a sample of size 25 is selected from this population. Find the probability that the sample mean for these 25 values is greater than 5.8.

Solution: The first question is simply a normal problem (pun intended!) that by now you are used to, the types of questions from Chapter 6. For one individual, we want to be greater than 5.8, so the lower limit is 5.8 and the upper limit is 999999, as seen in the following graph.

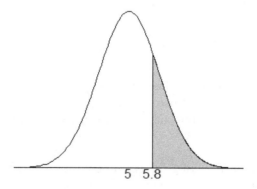

Thus,

$$P(X > 5.8) = normalcdf(5.8, 999999, 5, 1) = 0.21186$$

This means that the probability that one individual is above 5.8 is 0.30854.

Next, given a sample of size 25, we need the probability that the sample mean of those 25 values is greater than 5.8. This is a sampling distribution of sample means with $n = 25$, so we need to adjust the inputs in the graphing calculator. The lower limit is still 5.8, and the upper limit is still 999999. The mean is the population mean, still 5. However, the fourth number is now the standard error, equal to

$$\frac{\sigma}{\sqrt{n}} = \frac{1}{\sqrt{25}} = \frac{1}{5} = 0.20$$

All we need to do now is adjust the calculator inputs (the left side of the equation now says $\overline{X}$ to remind us that it is a sample mean rather than an individual point):

$$P(\overline{X} > 5.8) = normalcdf(5.8, 999999, 5, 0.20) = 0.00003$$

To be clear, the probability that one individual is above 5.8 is 0.21186. However, when given a sample of 25 subjects, the probability that their average is above 5.8 drops to 0.00003. This is a big decrease in probability because the standard error of 0.20 is a lot smaller than the original population standard deviation of 5, so there is less variability in how the average behaves than individual subjects. It is therefore far less likely that the average could be higher than 5.8 than an individual subject.

Δ

EXAMPLE
Suppose the scores on a test have a mean $\mu = 74$ and standard deviation $\sigma = 12$. We take a sample of $n = 36$.

    A) If we took many samples of size 36 and computed a sample mean test score for each sample, what would the standard deviation (spread) for these sample mean test scores be?
    B) Describe the shape of the sampling distribution of the sample mean.
    C) What is the probability that the sample mean of test scores for a sample of size $n = 36$ is between 76 and 79?

Solution: First, part A is describing a sampling distribution of sample averages because it concerns a bunch of sample averages and how they behave. The standard deviation of the sampling distribution is called standard error, and it is computed as

$$\text{standard error} = \frac{\sigma}{\sqrt{n}} = \frac{12}{\sqrt{36}} = \frac{12}{6} = 2$$

To use the normal distribution, we need to check the two possible requirements. First, we are not told what shape the population is, so we cannot use that assumption. The other item to check is whether the sample size is greater than 30, and it is. Thus, part B is that the sampling distribution of the sample means is approximately normal.

For part C, notice that the question is asking for the probability of the sample mean test scores, not the probability of an individual test score. That means we need to use the sampling distribution inputs of μ and $\sigma/\sqrt{n}$ instead of μ and σ. Here is our sketch for finding the sample average between 76 and 79.

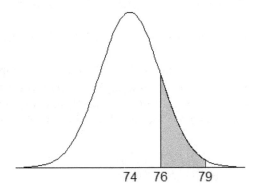

Noting that the mean of the sampling distribution is the population mean $\mu = 74$,

$$P(76 \leq \overline{X} \leq 79) = normalcdf(76, 79, 74, 2) = 0.15245$$

This means that the probability that a sample average of 36 test scores is between 76 and 79 is 0.15245.

Δ

EXAMPLE
The weight of a carton of strawberries is skewed right with mean 14 ounces and standard deviation 1.5 ounces. Suppose we take a random sample of 16 strawberry cartons. Can we use the normal distribution to find the probability that the sample average of the weights of these 16 cartons will be greater than 16 ounces? Why or why not?

Solution: To use the normal distribution and the $normalcdf($ $)$ function, we need to establish normality of the sampling distribution of the sample mean. The first thing to check is whether the population is normal. It is actually skewed right, so we cannot use that criterion.

Next, we see if the sample size is greater than 30. It is 16, which is less than 30, so we cannot use that criterion either. Thus, no conclusion can be made about the distribution shape, and it is not a good idea to use the normal distribution. (In reality, we could address this question using other methods called non-parametric techniques, but that is not taught in this class.)

Δ

EXAMPLE
Consider a population that is normal with mean 80 and standard deviation 5. Also suppose we select a sample of size $n = 625$. Which graph below represents the population? Which graph represents the sampling distribution of the sample mean?

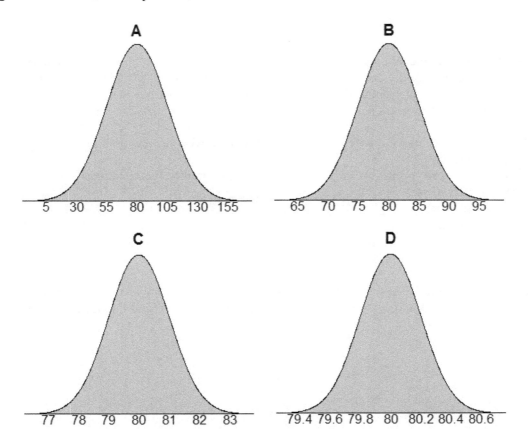

Solution: This is a good problem because we need to visually tell apart the population from the sampling distribution of the sample averages. First, let's get our notation nailed down: $\mu = 80$, $\sigma = 5$, and $n = 625$. The population mean appears in the center of the graph, but notice that all four graphs have a mean

185

of 80, so that does not rule out anything.

The other piece of information for the population is the population standard deviation, $\sigma = 5$. We need to find the graph whose standard deviation looks most closely like 5. Since there are three numbers on either side of the means, we may assume that these are the one, two, and three standard deviation values according to the Empirical Rule. That means that the distance from the mean to the immediate next number is approximately equal to the graph's standard deviation.

For example, Graph A's standard deviation is 25 because the distance between 80 and 105 is 25. Similarly, Graph B's standard deviation is $85 - 80 = 5$, Graph C's is $81 - 80 = 1$, while Graph D's is $80.2 - 80 = 0.2$. This means that Graph B represents the population since $\sigma = 5$.

Next, we need to select the graph that represents the sampling distribution of the sample means. The mean of the sampling distribution is the population mean, $\mu = 80$. The standard deviation of the sampling distribution, which is called standard error, is equal to

$$\frac{\sigma}{\sqrt{n}} = \frac{5}{\sqrt{625}} = \frac{5}{25} = 0.2$$

Graph D has a standard deviation of 0.2, matching the standard error, and so this graph is the correct one.

Δ

EXAMPLE

Suppose we have a machine that dispenses coffee into a cup. The cup can hold a maximum of 8.0 ounces, and the machine is supposedly set to dispense a mean of 7.9 ounces (to reduce the chances of coffee spilling over the cup edge). Assume that the amount of coffee dispensed is normally distributed with a standard deviation of 0.1 ounces.

  A) If we order one cup of coffee from this machine, what is the probability the machine will overflow the cup?
  B) Suppose we order 6 cups of coffee. What is the probability the average of the amounts will be less than 7.8 ounces?

Solution: For part A, notice the question is dealing with just one cup of coffee. This is not a sampling distribution question, so we will not have the standard error here. We would use $\mu = 7.9$ and $\sigma = 0.1$. The question is, what are the limits to use?

If the cup holds 8.0 ounces, and the machine overflows the cup, that means the machine must have dispensed more than 8.0 ounces. That means that the lower limit is 8.0 and the upper limit is 999999, as in the following sketch.

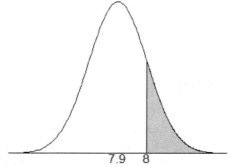

Thus,

$$P(X > 8.0) = normalcdf(8.0, 999999, 7.9, 0.1) = 0.15866$$

For part B, now we have a sample of $n = 6$ cups, and we need the probability that the average amount of coffee dispenses is less than 7.8 ounces, as in the following sketch.

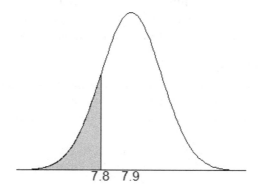

This is a sampling distribution of sample means question, since the question of interest is for an average. That means that we need to use a mean of $\mu = 7.9$ and a standard error of $\sigma/\sqrt{n} = 0.1/\sqrt{6} = 0.04082$.

We want the average to be less than 7.8 ounces, so the lower limit is -999999 and the upper limit is 7.8. Thus,

$$P\left(\overline{X} < 7.8\right) = normalcdf(-999999, 7.8, 7.9, 0.04082) = 0.00715$$

Δ

You will note that in the last example, the sample size of 6 was not a perfect square like the earlier sample sizes were. In general, situations will not always be so kind as to give you perfect square sample sizes like 16, 25, or 36. However, this is no problem since your calculator will easily find square roots of numbers:

"No need to fear – the calculator is here!"

Let's review the notation for the three possible distributions we are dealing with.

REVIEW

The **population distribution** describes the original population. It has mean μ and standard deviation σ, as well as its own shape that may be normal, skewed, something else, or undisclosed.

The **sample distribution** describes the one sample that is selected from the population. It has mean $\overline{x}$ and standard deviation s, and its shape is generally the same as the population's shape.

The **sampling distribution of the sample means** describes the way the possible sample averages, each of size n, behave and the probabilities that they can take. It has mean μ and a standard deviation equal to $\sigma/\sqrt{n}$, and this quantity is also called standard error. This distribution is approximately normal if either the original population is normal, or if the sample size n is greater than 30 (by the Central Limit Theorem).

For instance, if the population is normal, then one sample drawn from it will be normal as well. On the other hand, if a distribution is skewed left, one sample from it will also be skewed left.

However, if the sample size is large enough (greater than 30), then the sampling distribution of sample means will be approximately normal *regardless of the shape of the original population*.

EXAMPLE

Suppose the weight of a platypus (one of only two mammals that lays eggs) follows a distribution that is skewed right with mean 4.4 pounds and standard deviation 0.4 pounds. We sample 36 of these animals and get a sample mean and standard deviation of 3.1 and 0.35, respectively.

  A) What is the correct plural of platypus?
  B) What are the mean, standard deviation, and shape of the population distribution?
  C) What are the mean, standard deviation, and shape of the sample we selected?
  D) What are the mean, standard deviation, and shape of the sampling distribution of sample means, assuming a sample of size 36?
  E) Now suppose we instead sample 90 of these egg-laying mammals. What are the new mean, standard deviation, and shape of the sampling distribution of sample means, assuming a sample of size 90?

Solution: For part A, you will notice I wrote this question deliberately side-stepping the usage of the plural of platypus. Most people, as well as standard dictionaries, give the plural as platypuses, platypus itself, or platypi, since these terms are commonly used. Technically speaking, none of these words are correct. The word platypus comes from the Greek $\pi\lambda\alpha\tau\acute{\upsilon}\pi o\upsilon\varsigma$, which meant "flat-footed," and so the correct plural needs to derive from the grammar rules of ancient Greek. Thus, the correct plural of platypus is platypodes! (Another occurrence of this phenomenon is with octopus; the actual correct plural is octopodes, even though most people say octopi or octopuses.)

Having established that incredibly astounding piece of information, part B describes the characteristics of the original population. The population mean is $\mu = 4.4$, the population standard deviation is $\sigma = 0.4$, and the shape is skewed right.

Next, part C concerns the one sample selected. Its statistics are $\bar{x} = 3.1$ and $s = 0.35$, and since the shape of an individual sample mirrors the population's shape, it is skewed right also.

Heading into sampling distributions of the sample means, part D talks about samples of 36 platypodes. The mean is the same as the population mean, so $\mu = 4.4$. The standard deviation of the sampling distribution of sample means is the standard error formula:

$$\frac{\sigma}{\sqrt{n}} = \frac{0.4}{\sqrt{36}} = \frac{0.4}{6} = 0.06667$$

Finally, for part E, we repeat the questions for the sampling distribution of sample means but now for $n = 90$ platypodes. The mean is still the population mean, $\mu = 4.4$, so that does not change with sample size. However, the standard deviation of the sampling distribution of sample means, which is the standard error, does change:

$$\frac{\sigma}{\sqrt{n}} = \frac{0.4}{\sqrt{90}} = \frac{0.4}{9.48683} = 0.04216$$

Thus, when we increase sample size, the mean of the sampling distribution of sample means stays the same, but the standard error decreases.

Δ

> **REVIEW**
>
> As sample size n increases, the mean of the sampling distribution of sample means does not change.
>
> As sample size n increases, the standard error of the sampling distribution of sample means decreases.

Thus, for larger sample sizes, standard error will be smaller, which means that the sampling distribution of sample means will be less spread out.

Section 7.3 – The Sampling Distribution of the Sample Proportions

We have extensively covered the sampling distribution of sample means and studied the characteristics it has, along with several examples. A natural question to ask is whether there is a similar sampling distribution, only for sample proportions. The answer is yes, and in this section we extend the ideas we saw earlier in this chapter to cover sample proportions.

For example, consider a large population of students at a college, and it is known that 64% of the students are female, so $p = 0.64$. We write p here to denote the population proportion. Now suppose we draw a random sample of size $n = 50$ and calculate the sample proportion of female students in that sample. If 34 out of 50 students in our sample are female, then we write $\hat{p} = 34/50 = 0.68$.

In another random sample of 50 students, suppose 28 students are female, so the sample proportion from this new sample would be $\hat{p} = 28/50 = 0.56$. Finally, in one more random sample, perhaps 32 out of 50 students are female, in which case $\hat{p} = 32/50 = 0.64$.

As you can see from these samples, sometimes we will get a sample proportion below the population proportion (first sample), sometimes we will get a sample proportion above the population proportion (second sample), and occasionally we might get a sample proportion exactly equal to the population proportion (third sample).

Here is the idea: imagine we repeated this procedure by sampling a bunch of students in groups of 50, found the sample proportions of female students per group, and we did this over and over again a large number of times, so that we have many combinations of 50 students. Now we record all these sample proportions and graph them to look at their pattern. This distribution is called the **Sampling Distribution of the Sample Proportions**.

> **DEFINITION**
>
> The **sampling distribution of the sample proportions** is the distribution that describes the possible values that sample proportions of a specified sample size n can take, along with their corresponding probabilities. Under certain conditions, the sampling distribution of the sample proportions is normally distributed.

To be clear, the population proportion p stays the same, but the sample proportion $\hat{p}$ changes from sample to sample.

EXAMPLE
Draw all possible samples of size $n = 2$ from the population $\{1, 2, 3, 4\}$, and construct the sampling

distribution of the sample proportion of odd numbers in the sample.

Solution: To do this, recognize that there are 4 values in the population, from which we are choosing samples of size 2. (Just like before, you would hardly ever see a population this tiny! This is just for illustrative purposes!) Again, there are six possible combinations of values, so we can just list them all and compute the corresponding sample proportions of odd numbers:

$$\{1, 2\} \rightarrow \hat{p} = 0.50$$
$$\{1, 3\} \rightarrow \hat{p} = 1.00$$
$$\{1, 4\} \rightarrow \hat{p} = 0.50$$
$$\{2, 3\} \rightarrow \hat{p} = 0.50$$
$$\{2, 4\} \rightarrow \hat{p} = 0.00$$
$$\{3, 4\} \rightarrow \hat{p} = 0.50$$

To obtain the population proportion of odd numbers, we compute it from the original four points $\{1, 2, 3, 4\}$. It turns out to be $p = 0.50$ (because 2 out of 4 numbers are odd in this incredibly small population). The following is a graph of what this distribution looks like. Although a bit of a stretch, one could perhaps argue that it looks approximately normal.

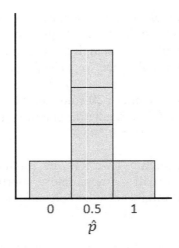

What is the probability that we would get a sample proportion of 0.00 from a sample of size 2 from this population? In this particular example, we can get the exact answer. There are six combinations, one of which has a sample proportion of 0.00. Thus, the probability is $1/6 = 0.16667$.

Δ

Again, in reality we will not have all the values from a population because most populations we look at are too large. Thus, to find probabilities involving sample proportions, we need to know what the distribution looks like. We need to know the mean, the standard deviation, and the shape.

EXAMPLE
Returning to the earlier scenario about a population of students with 64% of them being female, let's draw a random sample of size 50. Recall from Chapter 6 that this scenario is a binomial distribution with $n = 50$ and $p = 0.64$, and let X denote the number of female students in the sample. That means that X can be equal to 0, 1, 2, and so on through 50, so this is a discrete distribution. In fact, we could use the $binompdf(\ )$ function on the TI-84 to find all the possible probabilities for each value of X (for instance, $P(X = 34) = binompdf(50, 0.64, 34) = 0.10075$). The following graph shows the possible

outcomes for X along with the corresponding probabilities.

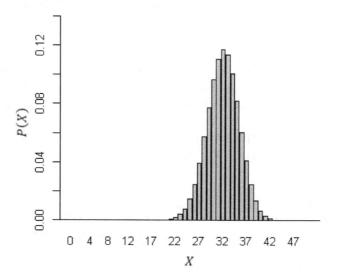

Where are we going with this example? First, notice that since $p = 0.64$, the distribution technically is skewed left. However, in Chapter 6 we worked with small sample sizes, whereas $n = 50$ is now quite larger. Notice that despite the fact that $p > 0.50$, the distribution of probabilities is starting to look approximately normal. That is because n is larger, and this is related to the Central Limit Theorem from the previous section.

This means that if n is large enough, we could potentially use the normal distribution to find binomial probabilities instead of the binomial distribution. This is good news since it is much easier to find a normal probability instead of a binomial probability.

However, let's change the situation a bit. Instead of finding the probability of a number of successes (meaning $X = 0, 1, 2, \dots, 50$), let's find the probability of specific sample proportions ($\hat{p} = 0/50, 1/50, 2/50, \dots, 50/50$). These are the possible sample proportions from a sample of size 50. Let's look at another graph of the possible sample proportions for $\hat{p}$ along with the corresponding probabilities $P(X)$.

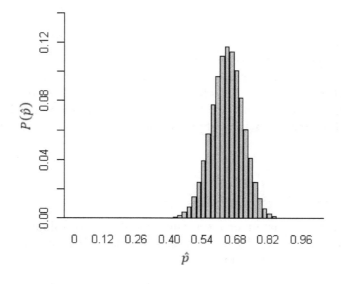

The probabilities are in fact the same! For instance, we showed above that $P(X = 34) = 0.10075$. This is the same as the probability of drawing a sample with a sample proportion of $\hat{p} = 34/50$; the probability of getting such a sample proportion is also 0.10075.

Δ

Thus, we are heading towards using a normal distribution as an approximation for the sampling distribution of sample proportions. What we need to do is find the mean, the standard error, and under what conditions it is approximately normal. We now discuss those characteristics.

Recall from earlier chapters that the population proportion is p. To answer these questions, this value will actually be told to us. (Again, in practice, this value is usually unknown, but in this chapter it will be given.)

First Characteristic: The Mean
The average of all possible sample proportions we could get will always be equal to the overall population proportion itself. In other words, the mean of the sampling distribution is p.

Second Characteristic: The Standard Deviation
As before, when we are talking about the spread, or standard deviation, of a sampling distribution, we call it the **standard error**.

DEFINITION

Analogous to earlier, the **standard error** is simply the standard deviation of the sampling distribution of the sample proportions. Given a sample of size n, the formula is

$$\text{standard error} = \sqrt{\frac{p(1-p)}{n}}$$

Be careful about the standard error formula. We have two possible expressions now: $\sigma/\sqrt{n}$ and $\sqrt{p(1-p)/n}$. The difference is that $\sigma/\sqrt{n}$ is used for the sampling distribution of the **sample mean**, while $\sqrt{p(1-p)/n}$ is used for the sampling distribution of the **sample proportion**. It is therefore critical that we first identify the problem as a means or proportions problem; otherwise we run the risk of using the wrong formulas!

Third Characteristic: The Shape of the Distribution
To find these probabilities associated with sample means, we need to ensure that the distribution of these sample means is in fact bell-shaped or normal, otherwise we cannot use the $normalcdf(\ )$ function. To check for this, we need the sample size n to be large enough so that the Central Limit Theorem can be used. To be large enough, both the following statements must be true:

1) $np \geq 15$.
2) $n(1-p) \geq 15$.

DEFINITION

The **Central Limit Theorem** says that given a sampling distribution of sample proportions, if the sample size used is large enough (meaning that $np \geq 15$ and $n(1-p) \geq 15$), then the shape of the sampling distribution of sample proportions is approximately normal.

> Caution: Some textbooks might suggest using other minimum numbers such as 10 or 20. In these notes, we will use 15.

We hinted earlier that having n large enough would ensure approximate normality. That was true, but the Central Limit Theorem further says that we need np and $n(1-p)$ to both be large enough, not just n alone. (In case you were wondering why 15 is selected as the threshold here and why 30 was used for the sample means, the answer is that statisticians have shown through computer simulations that those thresholds ensure approximate normality. Choosing smaller numbers may result in distributions that no longer look normal.)

There has been a lot of information here, so let's summarize the key points.

SUMMARY: SAMPLING DISTRIBUTION OF SAMPLE PROPORTIONS

Consider a population of values with proportion p. Now suppose we select a random sample of size n and compute $\hat{p}$, with the goal of describing the sampling distribution of the sample proportion. The following statements are true:

Statement 1: The mean of the sampling distribution is p.

Statement 2: The standard deviation of the sampling distribution is $\sqrt{\frac{p(1-p)}{n}}$. This is the **standard error**.

Statement 3: The shape of the sampling distribution is approximately normal if …
  a) $np \geq 15$, and …
  b) $n(1-p) \geq 15$.
  c) If either of those statements is false, then no conclusion can be made about the sampling distribution's shape.

EXAMPLE

Consider a very large population of adults where approximately 22% of the adults enjoy playing the game DDR (Dance Dance Revolution). Suppose samples of size 275 are selected from this population, and the value of $\hat{p}$ is recorded for each sample.

A) What are the mean and standard error of the sampling distribution of sample proportions?
B) Is the sampling distribution of sample proportions approximately normal?
C) According to the Empirical Rule, about 68% of the sample proportion values would be between what two values?
D) Find the probability that a random sample of size 275 produces a sample proportion of 0.25 or higher. (This means that 25% or more of the sampled adults enjoy playing DDR).
E) Would a sample proportion value of 0.35 or larger be unusual? If we did happen to get such a sample proportion, what can we say about the population proportion?

Solution: First, this is a proportion problem because a subject either plays DDR or does not. Thus, for part A we use the new formulas:

$$\text{Mean} = p = 0.22$$

$$\text{Standard Error} = \sqrt{\frac{p(1-p)}{n}} = \sqrt{\frac{0.22(1-0.22)}{275}} = \sqrt{0.000624} = 0.024979992$$

For part B, we need to check the two criteria:

$$np = 275 \times 0.22 = 60.5 \geq 15$$
$$n(1 - p) = 275 \times (1 - 0.22) = 214.5 \geq 15$$

Since both calculations are at least 15, the sampling distribution of sample proportions is approximately normal. Part C is a throwback to the Empirical Rule, which told us that approximately 68% of the data fall within one standard deviation of the mean. We use the same idea here, except recalling that the standard deviation of the sampling distribution is the standard error:

$$(\text{Mean} - 1 \times \text{St. Error}, \text{Mean} + 1 \times \text{St. Error}) = (0.22 - 0.024979992, 0.22 + 0.024979992)$$
$$= (0.19502, 0.24498)$$

This means that according to the Empirical Rule, approximately 68% of all sample proportions (all of size 275) will be between 0.19502 and 0.24498.

Next, part D requires us to use the $normalcdf(\ )$ function, now that we have established normality. Here is our sketch representing the probability of getting a $\hat{p}$ of 0.25 or greater:

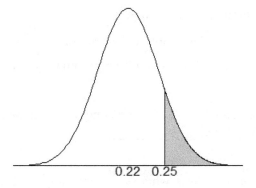

The lower limit is 0.25 and the upper limit is 999999. Thus,

$$normalcdf(0.25, 999999, 0.22, 0.024979992) = 0.11488$$

This tells us that the probability of getting a sample proportion of 0.25 or larger is 0.11488.

Lastly, part E concerns the probability of 0.35 or larger. We repeat the same process:

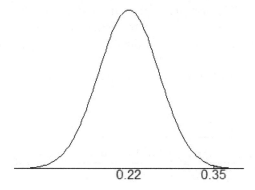

The lower limit is 0.35 and the upper limit is 999999. Thus,

$$normalcdf\,(0.35, 999999, 0.22, 0.024979992) = 9.76{\times}10^{-8}$$

This tells us that the probability of getting a sample proportion of 0.35 or larger is $9.76{\times}10^{-8}$, which is scientific notation for 0.0000000976 (seven zeros between the decimal and the first non-zero digit). Whenever we get a probability that is expressed in scientific notation from the calculator, it means an EXTREMELY small probability – or in other words, the event is incredibly unlikely. What this tells us is that if the population proportion really were 0.22 and the standard error really were 0.02498, it would be incredibly unusual to observe a sample proportion as extreme as 0.35 or higher.

Now suppose in our sample, we actually did get $p = 0.35$. Then one of two statements must be true:

    1) We have observed an extremely rare event, or…
    2) The assumption that the population proportion of $p = 0.22$ most likely is not correct after all. This
        is the more likely outcome.

Put another way, we would have strong evidence that the population proportion is not 0.22, as originally thought. (Make sure you understand this logic – Chapters 9, 10, and 11, all of which cover hypothesis testing, are based upon it!)

                                                           Δ

You may have been wondering why we stated in the $normalcdf(\;\;)$ function that the upper limit was 999999, and yet a proportion is necessarily between 0 and 1. That is a very fair point, but we program it that way just to keep consistency with the way we learned to find normal probabilities. In reality, using 1 as an upper limit instead would result in an answer that is usually almost exactly equal to the answer with 999999, so it is not a problem. (The same is true for using -999999 instead of 0 as a lower limit.)

SUMMARY: SCIENTIFIC NOTATION

You cannot go through an introductory statistics class and not see scientific notation at some point along your adventure! Depending on what your instructor says and what online homework website you may use, you may or may not need to convert the number into standard form. Let's go over how to do that.

A probability of $1.2{\times}10^{-5}$ means that to rewrite the number, we move the decimal point 5 places to the left (the number in the exponent). The negative sign indicates that the decimal moves left. Thus,

$$1.2{\times}10^{-5} = 0.000012$$

The consequence is that there are four zeros between the decimal and the first nonzero digit. As another example, the answer from the previous problem was $9.76{\times}10^{-8}$. This means that one moves the decimal 8 places to the left:

$$9.76{\times}10^{-8} = 0.0000000976$$

Here there are seven zeros between the decimal and the first non-zero digit. (The exponent in scientific notation can also be positive, but that would mean moving the decimal to the right, thereby making much larger numbers. We will not deal with that in this class – take an astronomy class for that application, where you will see measurements on an enormous cosmic scale!)

Anyway, the overall message here is that if you get a probability that is presented as scientific notation from the TI-84, it usually means that the probability is so incredibly small. That means that the event is extremely unlikely to happen!

EXAMPLE

Let's return to the problem earlier where we had a college population of 64% women, and we draw a sample of size 50. Find the mean, standard error, and shape of the sampling distribution of sample proportions, and find the probability that your sample proportion is greater than 0.67.

Solution: First, this is a proportion problem since an individual subject either is female or is not. Since $p = 0.64$ and $n = 50$, we have

$$\text{Mean} = p = 0.64$$

$$\text{Standard Error} = \sqrt{\frac{p(1-p)}{n}} = \sqrt{\frac{0.64(1-0.64)}{50}} = \sqrt{0.004608} = 0.067882251$$

Next, we check the two criteria:

$$np = 50 \times 0.64 = 32 \geq 15$$
$$n(1-p) = 50 \times (1-0.64) = 18 \geq 15$$

Since both calculations are at least 15, the sampling distribution of sample proportions is approximately normal, so we can use the $normalcdf(\ )$ function. To find the probability of getting a sample proportion greater than 0.67, you know what comes first – a sketch!

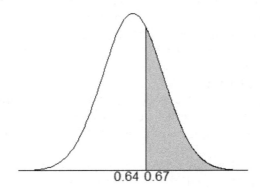

The lower limit is 0.67 and the upper limit is 999999, so we compute

$$normalcdf(0.67, 999999, 0.64, 0.067882251) = 0.32927$$

Thus, the probability is 0.32937, just under a one-third chance, that we draw a random sample of 50 students and get a $\hat{p}$ greater than 0.67.

Δ

Returning briefly to our earlier discussion of the binomial distribution, since np and $n(1-p)$ are both large enough, the Central Limit Theorem says that we can use the normal distribution as an approximation to get the probability above 0.67. The answer was 0.32927 using the normal approximation. Just to see what happens, let's find what the probability would have been had we used the binomial distribution.

We want all possible sample proportions greater than 0.67, and these occur for $\hat{p} = 34/50 = 0.68$, $\hat{p} = 35/50 = 0.70$, and so on through $\hat{p} = 50/50 = 1$. In other words, this is equivalent to $P(X \geq 34)$

for a binomial distribution with $n = 50$ and $p = 0.64$. Using our work from Chapter 6, this is equal to $1 - P(X \leq 33)$, and so

$$1 - binomcdf(50, 0.64, 33) = 1 - 0.66643 = 0.33357$$

Thus, our sampling distribution answer was 0.32927, whereas the exact answer was 0.33357. While not perfect, our answer from the normal approximation was very close.

EXAMPLE

In cricket (the sport, not the insect!), the bowler throws the ball to the batsman. The bowler's objective is to hit the wicket (the three wooden stumps) behind the batsman, since doing so will put the batsman out. Suppose a particular bowler claims to have a 20% success rate; that is, he will hit the wicket 20% of the time. Then in a match, he bowls 84 times and ends up hitting the wicket 6 times. (Assume this is a random sample of bowling.) If his claim is correct, what is the probability he could have taken out 6 or fewer batsmen?

A) First, can we use the normal approximation? Why or why not?
B) Find the sample proportion of times the bowler hits the wicket.
C) If the bowler's claim is correct, what should be the mean and standard error of the sampling distribution of the sample proportion?
D) Find the probability of hitting 6 or fewer wickets out of 84, using the above mean and standard error. Is this too small a probability?
E) Now suppose a rival bowler claims to have a 30% success rate in hitting the wicket, and he bowls 42 times and ends up taking 5 wickets (meaning he hits the wicket). Can we use the normal approximation here? Why or why not?

Solution: First, let's translate all the numbers given. This is a proportion problem because the bowler will either hit the wicket or will not. His claim is that he hits it 20% of the time, so $p = 0.20$. In a match, he bowls 84 times, so $n = 84$. He manages to hit the wicket 6 times, which is the number of successes.

For part A, to use the normal approximation, we need to check that np and $n(1 - p)$ are both at least 15. They are, and so we can use the approximation:

$$np = 84 \times 0.20 = 16.5 \geq 15$$
$$n(1 - p) = 84 \times (1 - 0.20) = 67.2 \geq 15$$

Part B wants the sample proportion. This is easier than it looks – the bowler bowls 84 times and hits the wicket 6 times, so

$$\hat{p} = \frac{6}{84} = 0.07143$$

Assuming the bowler is telling the truth, the mean and standard error for part C are

$$\text{Mean} = p = 0.20$$
$$\text{Standard Error} = \sqrt{\frac{p(1 - p)}{n}} = \sqrt{\frac{0.20(1 - 0.20)}{84}} = \sqrt{0.0019047619} = 0.043643578$$

Next, for part D we need the probability of hitting 6 or fewer wickets out of 84 attempts. This is equivalent to asking for the probability of getting a sample proportion of $\hat{p} = 0.07143$ or smaller when $n = 84$. Here is our sketch, noting that the mean is $p = 0.20$:

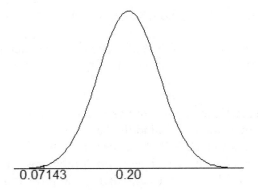

The lower limit is -999999 and the upper limit is 0.07143.

$$normalcdf(-999999, 0.07143, 0.20, 0.043643578) = 0.00161$$

Thus, if the bowler really does hit the wicket 20% of the time, he only has a 0.00161 chance of getting a sample proportion of 0.07143 or smaller. This is obviously a very low probability, so perhaps he is not telling the truth!

Finally, part E introduces another bowler who supposedly has a 30% success rate, then hits the wicket 5 times out of 42 attempts in a match. Here $p = 0.30$ and $n = 42$, and we check whether the normal approximation can be used:

$$np = 42 \times 0.30 = 12.6 < 15$$
$$n(1 - p) = 42 \times (1 - 0.30) = 29.4 \geq 15$$

Unfortunately $np < 15$, which means the normal approximation cannot be used to answer this question. (Like earlier, such a scenario can be answered using non-parametric techniques, but that is out of scope for this class.)

Δ

Chapter 8 – Confidence Intervals

Recall from the beginning of these notes that there are two branches of statistics: descriptive and inferential. The inferential branch uses sample information to draw conclusions about the population, and this chapter kicks off our study of inferential statistics.

Section 8.1 – Point Estimates and Interval Estimates

One of the most common uses of the inferential branch is to use sample statistics (such as $\bar{x}$) to estimate population parameters (such as μ). It makes sense that if we take a large enough sample, $\bar{x}$ should be fairly close to the actual value of μ. However, the chances are pretty small that $\bar{x}$ turns out to be exactly μ. Hopefully if we have a good sample, it will be close, but unfortunately the fact is that μ is unknown. This means that we do not know how close we are with our sample mean.

DEFINITION

A **point estimate** is a number, which is estimated from a sample, and that is used as a starting point to make inference about the population.

To estimate the unknown population mean μ, use $\bar{x}$ as the point estimate of μ.

To estimate the unknown population proportion p, use $\hat{p}$ as the point estimate of p.

Remember that **sample statistics** estimate **population parameters**.

The goal in this chapter is to obtain a reasonable set of estimates for the population parameters. It is a good start to say that $\bar{x}$ and $\hat{p}$ are reasonable estimates of μ and p, respectively, but at the same time it is rather unrealistic to declare that they will be exactly equal to the unknown population parameters. For instance, if the population mean turns out to be 30, then a sample mean might be equal to $25, 28, 31$, or other similar numbers, but it probably will not be exactly equal to the population mean.

A better approach is to instead report a range of likely values that the population mean could potentially take. This involves reporting an **interval estimate**, which is an interval of numeric values that are centered around $\bar{x}$ and $\hat{p}$. We would then state that μ and p are most likely somewhere inside these intervals.

EXAMPLE

A college has 20,000 students, and you are asked to estimate the average age of all the students. You survey 50 students at random and find that the average age in your sample is 20. The sample mean $\bar{x} = 20$ is a point estimate of μ, the population average age.

But why stop there? You could also express your answer by giving a range of ages that are centered around the sample average. For example, you might say that the average is 20, give or take 2 years. The additional part "give or take 2 years" is called the **margin of error**, which is defined below. It means we take our sample mean of 20 and add and subtract 2 to get an upper and lower bound, respectively, for our interval estimate. Thus, your interval estimate would be

$$(20 \pm 2) = (20 - 2, 20 + 2) = (18, 22)$$

This would say that the sample mean is 20 years, and the population mean age is most likely somewhere between 18 and 22 years.

Suppose you were then asked how confident you were that μ, the mean age of all students, was within your interval estimate of 18 to 22 years old. You could say "I am 95% confident that the mean age of all students is within 18 to 22 years old." (We will soon explain the choice of confidence percentage.)

Δ

DEFINITION

The **margin of error** is the number that we add to, and subtract from, the point estimate to form the upper and lower limits, respectively. It is the width of the resulting interval, the difference between the point estimate and one of the limits.

In the previous example about estimating ages, we had the following:

> Point estimate = 20
> Margin of error = 2
> Lower limit = 20 − 2 = 18
> Upper limit = 20 + 2 = 22
> Confidence level = 95%

Remember, it is usually impossible or unrealistic to find the population mean μ, so we estimate it by using the next best thing, the sample mean $\overline{x}$, plus and minus a margin of error. The resulting interval estimate is called a **confidence interval**. The following material explains the components of a confidence interval, and then we will summarize them all together afterwards.

A **confidence interval** of a population parameter consists of a range of numbers, and this interval is constructed as the **point estimate ± margin of error**. The value (point estimate − margin of error) is the **lower limit** or **lower bound** of the confidence interval. Similarly, the value (point estimate + margin of error) is the **upper limit** or **upper bound** of the confidence interval. The confidence interval is frequently written in parenthesis since this is common mathematical notation, as in (lower limit, upper limit).

Finally, the **confidence level** is important to note as well. This tells us how confident we are (as a probability) that the confidence interval does in fact contain the unknown population mean. A common confidence level that statisticians use is 95% confidence. As we shall see later, when the confidence level increases, the interval becomes wider.

That was a lot of information, so the following summary box contains everything you need to know.

DEFINITION

A **confidence interval** is a range of values, starting with a **lower limit** or **lower bound**, and ending with an **upper limit** or **upper bound**. This interval is a range of possible values that a population parameter could likely be, and the interval is constructed and centered around the sample statistic.

The corresponding **confidence level** tells us how confident we are that the population parameter falls somewhere inside the interval. A common choice of confidence is 95%, but other high values are possible too. To interpret a confidence interval, we are 95% confident that the population mean (or proportion) is somewhere between the lower limit and the upper limit. (If the confidence level is a different percentage, we simply change the percentage in that statement.)

In its basic format, a confidence interval can be written as the following:

> (point estimate) $\pm$ (margin of error)
>
> The point estimate is the center of the confidence interval, and the margin of error is the width of the confidence interval. Given a confidence interval, the point estimate can be found by averaging the endpoints:
>
> $$\text{point estimate} = \frac{\text{lower limit} + \text{upper limit}}{2}$$
>
> Given a confidence interval, the **margin of error** can be found by taking the distance between the point estimate and either of the endpoints:
>
> $$\text{margin of error} = \text{point estimate} - \text{lower limit}$$
> $$= \text{upper limit} - \text{point estimate}$$
>
> If we are estimating the population mean μ, the confidence interval is given by ($\bar{x} \pm$ margin of error). Likewise, if we are estimating the population proportion p, the confidence interval is given by ($\hat{p} \pm$ margin of error).

As we shall see in the coming sections of this chapter, the margin of error can be written as a specific formula that changes depending whether we are discussing a mean or a proportion, but the very basic formula of a confidence interval is just (point estimate $\pm$ margin of error).

If you come across a problem that asks you to compute a confidence interval, and you seem to have too little information to solve it, remember that very basic formula. It might just help you!

So far we have not covered exactly how to build these confidence intervals from scratch. We will get to that soon, but first we need to be comfortable with the basic concepts of what an interval is.

EXAMPLE
Suppose a farmer wants to estimate the average number of strawberries per bush on his farm. Instead of counting each strawberry on every single bush, he takes a random sample of 20 bushes and calculates a 95% confidence interval based on the sample. The interval turns out to be $(26, 34)$ strawberries per bush. Examine each important component of this situation.

Solution: The goal is to estimate the population mean μ, the average number of strawberries per bush on the farm. The farmer takes a sample of size $n = 20$ bushes, and the 95% confidence interval is $(26, 34)$. The lower limit is 26, and the upper limit is 34. We are 95% confident that the true mean number of strawberries per bush is between 26 and 34.

Next, what are the sample mean and the margin of error? The sample mean is always in the center of the interval, and we can find the center by averaging the endpoints:

$$\bar{x} = \frac{26 + 34}{2} = 30$$

The margin of error is always the distance between the center of the interval and either of the endpoints, so we can compute the middle minus the lower limit: $30 - 26 = 4$. We could also compute the upper limit minus the middle: $34 - 30 = 4$.

Δ

Remember the following: the sample mean is always inside the confidence interval. However, the population mean may or may not be inside the confidence interval. We certainly hope it is, and we are 95% (or some other percent) confident that it is, but we can never guarantee that it is inside. (For reasons we will see later, it is unrealistic to construct a 100% confidence interval.)

Section 8.2 – Confidence Interval for a Population Proportion

We have seen that the basic formula for a confidence interval is (point estimate) $\pm$ (margin of error). In this section we specialize it to the case where we are estimating a population proportion, in which case the confidence interval formula takes on a specific mathematical formula. Later in the chapter, we will study the case for the population mean.

First, the point estimate for the population proportion p is the sample proportion $\hat{p}$. If n is the sample size and there are x "successes" in the sample, then $\hat{p} = x/n$ is the point estimate, the center of the confidence interval. That is the easy part, but what about the margin of error? There is a specific formula for it when we are dealing with proportions, but first let's look at one more example. Again, the fundamental formula for a confidence interval is this:

$$\text{(point estimate)} \pm \text{(margin of error)}$$

If you have these two numbers given up front, that's all you need to construct the confidence interval. This is the easiest type of confidence interval question, and yet it is a great pity how many students incorrectly answer it!

EXAMPLE

Suppose we took a sample of 60 students and asked them whether they had ever sent a text message during a class. 44 of them said yes, and the margin of error (with 95% confidence) was 11 percentage points. Find the 95% confidence interval.

Solution: First, recognize that this is a proportion problem, not a mean problem, because we are dealing with a yes/no situation with the data (a student has either texted during class or has not). The point estimate is the sample proportion

$$\hat{p} = \frac{44}{60} = 0.73333$$

The margin of error is given to us as 11 percentage points, which as a proportion is 0.11. Since we have the point estimate and the margin of error, those are all we need to find the confidence interval:

$$\text{(point estimate)} \pm \text{(margin of error)} = 0.73333 \pm 0.11 = (0.62333, 0.84333)$$

The 95% confidence interval for this problem is $(0.62333, 0.84333)$. To interpret it, we are 95% confident that the true population proportion of students that have texted during class is somewhere between 0.62333 and 0.84333.

Δ

So far we have just been telling you what margin of error is without having you compute it yourself. It is now time to learn how!

DEFINITION

The **margin of error** is always a multiple of the **standard error**, meaning that it is equal to a specific number times the standard error. When building a confidence interval for a population proportion, the standard error is equal to

$$\text{Standard Error} = \sqrt{\frac{\hat{p}(1 - \hat{p})}{n}}$$

You will recognize this formula to be the same as the standard error formula we saw in Chapter 7, only this time we are using $\hat{p}$ instead of p. Why? In that chapter, we were told the true population proportion, but here we do not know what it is. (If we did, we would not need to estimate it now, would we?) The next best thing we can do is use $\hat{p}$ as a substitute in the equation.

Thus, the margin of error will always be a specific number multiplied by the standard error seen above. The number we multiply the standard error by to get the margin of error is determined by the level of confidence. Before we go further, let's introduce some new notation.

NOTATION

When we talk about a 95% confidence interval, for reasons that will become clear later when we make sketches, there is 5% left over. As a proportion, this leftover amount is denoted as $\alpha = 0.05$ (where α, pronounced "alpha," is a Greek letter). Similarly, given a 99% confidence interval, there is 1% left over, in which case $\alpha = 0.01$.

Generalizing, we can have a $100(1 - \alpha)\%$ confidence interval, corresponding to a proportion of α left over. For a proportion confidence interval, we will need to find a value from the standard normal distribution for the choice of α. This quantity is denoted as $Z_{\alpha/2}$ (we will see how to compute it later).

DEFINITION

The general formula for a $100(1 - \alpha)\%$ confidence interval for the population proportion is

$$\hat{p} \pm Z_{\alpha/2}\sqrt{\frac{\hat{p}(1 - \hat{p})}{n}}$$

The following parts are defined:

n is the sample size.
$\hat{p}$ is the sample proportion, the number of successes divided by n.
$Z_{\alpha/2}$ is a number that is determined by the confidence level. For a 95% confidence interval, we have $\alpha = 0.05$ and therefore $\alpha/2 = 0.025$. As a handy shortcut, it can be shown that $Z_{0.025} = 1.96$ (memorize that number – you will be using it a lot!)

$\sqrt{\frac{\hat{p}(1 - \hat{p})}{n}}$ is the standard error.

The product $Z_{\alpha/2}\sqrt{\frac{\hat{p}(1 - \hat{p})}{n}}$ is the margin of error.

Looking at the margin of error formula, you can see that it is equal to the $Z_{\alpha/2}$ number times the standard error. We will see later in this chapter exactly how to obtain this number, but for now just take my word that for 95% confidence, $Z_{0.025} = 1.96$. If we use a different confidence level such as 99% confidence, then $Z_{\alpha/2}$ will be different. (For 95% confidence, you can get away with using 1.96 as two decimals. However, for other levels, it is better to use all the decimals the TI-84 provides. For the record, $Z_{0.025} = 1.959963986$.)

Let's summarize the parts of the formula again.

SUMMARY: CONFIDENCE INTERVAL FOR A PROPORTION

For a confidence interval for a population proportion, we have the following, which can be computed in the four steps outlined below:

$$\text{Point Estimate} = \hat{p}$$

$$\text{Standard Error} = \sqrt{\frac{\hat{p}(1-\hat{p})}{n}}$$

$$\text{Margin of Error} = Z_{\alpha/2}\sqrt{\frac{\hat{p}(1-\hat{p})}{n}}$$

$$\text{Confidence Interval} = \hat{p} \pm Z_{\alpha/2}\sqrt{\frac{\hat{p}(1-\hat{p})}{n}}$$

If you want to write the formula in the form (lower limit, upper limit), it would look like this:

$$\left(\hat{p} - Z_{\alpha/2}\sqrt{\frac{\hat{p}(1-\hat{p})}{n}}, \hat{p} + Z_{\alpha/2}\sqrt{\frac{\hat{p}(1-\hat{p})}{n}}\right)$$

For a 95% confidence interval, which is the most commonly used, it can be shown that $Z_{0.025} = 1.96$. (In a few pages, we will see how to compute this number.)

These formulas can be derived using a nifty bit of calculus; however, the author of your notes cordially invites you to take his word for it instead!

Regarding the $Z_{0.025} = 1.96$ fact, this number should actually make sense. Recall the Empirical Rule, which said that for a bell-shaped distribution, about 95% of the data fall within 2 standard deviations of the mean. Stated as a formula, we wrote it like this:

$$(\text{mean}) \pm 2(\text{standard deviation})$$

Specializing to the proportion situation, we replace "mean" with $\hat{p}$ and "standard deviation" with the standard error, $\sqrt{\hat{p}(1-\hat{p})/n}$. That leaves the 2, which is very close to 1.96. In fact, when you first saw the Empirical Rule, you learned to use 2 simply because it was easy to remember. Now that you are a more advanced student of statistics, you can use a more accurate value of 1.96!

Note: For these last few chapters, when applicable we will usually use all available decimals that the TI-84 provides for intermediate steps. This will ensure that we get more accurate answers than if we round too early. We can still round our answers to however many digits are requested (usually we will round to five decimals in these notes). That said, for a 95% confidence interval, we can still use $Z_{0.025} = 1.96$ since a lot of computer assignments use that value for the Z-score.

EXAMPLE

We surveyed 1231 people in Florida and asked them whether they have cable TV in their homes. In our random sample, 541 replied that they do have cable. Find a 95% confidence interval for the population proportion of people in Florida who have cable, and interpret the interval. Does it appear likely that 50% of Floridians have cable TV? How about 45%?

Solution: First, we need to build the confidence interval from scratch. The first step is to compute the sample proportion, given that we are 541 successes out of a sample of size $n = 1231$:

$$\text{Point Estimate} = \hat{p} = \frac{541}{1231} = 0.4394800975$$

Since the margin of error was not provided to us, we need to compute it manually. The second step is to find the standard error:

$$\text{Standard Error} = \sqrt{\frac{\hat{p}(1 - \hat{p})}{n}} = \sqrt{\frac{0.4394800975(1 - 0.4394800975)}{1231}} = 0.0141460796$$

The third step is to compute the margin of error. Since this is a 95% confidence interval, $Z_{0.025} = 1.96$, and so the margin of error is

$$\text{Margin of Error} = Z_{0.025}\sqrt{\frac{\hat{p}(1 - \hat{p})}{n}} = 1.96 \times 0.0141460796 = 0.0277263161$$

Finally, the fourth step is to finish the job and compute the point estimate plus and minus the margin of error:

$$\hat{p} \pm Z_{0.025}\sqrt{\frac{\hat{p}(1 - \hat{p})}{n}} = 0.4394800975 \pm 0.0277263161$$
$$= (0.4394800975 - 0.0277263161, 0.4394800975 + 0.0277263161)$$
$$= (0.41175, 0.46721)$$

The 95% confidence interval is $(0.41175, 0.46721)$. To interpret it, we are 95% confident that the population proportion of Floridians who have cable TV is somewhere between 0.41175 and 0.46721. If you want to express these values as percentages, the population percentage is between 41.175% and 46.721% with 95% confidence.

Does it appear likely that 50% of all Floridians have cable? To answer that, we see whether 50%, or 0.50, is inside our interval of $(0.41175, 0.46721)$. It is not; it is above the interval. Thus, it is not likely that 50% of all Floridians have cable, with 95% confidence.

How about 45%? Observe that 0.45 is inside the interval, which means that 0.45 is a plausible value for the population proportion.

Consider the summary number line below. The middle region is the range of all plausible values that p could take, so anything outside this region (less than 0.41175 or more than 0.46721) is an unlikely value for the population proportion. As you can see, 0.50 falls in the unlikely region, but 0.45 is inside the likely region.

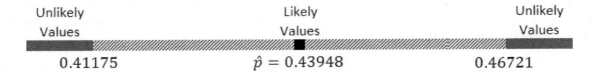

Unlikely Values	Likely Values	Unlikely Values
0.41175	$\hat{p} = 0.43948$	0.46721

Δ

Section 8.3 – Proportion Confidence Interval Assumptions and Interpretations

Although we can mathematically compute a confidence interval, it is only valid when three specific assumptions are met. If at least one of these assumptions is not true, then the confidence interval is invalid and should not be used.

PROPORTION CONFIDENCE INTERVAL ASSUMPTIONS

For a confidence interval for a proportion to be valid, three specific items need to be true about the sample:

<u>Assumption 1</u>: The sample must have been randomly selected.
<u>Assumption 2</u>: $n\hat{p} \geq 15$. That is, the number of successes should be at least 15.
<u>Assumption 3</u>: $n(1 - \hat{p}) \geq 15$. That is, the number of failures should be at least 15.

Again, we use $\hat{p}$ rather than p because p is unknown, so the next best thing to use is $\hat{p}$.

EXAMPLE

In the previous example about Floridians and cable TV, let's check that the three assumptions hold. Here is the background again: we surveyed 1231 people in Florida and asked them whether they have cable TV in their homes. In our random sample, 541 replied that they do have cable.

Solution: The background mentions that the sample was random. The number of successes (people who have cable) was 541, which is well above 15. The number of failures (people that do not have cable) was $1231 - 541 = 690$, which is also above 15. Thus, the three assumptions are met, and the confidence interval we created in that example is valid.

If we instead use the formulas for the second and third assumptions, we have the following:

$$n\hat{p} = 1231 \times 0.43948 = 541 \geq 15$$
$$n(1 - \hat{p}) = 1231 \times (1 - 0.43948) = 690 \geq 15$$

However, in general, if you are simply told the number of successes, you can quickly compute the number of failures. In this case, simply stating the number of successes and failures and noting that they are at least 15 each is sufficient, along with the random sample stipulation.

Δ

Regarding the interpretation of a confidence interval, a 95% confidence interval means we are 95% confident that the population proportion lies somewhere inside our interval of values. We cannot pin it down more accurately without having a larger sample size, but we can assert that with 95% confidence, it falls somewhere inside the found interval.

Be careful here: it is tempting to say "the population mean lies in the interval 95% of the time." This is **not** the correct way to interpret an interval. The reason is because the population mean, while unknown, is fixed. What changes from sample to sample is the confidence interval.

That is, the population mean will always be the same, but when we draw many samples from the population, we will get different confidence intervals. Most of them will contain p or μ inside, but there will be an unlucky few that by chance miss it.

How many intervals will capture p or μ? That depends on the level of confidence. As an example, suppose we draw 1000 samples and compute an interval for each (and suppose we are using 95% confidence). Then we can expect about 95% of these 1000 to contain p or μ inside somewhere. That number is $1000 \times 0.95 = 950$.

Of course, there is no reason to suppose this number is exact; maybe 948 of them will contain it. The 950 is only an approximation, so we could say that, say, between 945 and 955 of the intervals are expected to contain p or μ inside, and the rest not to contain the population parameter.

Now suppose we have 1000 99% confidence intervals. About how many will you expect contain p or μ? The answer is $1000 \times 0.99 = 990$, so approximately 990.

Here is an illustration of what it means for a population mean to fall inside or outside an interval. The rectangles are all confidence intervals draw from different samples, and most of them contain μ, while once in a great while one will miss it.

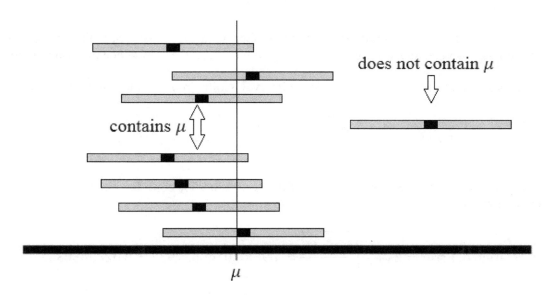

The following is a summary of how to interpret a confidence interval correctly, both an individual interval and a large number of intervals.

SUMMARY: INTERPRETATION OF A 95% CONFIDENCE INTERVAL
The following is a correct interpretation of an individual 95% confidence interval:

We are 95% confident that the true value for the population mean (or population proportion) falls somewhere inside the computed confidence interval.

The following is a correct long-run interpretation of 95% confidence intervals:

If we construct a large number of 95% confidence intervals, approximately 95% of them will contain μ (or p) somewhere inside them. As an extension, about 5% of those intervals will fail to contain μ (or p).

If we are working with a different confidence level, simply replace the 95% with the one of interest.

EXAMPLE

We take a survey of 884 people at random and ask each of them whether they have ever played on a team sport. 663 of them answered yes.

    A) Obtain a point estimate for p, the population proportion of people who have played on a team sport.
    B) Verify that the requirements for constructing a confidence interval about p are satisfied.
    C) Construct a 95% confidence interval for the population proportion of people that have played on a team sport.
    D) Interpret this interval.

Solution: First, this is a proportion problem because the data consist of successes (playing on a team sport) and failures (not playing). The point estimate is the sample proportion:

$$\hat{p} = \frac{663}{884} = 0.75$$

For the assumptions, the sample is random, and the number of successes is 663, which is above 15. The number of failures is $884 - 663 = 221$, which is also above 15, so the confidence interval will be valid.

Now the time has come to construct the confidence interval. Going in order, the standard error is

$$\text{Standard Error} = \sqrt{\frac{\hat{p}(1-\hat{p})}{n}} = \sqrt{\frac{0.75(1-0.75)}{884}} = 0.0145637932$$

The third step is to compute the margin of error. Since this is a 95% confidence interval, $Z_{0.025} = 1.96$, and so the margin of error is

$$\text{Margin of Error} = Z_{0.025}\sqrt{\frac{\hat{p}(1-\hat{p})}{n}} = 1.96 \times 0.0145637932 = 0.0285450347$$

Finally, the fourth step is to compute the point estimate plus and minus the margin of error:

$$\hat{p} \pm Z_{0.025}\sqrt{\frac{\hat{p}(1-\hat{p})}{n}} = 0.75 \pm 0.0285450347$$

$$= (0.75 - 0.0285450347, 0.75 + 0.0285450347)$$
$$= (0.72145, 0.77855)$$

Interpreting this interval, we are 95% confident that the population proportion of people that have ever played on a team sport is between 0.72145 and 0.77855.

Going for a long-run interpretation, if we were to take a large number of random samples (say 1000) and construct a 95% confidence interval for all of them, approximately 95% of all of those intervals (about 950) will contain the population proportion somewhere inside them.

Δ

Section 8.4 – Other Proportion Confidence Levels and the TI-84

So far we have just been creating 95% confidence intervals, so our margin of error has been 1.96 multiplied by the standard error. A while ago, I told you that $Z_{0.025} = 1.96$ and that at the time you should take my word for it. However, where does this 1.96 come from? And what if we want something different than a 95% confidence interval? In this section, we finally see how.

We cannot have a 100% confidence interval because we can never be 100% certain that the population proportion is within the interval if we do not know what it is. Another way to look at it is that a "true" 100% confidence interval would be suggesting that the population proportion is between 0 and 1. That is a correct statement, but it is rubbish since it tells us nothing useful! That is why we do not use it.

Similarly, if we made a 100% confidence interval for the population mean, we would be saying that it is somewhere between $-\infty$ and ∞. Again, this is absolutely true – but it is not exactly an earth-shattering revelation! A consequence of this, as you might have already guessed, is that there is a slight chance that our confidence interval misses the population proportion (or mean), and if this happens, it is due to the choice of sample we collected. That is why we can say that the population mean is "most likely" inside the interval somewhere, but we can never say that it is guaranteed to be inside.

Here is how we get the 1.96 for a 95% confidence interval. First, think of the normal curve with area 0.95 shaded in the middle like this:

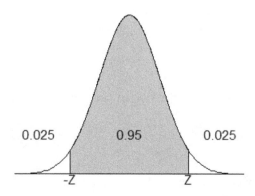

If 0.95 is in the middle region, that means that 0.05 is left over. This needs to go evenly in both tails, so half of 0.05 is 0.025 (remember symmetry). That is why we use the subscript 0.025 in the notation $Z_{0.025}$.

On the TI-84, go to $\boxed{\text{2nd}}$, $\boxed{\text{VARS}}$, and choose Option 3: $invNorm(\ \ )$. Typing in $invNorm(0.025)$ results in -1.95996. It is negative because the calculator computes the Z-score that has 0.025 of the normal curve *below* it. This is on the left side of the curve above, so you can see that Z must be negative since it is below 0. No need to worry; we can just drop the negative sign and declare that $Z_{0.025} =$

1.95996, or 1.96, since it is also true that 0.025 of the curve lies *above* $Z = 1.96$.

Incidentally, since $invNorm(\ )$ computes the Z-score with the given probability to the left, we could use it another way. The Z-score with probability 0.025 above (the right tail) also has probability 0.975 below, so $invNorm(0.975)$ results in 1.95996. However, you might find it easier just to compute $invNorm(0.025) = -1.95996$ and then drop the negative sign.

For a 95% confidence interval, we can usually get away with using the rounded $Z = 1.96$, which is easier to remember than 1.959963986 (and that value is very close to 1.96 anyway). However, for any other levels, we need to use more decimals to reduce potential round-off error (and as mentioned earlier, I'll generally use as many as the calculator shows).

This Z-score value is what we now take and multiply the standard error by to get the margin of error for a confidence interval, and it will always be a positive Z-score.

EXAMPLE
Let's find the Z-score to use for a 90% confidence interval. We draw the curve with 0.90 in the middle:

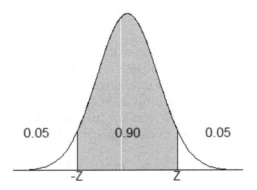

If 0.90 is in the middle of the curve, then 0.10 is left over, and half of that is 0.05. Thus, we need the Z-score that cuts the curve in such a way that it gives 0.05 area in the lower tail (and the upper tail). The TI-84 tells us that $invNorm(0.05) = -1.644853626$, and so dropping the negative sign, we would use $Z_{0.05} = 1.644853626$.

That means that when computing the margin of error for a 90% confidence interval, you multiply the standard error by 1.644853626.

Δ

EXAMPLE
In a class survey, 162 students were asked whether they had ever parasailed, and 47 said yes. Assume that this is a random sample of students.

   A) Obtain a point estimate for the population proportion of students who have parasailed.
   B) Verify that the requirements for constructing a confidence interval about p are satisfied.
   C) Construct a 90% confidence interval for the proportion of students who have parasailed.
   D) Interpret the 90% confidence interval.

Solution: For part A, the point estimate is the sample proportion:

$$\hat{p} = \frac{47}{162} = 0.2901234568$$

Noting that the sample is considered random and that there are 47 "yes's" and $162 - 47 = 115$ "no's", both of which are greater than 15, the assumptions in part B are met.

To construct the confidence interval in part C, we next compute the standard error:

$$\text{Standard Error} = \sqrt{\frac{\hat{p}(1 - \hat{p})}{n}} = \sqrt{\frac{0.2901234568(1 - 0.2901234568)}{162}} = 0.0356554012$$

The margin of error is equal to the correct Z-score multiplied by standard error. Since the confidence level is 90%, we have $\alpha = 0.10$ and therefore $\alpha/2 = 0.05$. From the previous example we have $Z_{0.05} = 1.644853626$, so

$$\text{Margin of Error} = Z_{0.05}\sqrt{\frac{\hat{p}(1 - \hat{p})}{n}} = 1.644853626 \times 0.0356554012 = 0.0586479159$$

Next, we compute the point estimate plus and minus the margin of error:

$$\hat{p} \pm Z_{0.05}\sqrt{\frac{\hat{p}(1 - \hat{p})}{n}} = 0.2901234568 \pm 0.0586479159$$

$$= (0.2901234568 - 0.0586479159, 0.2901234568 + 0.0586479159)$$
$$= (0.23148, 0.34877)$$

Interpreting this interval for part D, we are 90% confident that the population proportion of students that have parasailed is between 0.23148 and 0.34877.

Δ

EXAMPLE
Using the same example, let's now construct a 99% confidence interval and see how the interval changes from increasing the confidence level. The point estimate is the same sample proportion:

$$\hat{p} = \frac{47}{162} = 0.2901234568$$

The standard error is still the same:

$$\text{Standard Error} = \sqrt{\frac{\hat{p}(1 - \hat{p})}{n}} = \sqrt{\frac{0.2901234568(1 - 0.2901234568)}{162}} = 0.0356554012$$

However, we need to update the margin of error to have the 99% Z-score. Here is the normal curve:

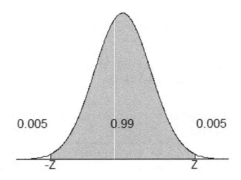

0.005   0.99   0.005

If 0.99 is in the middle of the curve, then 0.01 is left over, and half of that is 0.005. Thus, we need the Z-score that cuts the curve in such a way that it gives 0.005 area in the lower tail (and the upper tail). Thus, $invNorm(0.005) = -2.575829303$, and so dropping the negative sign, we would use $Z_{0.005} = 2.575829303$. The new margin of error is

$$\text{Margin of Error} = Z_{0.005}\sqrt{\frac{\hat{p}(1-\hat{p})}{n}} = 2.575829303 \times 0.0356554012 = 0.0918422272$$

Next, we compute the point estimate plus and minus the margin of error:

$$\hat{p} \pm Z_{0.005}\sqrt{\frac{\hat{p}(1-\hat{p})}{n}} = 0.2901234568 \pm 0.0918422272$$
$$= (0.2901234568 - 0.0918422272, 0.2901234568 + 0.0918422272)$$
$$= (0.19828, 0.38197)$$

Interpreting this interval, we are 99% confident that the population proportion of students that have parasailed is between 0.19828 and 0.38197.

Δ

Notice that the 99% confidence interval is wider than the 90% confidence interval. We can conclude the following points (assuming sample size stays the same):

1) As the level of confidence **increases**, the margin of error **increases** and the confidence interval gets **wider**.
2) As the level of confidence **decreases**, the margin of error **decreases** and the confidence interval gets **narrower**.

This applies to all confidence intervals, like in the picture below:

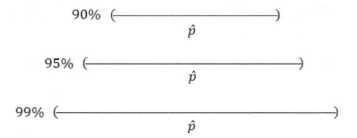

Why is this true? With a 95% confidence interval, we want to be 95% confident that the population parameter is within the interval. However, with a 99% confidence interval, we want to be even more confident that the population parameter is within the interval. Thus, to be that much more certain the proportion is on the interval, we need a wider interval.

We can also see it mathematically. Note that in the margin of error formula, the standard error is multiplied by $Z_{\alpha/2}$. Thus, if you increase $Z_{\alpha/2}$, the overall margin of error must increase as well:

$$\text{Margin of Error} = \boxed{Z_{\alpha/2}}\sqrt{\frac{\hat{p}(1-\hat{p})}{n}}$$

We have seen what happens when we change the confidence level. However, what about if we change the sample size? It turns out that the following is true:

1) As the sample size **increases**, the margin of error **decreases** and the confidence interval gets **narrower**.
2) As the sample size **decreases**, the margin of error **increases** and the confidence interval gets **wider**.

The opposite effects happen when we increase the sample size: the confidence interval gets narrower. Why is this true?

As we increase our sample size, the sample statistic we obtain (whether we are looking for a mean or a proportion) is a better representation of the population. That means that our point estimate is a better and better estimate, and we don't need such a wide confidence interval. That is, our error will be smaller, so we don't go out quite so much on both sides.

Here is another explanation. Notice that the sample size n is on the denominator of the margin of error. When the denominator gets larger, the overall number gets smaller:

$$\text{Margin of Error} = Z_{\alpha/2}\sqrt{\frac{\hat{p}(1-\hat{p})}{\boxed{n}}}$$

Now let's see how we can use the TI-84 to compute a confidence interval.

TI-84 COMMAND: CONFIDENCE INTERVAL FOR A PROPORTION

To find the confidence interval for a population proportion, press $\boxed{\text{STAT}}$, scroll right to TESTS, and choose Option A: $1 - propZInt$. Enter x (the number of successes), n the sample size), the desired confidence level, then scroll down to Calculate and press $\boxed{\text{ENTER}}$. The output shows the confidence interval, the sample proportion, and the sample size.

EXAMPLE

On the previous problem with the parasailing students, we can choose $1 - propZInt$ and enter $x = 47$, $n = 162$, and confidence level 0.90. The resulting confidence interval is $(0.23148, 0.34877)$, which matches what we computed earlier.

Δ

REVIEW: CONFIDENCE INTERVAL FACTS
These facts have been pointed out directly or indirectly earlier, so let's go over them again.

The sample mean is **always** inside the confidence interval. This is true because of the way the interval was constructed: we start with the point estimate and then go left and right the same number of units. Thus, the sample mean (or proportion) is always in the center of the interval.

Is the population mean (or proportion) ever inside the interval? As we have seen, maybe it is, and maybe it isn't. There is no way of assuring this.

The point here is that the sample mean (the statistic) is always inside the interval, at the center, but the population mean (the parameter) is in the interval only sometimes.

EXAMPLE
We have a 95% confidence interval that is $(0.20, 0.40)$.

   A) Can you find the sample proportion? If so, find it.
   B) Can you find the population proportion? If so, find it.
   C) Find the margin of error.
   D) Now suppose another confidence interval of the same sample size is drawn, and this interval is $(0.23, 0.37)$. Is it more likely a 92% or a 98% interval? Why?

Solution: For part A, the sample proportion is always inside the confidence interval, right at the center. We therefore need to find the middle of 0.20 and 0.40 by averaging those endpoints:

$$\hat{p} = \frac{0.20 + 0.40}{2} = \frac{0.60}{2} = 0.30$$

For part B, we cannot find the population proportion from this information alone. With 95% confidence, it is somewhere between 0.20 and 0.40, but that is the best we can do. The only way to compute the population proportion is to survey every single person in the whole population, and this is usually unfeasible to do.

To find the margin of error, remember that it is the distance between the point estimate and one of the endpoints. We have both, so we can compute the upper limit minus the point estimate:

$$\text{upper limit} - \text{point estimate} = 0.40 - 0.30 = 0.10$$

Alternatively, we could have computed the point estimate minus the lower limit.

Next, for part D, we have a new confidence interval $(0.23, 0.37)$, and the question is whether it is more likely to be a 92% or a 98% confidence interval. To answer this, recognize that this new interval $(0.23, 0.37)$ is shorter than $(0.20, 0.40)$. We are told that the sample sizes are the same, so the confidence level has to be a little different.

When you increase the confidence level, the interval becomes wider. By the same token, when you decrease the confidence level, the interval becomes shorter. That means that if the original $(0.20, 0.40)$ is at 95% confidence, the new interval $(0.23, 0.37)$ must have a lower confidence level. Thus, 92% is more likely than 98%.

Δ

This next example contains the necessary information, although it may not be that obvious at first. The key is to clearly identify what we have and do not have.

EXAMPLE
Given a sample, 71% of the subjects answered yes in a survey. The standard error is 0.034. Find a 93% confidence interval for the population proportion.

Solution: Yes, we are not told a sample size! No need to panic though; we can approach this problem by computing or stating the point estimate, standard error, margin of error, and confidence interval, in that order. First is the point estimate: although we are not told how many subjects answered yes, we know that 71% did. It is that simple – the point estimate is just 0.71!

Second, we need the standard error, which requires $\hat{p}$ and n, the latter of which we do not have. But look at the question again – we are told that the standard error is 0.034. We are in business!

Third, we need the margin of error, which means we need the Z-score for a 93% confidence interval. Here is the normal curve:

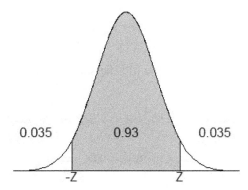

If 0.93 is in the middle of the curve, then 0.07 is left over, and half of that is 0.035. Thus, we need the Z-score that cuts the curve in such a way that it gives 0.035 area in the lower tail (and the upper tail). Thus, $invNorm(0.035) = -1.811910674$, and so dropping the negative sign, we would use $Z_{0.035} = 1.811910674$.

Even though we do not know the sample size, the margin of error is still Z times the standard error (which is given):

$$\text{Margin of Error} = Z_{0.035} \times \text{Standard Error} = 1.811910674 \times 0.034 = 0.0616049629$$

Next, we compute the point estimate plus and minus the margin of error:

$$\hat{p} \pm M\text{argin of Error} = 0.71 \pm 0.0616049629$$
$$= (0.71 - 0.0616049629, 0.71 + 0.0616049629)$$
$$= (0.64840, 0.77160)$$

Interpreting this interval, we are 93% confident that the population proportion of people who would answer yes in this survey is between 0.64840 and 0.77160.

Δ

Section 8.5 – Confidence Interval for a Population Mean

Recall that a confidence interval can be written in this general formula:

$$(\text{point estimate}) \pm (\text{margin of error})$$

The point estimate is a single number that is a reasonable guess for the parameter. The "best guess" for the population mean if we only have a sample is the sample mean. Thus, the point estimate is the sample mean $\bar{x}$, and it is at the center of the confidence interval.

What is the margin of error? Just like earlier, it is equal to a specific number times the standard error:

$$\bar{x} \pm (\text{something})(\text{standard error})$$

Remember from Chapter 7 that the formula for the standard error for a sampling distribution of sample means is $\sigma/\sqrt{n}$, and then the population standard deviation was given to us. In general, this is not realistic since this figure is almost always unknown (just like the population mean). The next best thing to use is the sample standard deviation s. That means that

$$\text{standard error} = \frac{s}{\sqrt{n}}$$

(Recall that with the proportion standard error, we did the same thing there – we replaced p with $\hat{p}$ in that formula.)

We are this far into our formula for the confidence interval for the population mean:

$$\bar{x} \pm (\text{something}) \times \frac{s}{\sqrt{n}}$$

The only question now is what number goes into the "something." With the proportion confidence interval, the number we used was a Z-score from the normal distribution, corresponding to the level of confidence. For a mean confidence interval, the number we need to use still corresponds to the confidence level, but it is from a new distribution called the T-distribution.

Before we see how to compute the T values, let's talk about the properties of the T-distribution and compare it to the standard normal distribution.

PROPERTIES OF THE T-DISTRIBUTION

The first three properties are the same as that of the standard normal distribution.

Property 1: The T-distribution has a mean of 0.
Property 2: The total area under the curve for the T-distribution is 1.
Property 3: The T-distribution is symmetric about 0.

The next three properties are unique to the T-distribution.

Property 4: The T-distribution takes on different shapes (and consequently different probabilities) for different values of the sample size n.

Property 5: The T-distribution is leptokurtic, which means that the area in the tails is a little larger than the area in the tails of the normal distribution. In addition, the □-distribution's apex juts higher than that of the standard normal.

Property 6: As the sample size n increases, the T-distribution looks more and more like the standard normal curve.

Let's discuss these points further.

Property 1: Just like the standard normal distribution, the mean and center of the T-distribution is 0.

Property 2: Like the standard normal distribution, the total probability under the T-distribution curve is 1, so the same techniques of finding the area of one side given the other side still apply here.

Property 3: Just like the standard normal distribution, the T-distribution is symmetric about 0, so the area to the right of $T = 0$ is 0.50 and the area to the left of $T = 0$ is 0.50.

Property 4: The shape of the T-distribution is different depending on the sample size. That means that, for instance, $P(T > 1)$ would be a different value for $n = 5$ than for $n = 50$. In contrast, on the normal distribution, $P(Z > 1) = 0.15866$ regardless of the sample size. The following graphs show what the T-distribution looks like for $n = 5$ and $n = 50$.

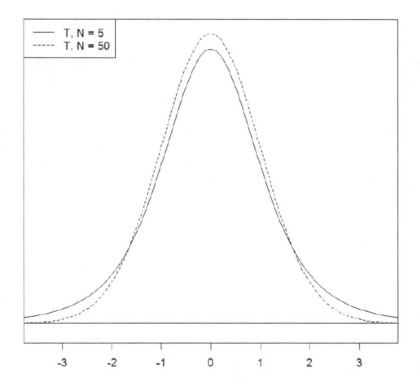

Property 5: The T-distribution is more "peaked" with "fatter" tails than the normal distribution, as shown in the following graph.

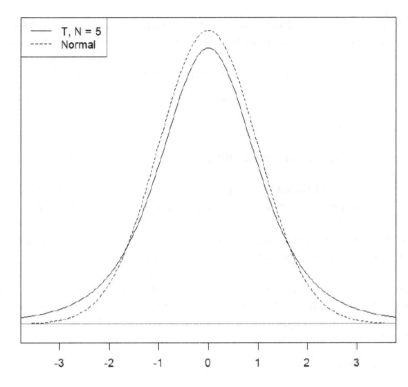

<u>Property 6</u>: As the sample size gets larger, the T-distribution looks more and more like the normal distribution. For instance, $P(Z > 1.959963986) = 0.025$ for the normal distribution. Switching to the T-distribution, $P(T > 1.959963986) = 0.02639$ for $n = 100$, and it is equal to 0.02514 for $n = 1000$. If we keep increasing the sample size, the probability would get closer to 0.025.

Although we will not go through the details of it, notice we did not mention the standard deviation of the T-distribution and whether it was equal to 1 like for the standard normal distribution. The answer is no – it can be shown that the standard deviation is in fact equal to $\sqrt{(n-1)/(n-3)}$ provided $n > 3$. However, for large sample sizes, this value will get closer to 1.

ETYMOLOGY

An interesting backstory here is that in 1908, the English statistician William Sealy Gosset created the T-distribution. However, at the time he also worked at – of all places – the Guinness Brewery in Dublin! The employees at the brewery were required to use pseudonyms when publishing scholarly papers instead of their real names, so Gosset chose Student as his name, thereby calling his discovery "Student's T-distribution." As for the choice of the letter T, one possibility is that the first letter of Student was skipped due to s already being used for the sample standard deviation, so T was the next letter.

The word leptokurtic defined earlier comes from the Greek $\lambda\varepsilon\pi\tau\acute{o}\varsigma$ (meaning "thin") and $\kappa\upsilon\rho\tau\acute{o}\varsigma$ (meaning "bulging"), which is a rather appropriate description of the T-distribution.

The following photo is a plaque from the Guinness Brewery dedicated to Gosset (I took this photo on a tour of this brewery in 2017).

To use the T-distribution, instead of entering the mean and standard deviation, we need to enter a quantity called degrees of freedom.

DEFINITION

The **degrees of freedom** (abbreviated DF) is a quantity that influences the overall shape of the T-distribution. For a confidence interval for a population mean, $DF = n - 1$ where n is the sample size, so here degrees of freedom is equal to sample size minus one. (And by convention, we treat "degrees of freedom" as singular, hence "is equal to.")

We also need to discuss how to use the T-distribution on the TI-84. (Although we won't pursue it in these notes, Appendix D features a T-table in case you need to use one for your class.)

TI-84 COMMAND: T-DISTRIBUTION

To find the probability between a lower limit and an upper limit given a specified DF, press $\boxed{\text{2nd}}$, $\boxed{\text{VARS}}$, and choose Option 6: $tcdf(\quad)$. The command is

$$tcdf(\text{lower limit}, \text{upper limit}, DF)$$

If there is no lower limit, use -999999, and if there is no upper limit, use 999999.

To find the T-score that gives a specified probability below (to the left) of that T-score given a specified DF, press $\boxed{\text{2nd}}$, $\boxed{\text{VARS}}$, and choose Option 4: $invT(\quad)$. The command is

$$invT(\text{probability}, DF)$$

EXAMPLE

First, let's find the probability above $T = 1.2$ for a sample size of 28 subjects. A sketch looks like the following:

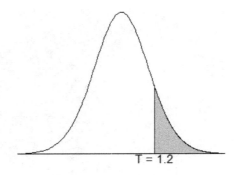

The lower limit is $T = 1.2$, and since there is no upper limit, we can say $T = 999999$. Since $n = 28$, $DF = 27$ and therefore

$$tcdf(1.2, 999999, 27) = 0.1202816196$$

Next, let's find the T-score associated with 95% confidence for a sample size of 45 subjects. Just like with the normal distribution, we draw a sketch with 0.95 in the middle:

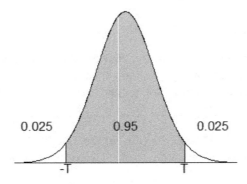

If 0.95 is in the middle region, then 0.05 is left over, and half of that is 0.025. Since $n = 45$, $DF = 44$ and therefore

$$invT(0.025, 44) = -2.015367547$$

We denote the quantity as $T_{\alpha/2}(n - 1)$, and for this problem, it is $T_{0.025}(44)$. As before, we can drop the negative sign and say that the T-score to use for 95% confidence and $n = 45$ is $T_{0.025}(44) = 2.015367547$.

Δ

We can finally complete the formula for the confidence interval for the population mean, and just like the previous confidence intervals, there are some assumptions that must be met for it to be valid.

DEFINITION

The general formula for a $100(1 - \alpha)\%$ confidence interval for the population mean is

$$\bar{x} \pm T_{\alpha/2}(n - 1) \times \left(\frac{s}{\sqrt{n}}\right)$$

The following parts are defined:

---

n is the sample size.

$\overline{x}$ is the sample mean.

s is the sample standard deviation.

$T_{\alpha/2}(n-1)$ is a number that is determined by the confidence level and the degrees of freedom, using $DF = n - 1$.

The fraction $\frac{s}{\sqrt{n}}$ is the standard error.

The product $T_{\alpha/2}(n-1) \times \left(\frac{s}{\sqrt{n}}\right)$ is the margin of error.

Caution: Some textbooks teach an alternative formula to use for the unlikely event that the population standard deviation σ is known. If this is the case, replace s with σ and use the normal distribution to find $Z_{\alpha/2}$ instead of $T_{\alpha/2}(n-1)$. We won't pursue any problems like this in these notes, however, since the population standard deviation is almost always unknown.

MEAN CONFIDENCE INTERVAL ASSUMPTIONS

For a confidence interval for a population mean to be valid, two specific items need to be true about the sample:

Assumption 1: The sample must have been randomly selected.
Assumption 2: At least one of the following is true:
      A) We are sampling from a population that is normally distributed, or …
      B) $n > 30$ (cf. the sampling distribution of sample means)

Let's summarize the parts of the formula again.

SUMMARY: CONFIDENCE INTERVAL FOR A MEAN

For a confidence interval for a population mean, we have the following, which can be computed in the four steps outlined below:

$$\text{Point Estimate} = \overline{x}$$
$$\text{Standard Error} = \frac{s}{\sqrt{n}}$$
$$\text{Margin of Error} = T_{\alpha/2}(n-1) \times \left(\frac{s}{\sqrt{n}}\right)$$
$$\text{Confidence Interval} = \overline{x} \pm T_{\alpha/2}(n-1) \times \left(\frac{s}{\sqrt{n}}\right)$$

If you want to write the formula in the form (lower limit, upper limit), it would look like this:

$$\left(\overline{x} - T_{\alpha/2}(n-1) \times \left(\frac{s}{\sqrt{n}}\right), \overline{x} + T_{\alpha/2}(n-1) \times \left(\frac{s}{\sqrt{n}}\right)\right)$$

EXAMPLE

In England, a popular silly contest is to get as many people as possible inside what is known as a phone box (a phone booth). Here is a random sample of 7 such contests, and the number of people inside the phone box per contest is recorded. We will assume that the number of successful contestants per contest is normally distributed (so that the assumptions are satisfied).

$$5, 7, 10, 8, 9, 12, 9$$

It is of interest to build a 95% confidence interval for the average number of people a contest can squeeze inside a phone box.

Solution: We first solve this using the formulas. Noting that $n = 7$, we first need the sample mean and sample standard deviation. Using the TI-84's lists and getting the one-variable statistics, it can be shown that $\bar{x} = 8.571428571$ and $s = 2.225394561$. (Be careful not to confuse standard deviation with standard error!) Thus,

$$\text{Point Estimate} = \bar{x} = 8.571428571$$

The standard error is

$$\text{Standard Error} = \frac{s}{\sqrt{n}} = \frac{2.225394561}{\sqrt{7}} = 0.8411200825$$

To find the T-score associated with 95% confidence, note that $DF = 7 - 1 = 6$ and create a sketch:

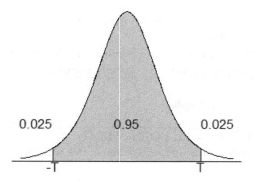

Next, $invT(0.025, 6) = -2.446911839$, which means that the T-score is $T_{0.025}(6) = 2.446911839$. That means that the margin of error is

$$\text{Margin of Error} = T_{0.025}(6) \times \text{Standard Error} = 2.446911839 \times 0.8411200825 = 2.058146688$$

We then compute the point estimate plus and minus the margin of error:

$$\begin{aligned} \bar{x} \pm \text{Margin of Error} &= 8.571428571 \pm 2.058146688 \\ &= (8.571428571 - 2.058146688, 8.571428571 + 2.058146688) \\ &= (6.51328, 10.62958) \end{aligned}$$

Interpreting this interval, we are 95% confident that the population mean number of people who could fit inside a phone box during a contest is between 6.51328 and 10.62958.

Δ

EXAMPLE
According to the confidence interval from the previous example, is it likely that the population mean number of successful contestants is 12? How about 7?

Solution: Like before, any value that is inside the interval is a likely value for the population mean μ, while any number below or above the value is not. The confidence interval $(6.51328, 10.62958)$ does not contain 12, so 12 is not a plausible value for the population mean. However, the interval does contain 7, so 7 is a plausible value for the population mean.

Δ

Just as we learned how to use the TI-84 to compute the confidence interval for a population proportion, there are analogous ways to do this for the confidence interval for a population mean.

TI-84 COMMAND: CONFIDENCE INTERVAL FOR A MEAN

To find the confidence interval for a population mean, if the data numbers are provided, first put them into a list by pressing $\boxed{\text{STAT}}$, choosing Option 1: Edit ..., and typing in the numbers into the L_1 column.

From the home screen, press $\boxed{\text{STAT}}$, scroll right to TESTS, and choose Option 8: *TInterval*.

If you have your data typed into L_1, choose Data for the input, L_1 for the List, select your desired confidence level, then scroll down to Calculate and press $\boxed{\text{ENTER}}$. On the other hand, if you are instead given $\bar{x}$, s, and n instead of the data values, under the *TInterval* option choose Stats. Type the values for $\bar{x}$, s, n, and the confidence level, then scroll down to Calculate and press $\boxed{\text{ENTER}}$. The output shows the confidence interval, the sample mean, the sample standard deviation, and the sample size.

EXAMPLE

On the previous problem with the phone boxes, we can put in our seven data values into L_1. Choosing *TInterval* and Data provides us with a lower limit of 6.5133 and an upper limit of 10.63, which matches what we computed earlier (although the output has been rounded).

On the other hand, choosing *TInterval* and Stats, we can instead enter $\bar{x} = 8.571428571$, $s = 2.225394561$, $n = 7$, and a confidence level of 0.95, and we get the same results.

Δ

EXAMPLE

We want to build a 90% confidence interval for the average wingspan (in meters) of a Sandhill Crane (*Grus canadensis*). A random sample of 20 cranes shows that $\bar{x} = 1.6$ and $s = 0.1$. Assume that the population of Sandhill Crane wingspans is normal. (This problem is based on my photograph on the cover of this book, which features 20 Sandhill Cranes in flight at sunset. I took that photo in northern Georgia in 2013 when they were about to land on a mudflat for the night before taking off the next day.)

Solution: Let's solve this by hand first. The point estimate is

$$\text{Point Estimate} = \bar{x} = 1.6$$

The standard error is

$$\text{Standard Error} = \frac{s}{\sqrt{n}} = \frac{0.1}{\sqrt{20}} = 0.0223606798$$

To find the T-score associated with 90% confidence, note that $DF = 20 - 1 = 19$ and create a sketch:

223

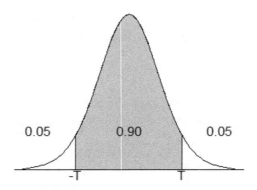

Next, $invT(0.05, 19) = -1.729132792$, which means that the T-score is $T_{0.05}(19) = 1.729132792$. That means that the margin of error is

Margin of Error = $T_{0.05}(19)\times$Standard Error = $1.729132792\times0.0223606798 = 0.0386645847$

We then compute the point estimate plus and minus the margin of error:

$$\bar{x} \pm \text{Margin of Error} = 1.6 \pm 0.0386645847$$
$$= (1.6 - 0.0386645847, 1.6 + 0.0386645847)$$
$$= (1.56134, 1.63866)$$

Interpreting this interval, we are 90% confident that the population mean wingspan of Sandhill Cranes is between 1.56134 and 1.63866 meters. Now let's compute this interval using the TI-84. Press $\boxed{\text{STAT}}$, scroll right to TESTS, and choose the 8th option, $TInterval$. Enter the given statistics $\bar{x} = 30.1$, $s = 3.68$, $n = 16$, and confidence level 0.90. The result is a confidence interval of $(1.5613, 1.6387)$, the same interval except for some rounding.

Δ

EXAMPLE
Suppose we obtain a sample mean of 2000 and a standard error of 300 on a sample size of 9. Assuming a normal population, we want to build a 92% confidence interval for the population mean. There appears to be just enough information that the $TInterval$ command cannot be used directly, so we need to find the confidence interval by hand. (Problems like this are one reason not to get too comfortable using the TI-84 commands alone – doing so will likely get you stumped when some piece of information is withheld!)

A) Find the 92% confidence interval.
B) Actually, the $TInterval$ command can be used if you are sneaky. How?
C) What are the two ways we can decrease the width of the confidence interval?
D) Another study conducted made three different confidence intervals from the same sample (and therefore the sample size is the same). These intervals are $(1400, 1600)$, $(1300, 1700)$, and $(1470, 1530)$. We are told that in some order, these are 89%, 93%, and 97% confidence intervals. Match up each interval with its most likely confidence level.
E) What is the point estimate in this new sample?

Solution: For part A, the point estimate is $\bar{x} = 2000$ and the standard error is 300. To find the T-score associated with 92% confidence, note that $DF = 9 - 1 = 8$ and create a sketch:

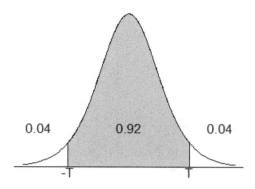

Next, $invT(0.04, 8) = -2.004151525$, which means that the T-score is $T_{0.04}(8) = 2.004151525$. That means that the margin of error is

$$\text{Margin of Error} = T_{0.04}(8) \times \text{Standard Error} = 2.004151525 \times 300 = 601.2454574$$

We then compute the point estimate plus and minus the margin of error:

$$\bar{x} \pm \text{Margin of Error} = 2000 \pm 601.2454574$$
$$= (2000 - 601.2454574, 30.1 + 601.2454574)$$
$$= (1398.75454, 2601.24546)$$

Interpreting this interval, we are 92% confident that the population mean is between 1398.75454 and 2601.24546.

For part B, to use the $TInterval$ command we need $\bar{x}$, s, and n. The only piece we are missing is s – or are we? The standard error is 300, so notice that we can solve for s:

$$\text{Standard Error} = \frac{s}{\sqrt{n}} \Rightarrow 300 = \frac{s}{\sqrt{9}} \Rightarrow s = 300 \times \sqrt{9}$$
$$\Rightarrow s = 900$$

For part C, there are two ways we can decrease the width of the confidence interval. Just like we discussed earlier in this chapter, the first method is to decrease the confidence level (holding the sample size constant). The second method is to increase the sample size (holding the confidence level constant).

Next, part D gives us three new confidence intervals. Arranging them from narrowest to widest, we have $(1470, 1530)$, $(1400, 1600)$, and $(1300, 1700)$. Since the sample size is the same, they all must have different confidence levels. Lower confidence levels are associated with narrower intervals, and so the most likely outcome is that $(1470, 1530)$ is the 89% confidence interval, $(1400, 1600)$ the 93%, and $(1300, 1700)$ the 97%.

Finally, since the three confidence intervals came from the same sample, they all have the same sample mean and therefore point estimate. The point estimate is in the middle of the confidence interval, so choose any of the intervals and find the midpoint. Picking the first interval, we have

$$\bar{x} = \frac{1400 + 1600}{2} = 1500$$

Δ

225

There is one issue that needs to be addressed, which otherwise can lead to some confusion. Therefore, let's derail that confusion right now. In the confidence interval equations, when do we use Z, and when do we use T? The answer is straightforward:

1) For a proportion problem, you use Z.
2) For a mean problem, you use T.

MNEMONIC

Suppose we are going to stick the letter T onto the end of the words "proportion" and "mean." Put it onto the end of "mean," and you get "meant," which is a proper word. Put it onto the end of "proportion," however, and you get "proportiont," which is not a proper word. This tells you that T goes with mean!

It is therefore critical to first identify the problem as a mean or proportion scenario!

EXAMPLES

Identify the following scenarios as a mean or proportion situation:

A) We want to estimate the number of collect calls made per day in a certain city.
B) In a random sample of size 55, 33 people own a dog.
C) A random sample of two hundred people shows that seventy-one percent of them have had chicken pox.
D) We sample ten roller coasters at random and calculate their maximum G force.

Solution: For part A, the number of collect calls (remember those before the days of mobile phones?) made per day is quantitative, so it is a mean problem. In contrast, part B involves people that either own a dog (success) or do not (failure), so this is a categorical scenario (yes/no) and therefore a proportion problem.

For part C, people either have had chicken pox (success) or not (failure), so this is a proportion problem since it is a yes/no scenario. Lastly, part D measures G forces, which are quantitative, so this is a mean problem.

Δ

Section 8.6 – Choosing Sample Sizes for a Study

Sometimes before setting up an experiment or a survey, we would like the margin of error to be a certain amount or less. To achieve such a margin of error, we need to have an idea of how many subjects to sample. The goal of this section is to figure out how many subjects we need to sample given a desired margin of error for the study.

In other words, earlier in this chapter we knew the sample size, along with the sample proportion (or sample standard deviation), and the next step was to compute the margin of error. In this section we turn it around: given the desired margin of error, along with good ideas for the sample proportion (or sample standard deviation), we want to know the required sample size.

First, borrowing some ideas from earlier in this chapter, it should make sense that when sample size increases, the margin of error gets smaller because the estimate becomes more precise. For example, if a study requires 200 people to have a margin of error of 5 percentage points, and we want to instead be within 3 percentage points (so more precise), we instead might need 300 people. In other words, the more subjects, the smaller the margin of error.

On the other hand, from a practical perspective, we often do not want to sample too many subjects. While more is better, keep in mind that surveying more subjects requires more time, effort, and money. Thus, there is a tradeoff between having a desired margin of error and the cost of conducting the survey.

First, let's discuss sample size estimations for proportions. Suppose we are trying to get results for an election, and we are looking for a sample proportion for the proportion of people who will vote for candidate A. Perhaps we know that whatever sample proportion we end up with, we want it to be within 3% of the true population proportion for ALL voters. Thus, we want the margin of error to be equal to 3%.

We can use a formula to tell us what sample size we need to take so that our margin of error will be 3%. In other words, we can be certain that whatever sample proportion we get will be within 3% of the true population proportion with a certain level of confidence.

ESTIMATING SAMPLE SIZE FOR A PROPORTION

The formula for choosing a sample size in estimating a population proportion is

$$n = \frac{\hat{p}(1 - \hat{p})\left(Z_{\alpha/2}\right)^2}{m^2}$$

Here $\hat{p}$ is a guess at the value we think we might get for the sample proportion. The rule is that if you have a previous study available, set $\hat{p}$ equal to that previous sample proportion. If you do not have a previous study available and therefore do not know what to expect, then set $\hat{p} = 0.50$.

The m is the margin of error we need to have.

The $Z_{\alpha/2}$ is the Z-score associated with the level of confidence (for 95%, $Z_{0.025} = 1.96$). It represents how confident we want to be that the sample proportion we will get will be within the required margin of error.

Why is this the formula to use for sample size? Recall that for proportions, the formula for margin of error (denoted by m) was given by the following:

$$m = Z_{\alpha/2}\sqrt{\frac{\hat{p}(1 - \hat{p})}{n}}$$

However, now we are given margin of error, and we want to know what n is necessary to achieve such a margin of error. That is, we want to solve for n in the above equation, which requires some basic algebra:

$$m = Z_{\alpha/2}\sqrt{\frac{\hat{p}(1 - \hat{p})}{n}} \Rightarrow \frac{m}{Z_{\alpha/2}} = \sqrt{\frac{\hat{p}(1 - \hat{p})}{n}} \Rightarrow \frac{m^2}{\left(Z_{\alpha/2}\right)^2} = \frac{\hat{p}(1 - \hat{p})}{n} \Rightarrow \frac{\left(Z_{\alpha/2}\right)^2}{m^2} = \frac{n}{\hat{p}(1 - \hat{p})}$$

$$\Rightarrow n = \frac{\hat{p}(1 - \hat{p})\left(Z_{\alpha/2}\right)^2}{m^2}$$

Why do we choose $\hat{p} = 0.50$ when nothing is known about what the sample proportion could be? The answer is as follows: both m (margin of error) and $Z_{\alpha/2}$ (from the confidence level) are specified, and so the only piece that is unknown is $\hat{p}(1 - \hat{p})$. We therefore want to assume the "worst-case scenario," which is taking a larger sample so that we will get within that margin of error, regardless of what sample proportion we end up obtaining.

Thus, the idea is to make $\hat{p}(1 - \hat{p})$ as large as possible. It can be shown (see the graph below) that choosing $\hat{p} = 0.50$ is the choice that maximizes $\hat{p}(1 - \hat{p})$. (If you have studied calculus, you can also show that $\hat{p} = 0.50$ maximizes $\hat{p}(1 - \hat{p})$.)

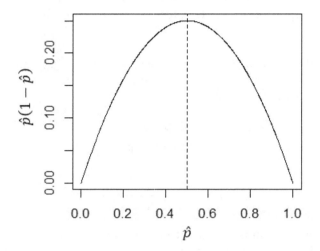

EXAMPLE

Some people enjoy dunking cookies into their cups of tea before eating the cookie. We are going to find a sample proportion of people that are "dunkers." How large a sample size should we take to estimate the proportion to within 0.03 with probability 0.95?

Solution: To rephrase everything, we want to take a sample and get a sample proportion. We then want to create a 95% confidence interval around that sample proportion, and we require the margin of error for that confidence interval to equal 0.03. (Watch for phrases such as "estimate to within 0.03" as that indicates the margin of error.) The sample size formula is

$$n = \frac{\hat{p}(1 - \hat{p})\left(Z_{\alpha/2}\right)^2}{m^2}$$

It is enormously helpful to label each number before putting it into the formula!

$$m = 0.03$$
$$\alpha = 0.05$$
$$\frac{\alpha}{2} = 0.025$$
$$Z_{0.025} = 1.96$$
$$\hat{p} = 0.50$$

Be careful with the "with probability 0.95" piece – that means having 95% confidence in our answer. That is the reason that $Z_{0.025} = 1.96$.

As for $\hat{p}$, notice that the problem does not mention a sample proportion from a previous study. When this happens, we assume the worst-case scenario and set $\hat{p} = 0.50$.

Now let's put everything into the formula:

$$n = \frac{\hat{p}(1-\hat{p})(Z_{\alpha/2})^2}{m^2} = \frac{0.50 \times (1-0.50) \times 1.96^2}{0.03^2} = \frac{0.9604}{0.0009} = 1067.11111$$

As will usually be the case, we get a decimal answer. However, sample size obviously must be a whole number, so the question is how do we round. The answer is that with these sample size estimation problems, if you get a decimal answer, always round up, regardless of what the decimal is. (In the unlikely event you get a whole number answer, then the answer is just that, with no rounding.)

The reason is because if you round down to 1067, you will likely get a margin of error that is just barely above 0.03, but you want to be within 0.03 – meaning 0.03 or smaller. The problem is solved when you take just one more subject, so you round up to 1068. Thus, the answer is that you need 1068 subjects:

$$n = \frac{\hat{p}(1-\hat{p})(Z_{\alpha/2})^2}{m^2} = 1067.11111 \rightarrow 1068$$

Δ

EXAMPLE
Consider the previous scenario, only this time a similar study conducted in Edinburgh gave a sample estimate of 78% of people dunking cookies in their tea.

A) Using that study as a guideline, find the new sample size required.
B) What is the advantage to having an idea what the sample proportion might be?
C) Now suppose, all other things being equal, we wanted to be 98% confident of our answer rather than 95%. Will we need to take a larger or smaller sample size?

Solution: For part A, we state the numbers again, only this time using the 78% from a previous study:

$$m = 0.03$$
$$\alpha = 0.05$$
$$\frac{\alpha}{2} = 0.025$$
$$Z_{0.025} = 1.96$$
$$\hat{p} = 0.78$$

Now let's put everything into the formula again:

$$n = \frac{\hat{p}(1-\hat{p})(Z_{\alpha/2})^2}{m^2} = \frac{0.78 \times (1-0.78) \times 1.96^2}{0.03^2} = \frac{0.65921856}{0.0009} = 732.46507 \rightarrow 733$$

For part B, recognize that when we had no idea what sample proportion we would get, we needed to sample 1068 subjects. However, when we had an idea of what to expect, the required number dropped to a mere 733 subjects. Thus, the advantage is that you will not need to sample as many people for the study, which will save time, effort, and money.

For part C, let's first answer the question just by examining the necessary pieces of the formula. If confidence increases from 95% to 98%, then $Z_{\alpha/2}$ will increase. All other terms are the same, so $\hat{p}$ and m will remain the same. If $Z_{\alpha/2}$ increases, then the numerator in the formula will increase, resulting in an overall larger number, the sample size:

$$n = \frac{\hat{p}(1 - \hat{p})(Z_{\alpha/2})^2}{m^2}$$

You can also visualize this by arguing that if you want to be more confident in your answer, having a larger sample size will accomplish that.

Δ

The mathematical argument used in that last problem uses these fundamental facts:

1) When the numerator of a fraction increases, the overall number increases.
2) When the numerator of a fraction decreases, the overall number decreases.
3) When the denominator of a fraction increases, the overall number decreases.
4) When the denominator of a fraction decreases, the overall number increases.

If you forget this, make up some simple examples. For instance, consider 1/3 and 1/2. The fraction 1/3 has a larger denominator than 1/2, and it is a smaller number overall (because 0.333 is less than 0.50).

Next, we turn our attention to choosing sample size for estimating a population mean. For example, maybe we want to estimate the income for an entire company. We want to take a sample of their employees and get a sample mean of their income. Furthermore, suppose we want this sample mean income to be within $5000 of the entire company's mean income with 95% confidence.

ESTIMATING SAMPLE SIZE FOR A MEAN
The formula for choosing a sample size in estimating a population mean is

$$n = \frac{\sigma^2(Z_{\alpha/2})^2}{m^2}$$

Here σ is the provided standard deviation (in these problems, this will be given, which is why it is σ and not s), m is the margin of error, and $Z_{\alpha/2}$ is the Z-score associated with the level of confidence (for 95%, $Z_{0.025} = 1.96$). It represents how confident we want to be that the sample mean we will get will be within the required margin of error.

Why is this the formula? Recall that for means, the formula for margin of error (denoted by m) was given by the following:

$$m = T_{\alpha/2}(n - 1) \times \left(\frac{\sigma}{\sqrt{n}}\right)$$

However, now we are given margin of error, and we want to know what n is necessary to achieve such a margin of error. That is, we want to solve for n in the above equation, which requires some basic algebra:

$$m = T_{\alpha/2}(n - 1) \times \left(\frac{\sigma}{\sqrt{n}}\right) \Rightarrow \frac{m}{T_{\alpha/2}(n - 1)} = \frac{\sigma}{\sqrt{n}} \Rightarrow \frac{T_{\alpha/2}(n - 1)}{m} = \frac{\sqrt{n}}{\sigma}$$

$$\Rightarrow \frac{\left(T_{\alpha/2}(n-1)\right)^2}{m^2} = \frac{n}{\sigma^2} \Rightarrow n = \frac{\sigma^2\left(T_{\alpha/2}(n-1)\right)^2}{m^2}$$

The problem is that the T-score in the above last step depends on degrees of freedom, which depends on sample size ... which is what we are trying to estimate. Thus, the next best thing we can do to get an estimate is to use $Z_{\alpha/2}$ instead of $T_{\alpha/2}(n-1)$. That is why the formula to use is

$$n = \frac{\sigma^2\left(Z_{\alpha/2}\right)^2}{m^2}$$

EXAMPLE
An estimate is needed of the mean height of women in Ontario, Canada. A 95% confidence interval should have a margin of error of 3 inches. A study ten years ago in this province had a standard deviation of 10 inches.

   A) About how large a sample of women is needed?
   B) About how large a sample of women is needed for a 99% confidence interval to have a margin of error of 3 inches?
   C) All other things being equal, what will happen to the required sample size if we only require a margin of error of 4 inches rather than 3?

Solution: For part A, let's label the numbers:

$$m = 3 \text{ inches}$$
$$\alpha = 0.05$$
$$\frac{\alpha}{2} = 0.025$$
$$Z_{0.025} = 1.96$$
$$\sigma = 10 \text{ inches}$$

Putting everything into the formula,

$$n = \frac{\sigma^2\left(Z_{\alpha/2}\right)^2}{m^2} = \frac{10^2 \times 1.96^2}{3^2} = \frac{384.16}{9} = 42.68444 \rightarrow 43$$

A sample of 43 women is needed to achieve a margin of error within 10 inches. For part B, we need to go to 99% confidence, which means that now $\alpha = 0.01$, $\alpha/2 = 0.005$, and therefore by earlier work, $Z_{0.005} = 2.575829303$. Otherwise $\sigma = 10$ and $m = 3$, and so

$$n = \frac{\sigma^2\left(Z_{\alpha/2}\right)^2}{m^2} = \frac{10^2 \times 2.575829303^2}{3^2} = \frac{663.4896498}{9} = 73.72107 \rightarrow 74$$

For part C, all other things being equal, what happens when $m = 4$ instead of 3? We can see that margin of error is on the denominator, and when the denominator increases, the overall fraction (the sample size) decreases. We can also think of it this way: if margin of error is larger, it means that the estimate is not as precise. Thus, fewer subjects are needed.

Δ

SUMMARY: SAMPLE SIZE ESTIMATION
The formulas for estimating sample size for a proportion and mean are

$$n = \frac{\hat{p}(1 - \hat{p})\left(Z_{\alpha/2}\right)^2}{m^2}$$
$$n = \frac{\sigma^2\left(Z_{\alpha/2}\right)^2}{m^2}$$

All other things being equal…

As confidence increases, $Z_{\alpha/2}$ increases and therefore sample size increases.
As confidence decreases, $Z_{\alpha/2}$ decreases and therefore sample size decreases.

As margin of error increases, sample size decreases.
As margin of error decreases, sample size increases.

When $\hat{p}$ is unknown, sample size increases because $\hat{p} = 0.50$.
When $\hat{p}$ is known from a previous study, sample size decreases.

As standard deviation increases, sample size increases.
As standard deviation decreases, sample size decreases.

Chapter 9 – Hypothesis Testing of One Population

In this chapter we turn our attention to another of the most important concepts in introductory statistics, hypothesis testing. We begin with a basic overview of the topic, and then we gradually introduce the formulas and diagrams, along with plenty of examples to keep you busy. The remaining chapters in these notes all build upon the concepts in this chapter, so be prepared! Further, in certain places we shall see that confidence intervals and hypothesis testing are two different approaches to getting equivalent answers to the research problem at hand.

Section 9.1 – The Basic Concepts of Hypothesis Testing

In Chapter 8 we made confidence intervals for the population proportion and mean. These intervals gave ranges of plausible values for the population parameters. In this chapter we instead focus on testing whether the population parameter is realistically equal to a specified value of interest, along with the probability that it can realistically be equal to this value.

Here is a general example. A factory that produces cookies claims that only 12% of the cookies contain traces of nuts. A quality control team suspects that the percentage is in fact higher. This means that the two competing statements are "The proportion of cookies with nuts is 0.12" and "The proportion of cookies with nuts is greater than 0.12." The question is, which statement is correct? The team would then collect a random sample of cookies and calculate the sample proportion of cookies with nut traces.

A test statistic is then calculated which determines how close to 0.12 the sample proportion is. This statistic leads to a probability of being able to observe such a sample proportion, or a more extreme one, if the factory's claim is true. The quality control team makes a conclusion as to which of the two statements is most likely correct. This example illustrates, in basic terms, how hypothesis testing works.

DEFINITION

A **hypothesis** (plural: **hypotheses**) is a conjecture or claim that has not yet been proven but is suspected to be true before evidence is gathered. Thus, **hypothesis testing** (also called **significance testing**) is the act of setting up a claim about a population proportion or mean, then studying a random sample to verify the truth of the claim.

ETYMOLOGY

The word **hypothesis** comes from the Greek ὑπό and θέσις, which meant "under" and "placing," so the two words combined meant "foundation."

Just like the previous chapter on confidence intervals, we will go through the general concepts of hypothesis testing, followed by detailed testing of population proportions, and lastly with detailed testing of population means. The five basic steps of hypothesis testing are as follows (we will cover each one in depth later, so don't worry if the names of the steps don't make sense right now). Note "Step 0" as well!

Step 0: Determine if the problem is a proportion or mean situation.
Step 1: Set up the hypotheses.
Step 2: Check the assumptions.
Step 3: Compute the test statistic.
Step 4: Compute the p-value.
Step 5: State the conclusion.

Step 0: Determine if the problem is a proportion or mean situation
As we will stress in this chapter, it is very important to first identify the problem as a proportion or a mean situation, just like we did for confidence intervals. You probably already guessed that although the general hypothesis testing process is the same for both scenarios, the formulas change, so you need to recognize whether we are working with proportions or means!

Step 1: Set up the hypotheses
In Stage 1, we set up a null hypothesis and an alternative hypothesis.

DEFINITION
A **null hypothesis** is a statement about a population parameter that needs to be tested. It is assumed to be true until evidence suggests otherwise. The null hypothesis is written as H_0 (pronounced "H-naught").

If we are studying a population proportion, we write the null hypothesis as

$$H_0 : p = p_0$$

If we are studying a population mean, we write the null hypothesis as

$$H_0 : \mu = \mu_0$$

The values p_0 and μ_0 (pronounced "p-naught" and "mu-naught") are values that are assumed to be correct, and they will be provided in the background of the problem. The null hypothesis (in this introductory class) is always written with an equals sign. (Caution: Some textbooks may write them with a $\leq$ or $\geq$ sign in certain contexts, but for simplicity we will not do that here.)

DEFINITION
An **alternative hypothesis** is a statement about a population parameter that you suspect is the true statement. It is a claim that is different from the null hypothesis and can be written one of three different ways. It claims that the population parameter is greater than, less than, or not equal to the assumed value from the null hypothesis. The alternative hypothesis is written as H_A (but some textbooks write it as H_1).

If we are studying a population proportion, we write the alternative hypothesis as one of the following, depending on context:

$$H_A : p > p_0 \qquad\qquad H_A : p < p_0 \qquad\qquad H_A : p \neq p_0$$

If we are studying a population mean, we write the alternative hypothesis as one of the following, depending on context:

$$H_A : \mu > \mu_0 \qquad\qquad H_A : \mu < \mu_0 \qquad\qquad H_A : \mu \neq \mu_0$$

If the alternative hypothesis has a greater than sign ($p > p_0$ or $\mu > \mu_0$), the hypothesis test is said to be a **right-tailed test**.

If the alternative hypothesis has a less than sign ($p < p_0$ or $\mu < \mu_0$), the hypothesis test is said to be a **left-tailed test**.

If the alternative hypothesis has a not equals sign ($p \neq p_0$ or $\mu \neq \mu_0$), the hypothesis test is said to be a **two-tailed test**.

EXAMPLE

Consider the earlier scenario presented. A factory that produces cookies claims that only 12% of the cookies contain traces of nuts. A quality control team suspects that the percentage is in fact higher. This means that the two competing statements are "The proportion of cookies with nuts is 0.12" and "The proportion of cookies with nuts is greater than 0.12."

This is a proportion problem because a cookie either has nut traces or does not. The proportion value of interest is 0.12, so when setting up the hypotheses, $p_0 = 0.12$. Since the null always has an equals sign, that means that $H_0: p = 0.12$.

As for the alternative, the claim is that the proportion of cookies with nut traces is higher than 0.12. In mathematical terms, that means that $p > 0.12$ if this turns out to be correct, so we write $H_A: p > 0.12$, making this a right-tailed test. Thus, the hypotheses are written together as

$$H_0: p = 0.12$$
$$H_A: p > 0.12$$

Δ

EXAMPLE

A radio station needs to play, on average, 6 songs between any two breaks to achieve a fair balance of music and adverts. The station manager thinks the actual average is different from 6.

This is a mean problem because the number of songs played between breaks is quantitative. Since 6 is the average number of interest, the null hypothesis is $H_0: \mu = 6$. It is believed that the actual average number of songs between breaks is different from 6. Since we do not specify how different (meaning it is unclear whether we think it is greater than or less than), we need to use the not equals sign, making this a two-tailed test, so we have $H_A: \mu \neq 6$. The hypotheses are

$$H_0: \mu = 6$$
$$H_A: \mu \neq 6$$

Δ

EXAMPLE

A gumball machine supposedly contains 20% red balls, but you suspect the actual proportion is smaller than this.

This is a proportion problem because a gumball either is red or is not red. The proportion value of interest is 0.20, so we have $H_0: p_0 = 0.20$. It is believed that the actual proportion of red gumballs is less than 0.20, which means that $p < 0.20$ if this turns out to be correct, making this a left-tailed test. Thus, the hypotheses are written together as

$$H_0: p = 0.20$$
$$H_A: p < 0.20$$

Δ

The following summary box recaps what we just talked about with the hypotheses.

REVIEW: SETTING UP THE HYPOTHESES

The hypotheses are written with population parameters (p and μ) and are concerned with specific values (p_0 and μ_0) that are given in the problem. The null hypothesis is always written with an equals sign:

$$H_0: p = p_0 \qquad\qquad H_0: \mu = \mu_0$$

The alternative hypothesis is always written with a greater than, less than, or not equal to sign depending on the context of the problem:

$H_A: p > p_0$	$H_A: \mu > \mu_0$	Right-tailed test
$H_A: p < p_0$	$H_A: \mu < \mu_0$	Left-tailed test
$H_A: p \neq p_0$	$H_A: \mu \neq \mu_0$	Two-tailed test

Look for context clues in the problem for which sign to choose. For instance, "you think the proportion is higher" or "you suspect the actual mean has increased" indicates a greater than sign, while "you want to see if the proportion has changed" or "you are testing whether the mean is different from a specified number" suggests a not equal to sign.

As we continue on our adventure through hypothesis testing, it is important to keep in mind that we assume the null hypothesis is true unless we encounter sufficient evidence to prove otherwise.

MNEMONIC

Think of hypothesis testing as like a court case. Just like the defendant is assumed to be not guilty unless evidence shows he/she is guilty, we assume the null hypothesis is the true statement unless our sample shows evidence supporting the alternative hypothesis instead.

The remaining examples in this chapter will give us plenty of practice setting up hypotheses, so we now give a brief overview of the remaining stages of hypothesis testing.

Step 2: Check the assumptions

In Chapter 7, we had a set of assumptions for using a valid sampling distribution of sample proportions and means. These same assumptions with slight adjustments carried over into Chapter 8 when we studied confidence intervals. In this chapter, we shall see the same assumptions, again with slight adjustments, come into play again for hypothesis testing to be valid. We delay stating what the assumptions are until further on.

Step 3: Compute the test statistic

Having set up the hypotheses and verified that the necessary assumptions are met, the next step is to compute a **test statistic** that is derived from the sample. The formula changes for proportion and mean problems, but the basic formula boils down to

$$\text{test statistic} = \frac{(\text{sample statistic}) - (\text{null value})}{\text{standard error}}$$

If this formula looks familiar, this is essentially an extension of the Z-score formula. The sample statistic is the sample proportion (or mean), and the null value is the number that is stated in the null hypothesis. The standard error changes formula depending whether we are studying a proportion or a mean. As a whole, the test statistic tells us how many standard errors above (or below) the assumed null value our sample statistic falls if the null hypothesis is correct.

Step 4: Compute the _p_-value

Armed with a test statistic from our sample, the next step is to find the probability that we realistically could have observed such a sample statistic, or a more extreme one, if the null hypothesis is correct. We find this probability using the normal distribution or the _T_-distribution, depending whether we are working with a proportion or mean scenario. This probability is called a **_p_-value**, and the method of computing it depends on the chosen symbol for the alternative hypothesis. We will explore these methods later in this chapter.

It is important to remember that a _p_-value is a probability, so it is between 0 and 1. The closer it is to 0, the less likely we could have observed the sample statistic we obtained (or a more extreme one). The answer for the _p_-value drives Step 5, which is where we make our conclusion.

Again, the _p_-value can be thought of as the probability of observing the sample proportion (or mean), or a more extreme one, if the null hypothesis is in fact correct.

Step 5: State the conclusion

Remember, we conduct hypothesis testing assuming the null hypothesis is correct. In the end, we will make one of two possible conclusions:

1) There is insufficient evidence that the null hypothesis is incorrect.
2) There is sufficient evidence that the null hypothesis is incorrect.

The question is, which one do we choose and why? It all depends on the _p_-value from Step 4. The logic is that if the _p_-value is not too small (above a predetermined value), then there is a reasonable chance the null hypothesis is in fact correct. In other words, we have not provided enough evidence against it.

On the other hand, if the _p_-value is too small (reasonably close to 0), then either we have observed an extremely unusual sample statistic, or the null hypothesis is probably not correct after all. In other words, we have strong evidence against it.

What happens here is that we have a predetermined threshold value (called the **significance level**). If the _p_-value is above this threshold, we do not have enough evidence against the null hypothesis. If the _p_-value is below this threshold, we have strong evidence against the null hypothesis.

You have been presented with some new definitions here, so let's define them officially.

DEFINITION

A **test statistic** indicates how many standard errors above (or below) the assumed null value the sample statistic falls if the null hypothesis is correct. The basic formula is

$$\text{test statistic} = \frac{(\text{sample statistic}) - (\text{null value})}{\text{standard error}}$$

A **_p_-value** is the probability of being able to observe the sample proportion (or mean), or a more extreme one, if the null hypothesis is in fact correct. The exact way to compute it depends on what symbol is chosen for the alternative hypothesis, as well as whether the problem is a proportion or mean situation.

A **significance level** is a predetermined threshold value to which we compare the _p_-value. If the _p_-value is above this threshold, we do not have enough evidence against the null hypothesis. If the _p_-value is below this threshold, we have strong evidence against the null hypothesis.

NOTATION

The significance level is denoted by the Greek letter α. The choice of significance level is to some extent subjective, depending on the nature of the study. In statistics, the most common threshold of choice is $\alpha = 0.05$, in which case we would have strong evidence against the null hypothesis if the p-value is below 0.05. However, you might sometimes see other small numbers such as $\alpha = 0.01$ or $\alpha = 0.10$ (usually no higher than that).

In case you were wondering, the α is indeed connected to the same α we used for confidence intervals, and we shall explore that later in this chapter.

We also have to define the correct choice of words for stating a conclusion.

NOTATION

If the p-value is below the significance level (p-value $< \alpha$), then…

    1) We reject the null hypothesis.
    2) There is sufficient evidence against the null hypothesis.
    3) There is sufficient evidence for the alternative hypothesis.

If the p-value is above the significance level (p-value $> \alpha$), then…

    1) We fail to reject the null hypothesis.
    2) There is insufficient evidence against the null hypothesis.
    3) There is insufficient evidence for the alternative hypothesis.

Caution: Despite what you might see in occasional sources, it is incorrect to say "accept the null hypothesis." We can only fail to reject it!

MNEMONIC

If the p-value is below the significance level (p-value $< \alpha$), then you reject the null hypothesis. To remember this, imagine you go on a date with someone. If your date turns out to be below your standards, you reject them!

Without computing anything yet, let's look at some examples of what we have covered.

EXAMPLE

Going back to the cookie example, a factory that produces cookies claims that only 12% of the cookies contain traces of nuts. A quality control team suspects that the percentage is in fact higher. We already determined the null and alternative hypotheses:

$$H_0: p = 0.12$$
$$H_A: p > 0.12$$

In one sample of cookies, suppose we discover that $\hat{p} = 0.14$. It is true that $\hat{p} = 0.14$ is larger than $p_0 = 0.12$ (higher by 2 percentage points), but one could argue that 0.14 is "reasonably close" to 0.12 that it probably is not a concern. (We have to allow for some natural variation to occur.) Suppose this results in a test statistic of 0.81 and a p-value of 0.20897. As we shall see in the next section, the following graph (of the normal distribution) shows the test statistic of 0.81, and the probability above 0.81 is equal to the p-value (which is 0.20897).

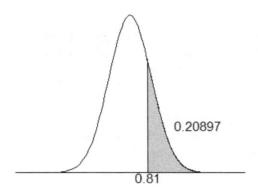

To interpret these numbers, the sample proportion $\hat{p} = 0.14$ is 0.81 standard errors above the assumed null value $p_0 = 0.12$ (above because the test statistic is positive). The p-value is 0.20897, so the probability of observing a sample proportion of 0.14 or higher, if the population proportion really were 0.12, is equal to 0.20897.

Next, comparing the p-value to a significance of $\alpha = 0.05$, the p-value is greater than 0.05. As a result, we fail to reject the null hypothesis, and there is insufficient evidence that the proportion of cookies containing traces of nuts is greater than 0.12. (Again, we do not accept the null hypothesis; we only fail to reject it.)

Now let's change the numbers to further illustrate how the testing works. Suppose in a new sample, we compute $\hat{p} = 0.30$. This time 0.30 is a lot higher than 0.12, so already this likely casts some doubt on the null hypothesis. Suppose the test statistic is now 2.4 with a corresponding p-value of 0.00820. The following graph shows the test statistic of 2.4, and the probability above 2.4 is equal to the p-value (which is 0.00820). Notice that the test statistic is further away from the middle of the graph, which results in a smaller p-value.

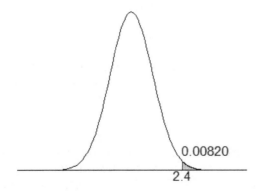

Interpreting these numbers, the sample proportion $\hat{p} = 0.30$ is 2.4 standard errors above the assumed null value $p_0 = 0.12$. The p-value is 0.00820, so the probability of being able to observe a sample proportion of 0.30 or higher, if the population proportion really were 0.12, is equal to a mere 0.00820.

This time the p-value is less than 0.05. As a result, we reject the null hypothesis, and there is strong evidence that the proportion of cookies containing traces of nuts is greater than 0.12.

Δ

EXAMPLE

A teashop is supposed to pour, on average, 16 fluid ounces of tea per cup to customers. The owner of the teashop suspects the staff members are distributing less tea, so he randomly samples 40 served cups and measures the amount of tea per cup, obtaining $\overline{x} = 15.8$. Given a test statistic of -0.57 and a corresponding p-value of 0.28597, interpret the results and state the conclusion using the 0.05 significance level.

Solution: First, notice that this is a mean problem because the quantity of interest is the average amount of tea, in fluid ounces. It is of interest to see whether the average is less than 16, so this is a left-tailed test, and the hypotheses are

$$H_0: \mu = 16$$
$$H_A: \mu < 16$$

The test statistic of -0.57 indicates that the sample mean of 15.8 fluid ounces lies 0.57 standard errors below the assumed null population mean of 16 fluid ounces (below because the test statistic is negative). The p-value is 0.28597, so the probability of observing a sample mean of 15.8 or lower, if the population mean really were 16, is equal to 0.28597. The following graph represents what the p-value looks like graphically.

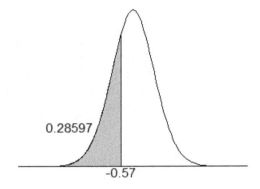

Next, comparing the p-value to a significance of $\alpha = 0.05$, the p-value is greater than 0.05. As a result, we fail to reject the null hypothesis, and there is insufficient evidence that the mean amount of tea given per customer is less than 16 fluid ounces.

Δ

You will notice a couple of important differences with this example and the preceding one. First, the graph of the p-value above involves the area to the left of the test statistic, whereas in the previous example we shaded to the right of the test statistic. This is because the tea example is a left-tailed test, and the cookie example is a right-tailed test, so we shade the area in the corresponding direction of the graph. That is, we shade to the right of the test statistic for a right-tailed test, and for a left-tailed test, we shade to the left of the test statistic.

Second, notice how we interpreted the p-value. For the cookie example, we said it was the probability of observing a sample proportion of 0.14 or larger. This was a right-tailed test, and so we concentrated on the area to the right of the test statistic, and consequently to the right of $\hat{p} = 0.14$. However, for the tea example, we said the p-value was the probability of observing a sample mean of 15.8 or smaller. This was a left-tailed test, so we instead looked at the area to the left of the test statistic, and consequently to the left of $\overline{x} = 15.8$. It is very important to realize which direction we are looking at!

A natural next question to ask is how do we handle a two-tailed test. We will address that in the next section, and we will also finally introduce the mathematical steps of hypothesis testing. For now, we conclude this section with a couple of extra pointers.

First, the hypotheses are written with population parameters p or μ. They are never written with sample statistics $\hat{p}$ or $\bar{x}$. This is because we do not know what the population parameters are, so we are trying to make inference about them. For instance, if you see hypotheses such as $H_A: \hat{p} > 0.12$ or $H_A: \bar{x} < 16$, they are definitely incorrect.

Second, we must state our hypotheses **before** we look at the data, not after. We set up the hypotheses based on an expectation we have going into the experiment, so if we instead look at the data first, we have biased our expectations. For example, in the tea example, suppose we first got our sample average of $\bar{x} = 15.8$ and then chosen some hypotheses. We could deliberately fix them so that the null hypothesis would definitely be rejected since we have "peeked" at the data in advance. This is a no-no – I like to think of this situation as like opening a Christmas present early since then you know what you are receiving!

Section 9.2 – Hypothesis Testing of a Proportion

Now that we have covered the general steps of hypothesis testing, the next step is to see them play out in detail. We start with hypothesis testing of proportions, and along the way we will discuss specific details that might not be obvious at first. Testing for means is delayed until Section 9.3. We now state the hypothesis testing steps for proportions, and then we will delve into some illustrative examples.

First, to verify that the problem really is a proportion problem, look for context clues such as what proportion/percentage is of interest, or a situation where a characteristic is true or is not. Here are the five steps to follow.

Step 1: Set up the hypotheses.
After determining p_0, the assumed population proportion, as well as what kind of alternative test to use, the null hypothesis is

$$H_0: p = p_0$$

The alternative hypothesis is one of the following:

$$
\begin{array}{ll}
H_A: p > p_0 & \text{(right-tailed test)} \\
H_A: p < p_0 & \text{(left-tailed test)} \\
H_A: p \neq p_0 & \text{(two-tailed test)}
\end{array}
$$

Step 2: Check the assumptions.
For the hypothesis test to be valid, four assumptions need to be true, assuming a sample size n:

1) The data must be categorical (meaning a characteristic is either true or is not).
2) The subjects must be randomly selected.
3) $np_0 \geq 15$.
4) $n(1 - p_0) \geq 15$

These assumptions should look familiar by now. When we studied sampling distributions, we used the population proportion p, which was told to us. For confidence intervals, we used $\hat{p}$ as a substitute since the population proportion was unknown. It is still unknown for hypothesis testing, except now we use the null value of p_0 (from the null hypothesis). The reason is because we are assuming the null hypothesis is correct to conduct the test. It would be incorrect to use the sample proportion here for that reason.

Step 3: Compute the test statistic.

Recall that the general test statistic formula is

$$\text{test statistic} = \frac{(\text{sample statistic}) - (\text{null value})}{\text{standard error}}$$

For a hypothesis test of proportions, the formula becomes

$$Z = \frac{\hat{p} - p_0}{\sqrt{\frac{p_0(1 - p_0)}{n}}}$$

Stated a simpler way, we can write

$$Z = \frac{\hat{p} - p_0}{\text{standard error}} \quad \text{where} \quad \text{standard error} = \sqrt{\frac{p_0(1 - p_0)}{n}}$$

Notice the test statistic is called a Z-statistic because we are dealing with proportions. Again, we now use p_0 in the standard error formula because the null hypothesis is assumed to be true during the hypothesis test.

Step 4: Compute the p-value.

Since we have a Z-statistic, we must use the standard normal distribution to find the p-value (which, remember, is just a probability, so we compute it just like we did in Chapter 6). The question is, exactly how do we find the p-value? The answer depends on which symbol we chose for the alternative hypothesis. For a right-tailed test, we find the probability to the right of Z, as in the following graph.

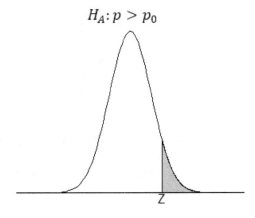

$$H_A: p > p_0$$

For a left-tailed test, we find the probability to the left of Z.

$$H_A: p < p_0$$

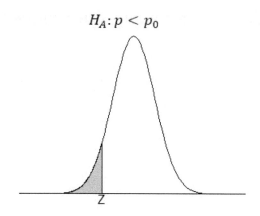

For a two-tailed test, we first plot Z and $-Z$ on the standard normal distribution. We then find the probability to the right of Z and add it to the probability to the left of $-Z$. Of course, these two probabilities are the same because the normal distribution is symmetric, so it suffices to find the right-tailed probability and double it.

$$H_A: p \neq p_0$$

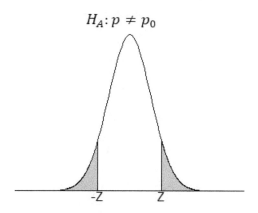

Step 5: State the conclusion.
Finally, we compare the p-value to a predetermined significance level α. If the p-value is below the significance level (p-value $< \alpha$), then…

1) We reject the null hypothesis.
2) There is sufficient evidence against the null hypothesis.
3) There is sufficient evidence for the alternative hypothesis.

If the p-value is above the significance level (p-value $> \alpha$), then…

1) We fail to reject the null hypothesis.
2) There is insufficient evidence against the null hypothesis.
3) There is insufficient evidence for the alternative hypothesis.

REVIEW: HYPOTHESIS TESTING FOR A POPULATION PROPORTION

Step 1: Set up the hypotheses.

$$H_0: p = p_0$$
$$H_A: p > p_0 \quad \text{or} \quad H_A: p < p_0 \quad \text{or} \quad H_A: p \neq p_0$$

Step 2: Check the assumptions.

1) Categorical data
2) Random sample
3) $np_0 \geq 15$
4) $n(1 - p_0) \geq 15$

Step 3: Compute the test statistic.

$$Z = \frac{\hat{p} - p_0}{\text{standard error}} \quad \text{where} \quad \text{standard error} = \sqrt{\frac{p_0(1 - p_0)}{n}}$$

Step 4: Compute the p-value.

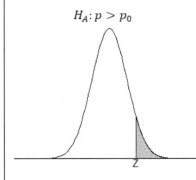
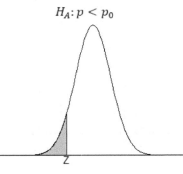
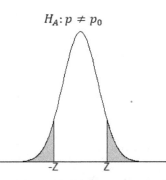

Step 5: State the conclusion.

If the p-value is below the significance level (p-value $< \alpha$), then …
  1) We reject the null hypothesis.
  2) There is sufficient evidence against the null hypothesis.
  3) There is sufficient evidence for the alternative hypothesis.

If the p-value is above the significance level (p-value $> \alpha$), then…
  1) We fail to reject the null hypothesis.
  2) There is insufficient evidence against the null hypothesis.
  3) There is insufficient evidence for the alternative hypothesis.

The following sketch might be helpful as it illustrates the concept of when to reject the null hypothesis for two different choices of α.

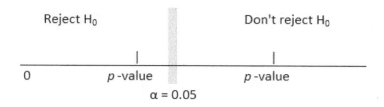

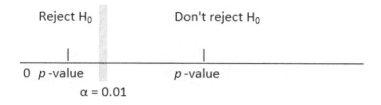

I do believe some examples are in order!

EXAMPLE
Your friend Claire Voyant claims to be psychic. To test her claim, you randomly draw a card from a shuffled standard deck of cards, have Claire guess the suit of the card, then you replace the card in the deck, shuffle, and repeat this process. You note that she guesses the suit correctly in 22 out of 80 draws. If Claire Voyant were guessing at random, then she should be correct approximately 25% of the time. Test at the 0.05 significance level to see if she really could be psychic; that is, if the percentage of correct guesses is significantly greater than 25%.

Solution: This is a proportion scenario because a guess is either correct or is not. The hypotheses are

$$H_0: p = 0.25$$
$$H_A: p > 0.25$$

For the assumptions, each card draw is random since the deck was shuffled each time. Noting that $n = 80$ and $p_0 = 0.25$ (the null value), we check the assumptions:

$$np_0 = 80 \times 0.25 = 20 \geq 15$$
$$n(1 - p_0) = 80 \times (1 - 0.25) = 60 \geq 15$$

The assumptions are met, so we may proceed with the test statistic. It might be easier to find the sample proportion and standard error first:

$$\hat{p} = \frac{22}{80} = 0.275$$

$$\text{standard error} = \sqrt{\frac{p_0(1 - p_0)}{n}} = \sqrt{\frac{0.25(1 - 0.25)}{80}} = \sqrt{0.00234375} = 0.0484122918$$

The Z-statistic is

$$Z = \frac{\hat{p} - p_0}{\text{standard error}} = \frac{0.275 - 0.25}{0.0484122918} = 0.51640$$

To find the p-value, noting that this is a right-tailed test, we plot $Z = 0.51640$ on the standard normal distribution and find the probability to the right.

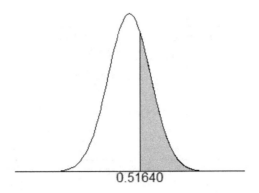

0.51640

The lower limit is 0.51640 and the upper limit is 999999, so the p-value is

$$normalcdf(0.51640, 999999) = 0.30279$$

The p-value says that if the null hypothesis were true (if Claire were indeed guessing at random), then the probability of getting a sample proportion of 0.275 or higher of correct guesses is 0.30279. Noting that the p-value is above 0.05, we do not reject the null hypothesis. There is no strong evidence that Claire's proportion of correct guesses is greater than 0.25. Put another way, we have insufficient evidence that Claire Voyant lives up to her name!

Δ

EXAMPLE
Suppose a credit card company says that 60% of college students carry a credit card balance from month to month. You want to test whether the percentage is different from 60% at the 0.01 significance level. In a random sample of 400 college students, 268 of them carry a balance each month. Perform the hypothesis testing steps.

Solution: This is a proportion problem because a student either carries a credit card balance or does not. The proportion of interest is 0.60, and so

$$H_0: p = 0.60$$
$$H_A: p \neq 0.60$$

We use the not equals sign because we are testing for a difference from 0.60, not specifically for greater than or less than. Testing for a difference allows for the possibility that the population proportion could be greater than 0.60 or less than 0.60.

Next, noting that the data are categorical and randomly selected, $n = 400$ and $p_0 = 0.60$, so we check the other two assumptions:

$$np_0 = 400 \times 0.60 = 240 \geq 15$$
$$n(1 - p_0) = 400 \times (1 - 0.60) = 160 \geq 15$$

The assumptions are met, so we now compute the test statistic.

$$\hat{p} = \frac{268}{400} = 0.67$$

$$\text{standard error} = \sqrt{\frac{p_0(1 - p_0)}{n}} = \sqrt{\frac{0.60(1 - 0.60)}{400}} = \sqrt{0.0006} = 0.0244948974$$

The Z-statistic is

$$Z = \frac{\hat{p} - p_0}{\text{standard error}} = \frac{0.67 - 0.60}{0.0244948974} = 2.85774$$

To find the p-value, noting that this is a two-tailed test, we plot $Z = 2.85774$ on the standard normal distribution, but we also plot $-Z$, which is -2.85774. We then find the probability below -2.85774 and the probability above 2.85774 and add them, but it suffices to find the probability above 2.85774 and double it.

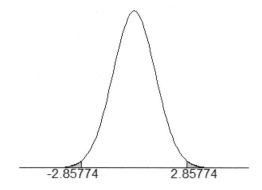

The lower limit is 2.85774 and the upper limit is 999999, so the p-value (doubled) is

$$2 \times normalcdf(2.85774, 999999) = 0.00427$$

The p-value says that if the null hypothesis were true (if the population proportion of college students carrying a balance were 0.60), then the probability of getting a sample proportion of 0.67 or more extreme is only 0.00427. This time the p-value is below 0.01, so we reject the null hypothesis. There is strong evidence that the true proportion of college students who carry a credit card balance is different from 0.60. (The reason we said "a sample proportion of 0.67 or more extreme" is because of the two-tailed test. "More extreme" means further away from the assumed null value but on either side.)

Δ

EXAMPLE
In the previous example, what would our conclusion be if we were instead testing whether the percentage is greater than 60%? What about testing whether the percentage is less than 60%?

Solution: The previous problem involved a two-tailed test, and now we want to repeat it but using a right-tailed and later a left-tailed test. Here are the hypotheses for a right-tailed test.

$$H_0: p = 0.60$$
$$H_A: p > 0.60$$

The test statistic $Z = 2.85774$ is the same regardless of which alternative hypothesis we use. The only thing that changes is the manner in which we find the p-value, and consequently the p-value itself. We find the probability to the right of 2.85774:

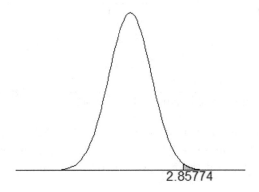

The lower limit is 2.85774 and the upper limit is 999999, so the p-value is

$$normalcdf(2.85774, 999999) = 0.00213$$

Using the same significance level of 0.01 as before, the p-value is below 0.01, so we still reject the null. Now we say that there is strong evidence that the proportion of college students carrying a credit card balance is greater than 0.60.

Now let's repeat the process for a left-tailed test.

$$H_0: p = 0.60$$
$$H_A: p < 0.60$$

This time we find the probability to the left of 2.85774:

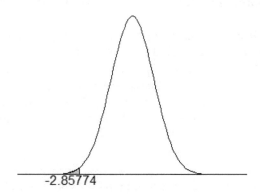

The lower limit is -999999 and the upper limit is 2.85774, so the p-value is

$$normalcdf(-999999, 2.85774) = 0.99787$$

Using the same significance level of 0.01 as before, the p-value is above 0.01 (well above!), so we fail to reject the null hypothesis. There is insufficient evidence that the proportion of college students carrying a credit card balance is less than 0.60.

Δ

The previous example illustrates an important connection among right-tailed, left-tailed, and two-tailed p-values. Notice that the left-tailed and right-tailed p-values added to 1 ($0.99787 + 0.00213 = 1$), and that the two-tailed probability was double the right-tailed p-value. You can see these observations by looking at the preceding normal sketches.

Actually, in general the two-tailed p-value is double the smaller of the left-tailed and right-tailed p-values. Remember, a p-value must be between 0 and 1, so if you double the incorrect side, you will get an answer greater than 1, which means you definitely made a mistake!

REVIEW: LINK WITH RIGHT-, LEFT-, AND TWO-TAILED *P*-VALUES

For a specific hypothesis testing situation, if you compute one of the three possible p-values (right-tailed, left-tailed, and two-tailed), you can mathematically derive the other two using these formulas:

$$\text{Left} + \text{Right} = 1$$
$$\text{Two} = 2 \times \min(\text{Left}, \text{Right})$$

We have done the last few examples by hand, using the provided formulas. I wanted to ensure that you feel comfortable with the process of computing these problems by hand so that you understand what is going on behind the scenes. If you simply take the numbers and dump them into a calculator or computer, it is harder to learn why you are doing what you are doing. However, now that we have practiced a bit, it is time to learn how to use the TI-84.

TI-84 COMMAND: HYPOTHESIS TESTING FOR A PROPORTION

To conduct a hypothesis test for a proportion, press $\boxed{\text{STAT}}$, scroll right to TESTS, and select Option 5: $1 - PropZTest$. On the next screen, type the null hypothesis value (p_0), the number of successes (x), the sample size (n), and the appropriate symbol for the alternative hypothesis ($\neq p_0, < p_0, > p_0$). Choose Calculate, and the resulting output shows the following:

The alternative hypothesis selected.
The Z-statistic.
The p-value (denoted as p, but don't confuse this with the population proportion).
The sample proportion $\hat{p}$.
The sample size n.

EXAMPLE

In the previous example about credit card balances, we had a sample of 400 college students, 268 of whom carried a balance. We tested whether the population proportion of all college students carrying a balance was greater than, less than, or not equal to 0.60. Let's run the test again on the TI-84, starting with the two-tailed test.

Using the $1 - PropZTest$ option, we enter 0.60 for p_0, 268 for number of successes, 400 for sample size, and $\neq$ for the symbol. The resulting screen tells us the following:

$$Z = 2.857738033$$
$$p = 0.0042668541$$
$$\hat{p} = 0.67$$

The Z-statistic and sample proportion match what we computed earlier. The two-tailed p-value of 0.00427 also matches the one from earlier. Going back to the same command, we now change the $\neq$ to $<$

for a left-tailed test:

$$Z = 2.857738033$$
$$p = 0.997866573$$
$$\hat{p} = 0.67$$

The Z-statistic and sample proportion stay the same since it is the same sample. The only thing that changes is the p-value. Repeating this exercise one more time but changing the alternative symbol to $>$ results in the following output for a right-tailed test, once again matching our result:

$$Z = 2.857738033$$
$$p = 0.002133427$$
$$\hat{p} = 0.67$$

Δ

Section 9.3 – Hypothesis Testing of a Mean

The next step in our journey to the center of hypothesis testing is to cover the same procedure for a means scenario. We will find that the steps are the same as for proportions; although the notation and formulas change somewhat, the overall concept is still the same, and so is the way we interpret the results.

First, to verify that the problem really is a mean problem, look for context clues such as quantitative data, or a number or average of interest. Here are the five steps to follow.

Step 1: Set up the hypotheses.
After determining μ_0, the assumed population mean, as well as what kind of alternative test to use, the null hypothesis is

$$H_0: \mu = \mu_0$$

The alternative hypothesis is one of the following:

$$H_A: \mu > \mu_0 \quad \text{(right-tailed test)}$$
$$H_A: \mu < \mu_0 \quad \text{(left-tailed test)}$$
$$H_A: \mu \neq \mu_0 \quad \text{(two-tailed test)}$$

Step 2: Check the assumptions.
For the hypothesis test to be valid, three assumptions need to be true, assuming a sample size n:

1) The data must be quantitative (meaning they are numbers that can be averaged).
2) The subjects must be randomly selected.
3) At least one of the following statements must be true:
    a. The population is normal.
    b. $n > 30$.

These assumptions should look familiar by now, just like the ones from proportions. We require the sample average to be approximately normal, and that occurs if the population is normal and/or if the sample size is large enough (by the Central Limit Theorem).

Step 3: Compute the test statistic.
Recall that the general test statistic formula is

$$\text{test statistic} = \frac{(\text{sample statistic}) - (\text{null value})}{\text{standard error}}$$

For a hypothesis test of means, the formula becomes

$$T = \frac{\overline{x} - \mu_0}{\frac{s}{\sqrt{n}}}$$

Stated a simpler way, we can write

$$T = \frac{\overline{x} - \mu_0}{\text{standard error}} \quad \text{where} \quad \text{standard error} = \frac{s}{\sqrt{n}}$$

Notice the test statistic is now called a T-statistic because we are dealing with a mean. Recall from Chapter 8 that we use Z for proportions and T for means (and remember the nice mnemonic I gave you for that too!), and this idea extends to hypothesis testing as well.

Step 4: Compute the p-value.
Since we have a T-statistic, we must use the T-distribution to find the p-value. This will work just like the standard normal distribution in terms of shading directions, only now it is on the T-distribution. That means that we must specify degrees of freedom, and just like in Chapter 8, $DF = n - 1$. Other than those adjustments, we use the same logic to find the p-value. For a right-tailed test, we find the probability to the right of T, as in the following graph.

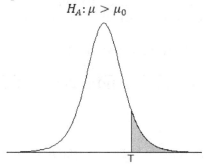

For a left-tailed test, we find the probability to the left of T.

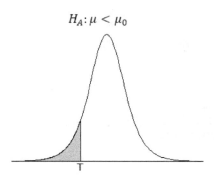

For a two-tailed test, we first plot T and $-T$ on the T-distribution. We then find the probability to the right of T and add it to the probability to the left of $-T$. As before, these two probabilities are the same because the T-distribution is symmetric, so it suffices to find the right-tailed probability and double it.

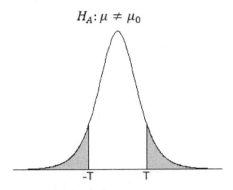

$$H_A: \mu \neq \mu_0$$

Step 5: State the conclusion.
Finally, we compare the p-value to a predetermined significance level α. If the p-value is below the significance level (p-value $< \alpha$), then...

1) We reject the null hypothesis.
2) There is sufficient evidence against the null hypothesis.
3) There is sufficient evidence for the alternative hypothesis.

If the p-value is above the significance level (p-value $> \alpha$), then...

1) We fail to reject the null hypothesis.
2) There is insufficient evidence against the null hypothesis.
3) There is insufficient evidence for the alternative hypothesis.

The following box recaps the steps for hypothesis testing of a mean.

REVIEW: HYPOTHESIS TESTING FOR A POPULATION MEAN
Step 1: Set up the hypotheses.

$$H_0: \mu = \mu_0$$
$$H_A: \mu > \mu_0 \quad \text{or} \quad H_A: \mu < \mu_0 \quad \text{or} \quad H_A: \mu \neq \mu_0$$

Step 2: Check the assumptions.

1) Quantitative data
2) Random sample
3) Normal population or $n > 30$

Step 3: Compute the test statistic.

$$T = \frac{\bar{x} - \mu_0}{\text{standard error}} \quad \text{where} \quad \text{standard error} = \frac{s}{\sqrt{n}}$$

Step 4: Compute the p-value.

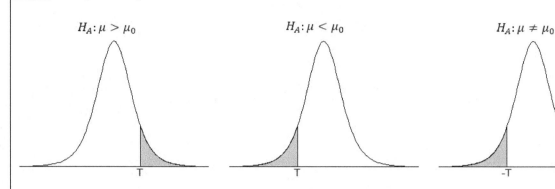

Step 5: State the conclusion.

If the p-value is below the significance level (p-value $< \alpha$), then …
      1) We reject the null hypothesis.
      2) There is sufficient evidence against the null hypothesis.
      3) There is sufficient evidence for the alternative hypothesis.

If the p-value is above the significance level (p-value $> \alpha$), then…
      1) We fail to reject the null hypothesis.
      2) There is insufficient evidence against the null hypothesis.
      3) There is insufficient evidence for the alternative hypothesis.

And now…for some examples!

EXAMPLE
You are interested to see if the average age at which a person has their first kiss is less than 15. You take the following random sample of people who state how old they were when they experienced their first kiss. The data are the following:

$$15, 14, 16, 13, 16, 16, 19, 15, 14, 16, 9, 15, 13, 6, 14, 10, 14, 10, 15, 12$$

Assuming that the mean age for a first kiss is normally distributed, conduct an appropriate hypothesis test at the $\alpha = 0.05$ significance level. What happens if we instead use the $\alpha = 0.01$ significance level?

Solution: This is a mean scenario because the data are quantitative. Noting that we want to see if the average is less than 15, the hypotheses are

$$H_0: \mu = 15$$
$$H_A: \mu < 15$$

For the assumptions, the sample was random, and the population is assumed to be normal. To proceed, we need to know the sample mean, standard deviation, and size, none of which are told to us. But no need to fear – the calculator is here! We can type all the numbers into a list on the TI-84 and do the summary stats option from Chapter 2. Also, we can simply count the number of responses to see that there are $n = 20$ subjects. Using the calculator, we discover that

$$\overline{x} = 13.6$$
$$s = 2.980639281$$
$$n = 20$$

The standard error is

$$\text{standard error} = \frac{s}{\sqrt{n}} = \frac{2.980639281}{\sqrt{20}} = 0.6664912049$$

The T-statistic is

$$T = \frac{\overline{x} - \mu_0}{\text{standard error}} = \frac{13.6 - 15}{0.6664912049} = -2.10055$$

To find the p-value, noting that this is a left-tailed test, we plot $T = -2.10055$ on the T-distribution with 19 degrees of freedom (because $DF = 20 - 1 = 19$) and find the probability to the left.

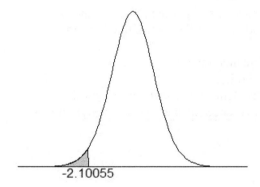

-2.10055

The lower limit is -999999 and the upper limit is -2.10055, so the p-value is

$$tcdf(-999999, -2.10055, 19) = 0.02463$$

The p-value says that if the null hypothesis were true (if the population mean age of a first kiss were 15), then the probability of getting a sample mean of 13.6 or lower is 0.02463. Noting that the p-value is below 0.05, we reject the null hypothesis. At the $\alpha = 0.05$ level, there is significant evidence that the mean age at which a first kiss is experienced is less than 15.

Now what happens had we used a significance level of 0.01 instead? This time, note that the p-value is greater than 0.01. So at that significance level, we don't reject the null hypothesis, and there would be insufficient evidence that the mean age is less than 15.

Δ

This previous example illustrates that the outcome of a hypothesis test depends on the choice of significance level α. Remember that $\alpha = 0.05$ is the most common choice used in statistical and scientific research, but it is not uncommon to see other similar small numbers. The significance level has to be a small number (usually the largest you will ever see is $\alpha = 0.10$).

Rejection of the null hypothesis occurs if the p-value is smaller than α. Thus, it follows that if α is smaller, it becomes harder to reject the null hypothesis since the p-value must be a lot smaller for this to happen. We say that a smaller significance level is more conservative (for instance, $\alpha = 0.01$ is a more conservative significance level than $\alpha = 0.05$) because rejection at a smaller level means there is stronger evidence for the alternative hypothesis.

Let's say we have a p-value of 0.005. This number is smaller than the significance level 0.05, but it is also smaller than 0.01. For that reason, the corresponding hypothesis test gives a stronger and more "impressive" result using $\alpha = 0.01$. Now let's say in another hypothesis test, we get a p-value of 0.045. Both this number and 0.005 are smaller than $\alpha = 0.05$, so we would reject them both at the 0.05 significance. However, the test with the p-value of 0.005 produces a stronger result since it is smaller and therefore more significant.

The moral here is that the smaller the p-value, the more significant it is. If we simply declare "p-value less than 0.05" each time without reporting the p-value, we lose the important information of how significant is the significant result.

EXAMPLE
Suppose in a hypothesis test, we know the null hypothesis was rejected at the $\alpha = 0.02$ significance level. Would it also be rejected at the $\alpha = 0.05$ and $\alpha = 0.01$ scenarios? Why or why not?

Solution: If the null hypothesis is rejected at the $\alpha = 0.02$ level, it means that whatever the p-value is, it must be less than 0.02. That means it is also less than 0.05, so we would also reject the null hypothesis at the $\alpha = 0.05$ significance level.

How about at $\alpha = 0.01$? We would reject the null hypothesis in that case if the p-value were less than 0.01. However, all we know is that it is less than 0.02. Maybe it is greater than 0.01 (such as a p-value of 0.012), or perhaps it is less (such as a p-value of 0.008). The point is that we cannot answer the question definitively. The null hypothesis may or may not be rejected at the $\alpha = 0.01$ level.

Δ

EXAMPLE
Suppose in a certain state, the average number of students graduating high school in a given year used to be 210 per school. You care to see if that number has changed. A random sample of 45 schools reveals a mean of 215.3 students and a standard deviation of 18.2 students in the sample. Conduct the hypothesis test at the 0.05 significance level.

Solution: We want to see if the population mean number of students graduating per high school has changed from 210. Due to this choice of words (no reference to "greater" or "less"), we do a two-tailed test. This is a mean question because it concerns the average number of students. The hypotheses are

$$H_0: \mu = 210$$
$$H_A: \mu \neq 210$$

For the assumptions, the sample was random, and the sample size is larger than 30, so we can move forward. Labeling the numbers given, we have $\overline{x} = 215.2$, $s = 18.2$, and $n = 45$, so

$$\text{standard error} = \frac{s}{\sqrt{n}} = \frac{18.2}{\sqrt{45}} = 2.713095813$$

The T-statistic is

$$T = \frac{\overline{x} - \mu_0}{\text{standard error}} = \frac{215.3 - 210}{2.713095813} = 1.95349$$

To find the p-value, noting that this is a two-tailed test, we plot $T = 1.95349$ on the T-distribution with 44 degrees of freedom (because $DF = 45 - 1 = 44$), but we also plot $-T$, which is -1.95349. We then find the probability below -1.95349 and the probability above 1.95349 and add them, but it suffices to find the probability above 1.95349 and double it.

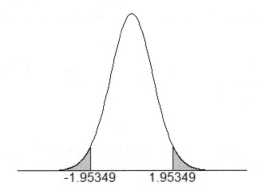

The lower limit is 1.95349 and the upper limit is 999999, so the p-value (doubled) is

$$2 \times tcdf(1.95349, 999999, 44) = 0.05714$$

The p-value says that if the null hypothesis were true (if the population mean number of students graduating from a high school per year were 210), then the probability of getting a sample mean of 215.3 (or a more extreme result) is 0.05714. Noting that the p-value is above 0.05, we fail to reject the null hypothesis. At the $\alpha = 0.05$ level, there is insufficient evidence that the mean number of students graduating per high school per year has changed from 210.

Δ

Let's now see how the TI-84 can help us.

TI-84 COMMAND: HYPOTHESIS TESTING FOR A MEAN

To conduct a hypothesis test for a mean, press $\boxed{\text{STAT}}$, scroll right to TESTS, and select Option 2: $T - Test$. For input, if your data are already stored in a list (say L_1), select Data, but if you instead have the sample mean, standard deviation, and size, select Stats.

If you chose Data, type the null hypothesis value (μ_0) and your list name (in our example, L_1). If you chose Stats, type the null hypothesis value, the sample mean ($\overline{x}$), the sample standard deviation (s), and the sample size (n). After these necessary inputs, select the appropriate symbol for the alternative hypothesis ($\neq \mu_0, < \mu_0, > \mu_0$). Choose Calculate, and the resulting output shows the following:

The alternative hypothesis selected.
The T-statistic.
The p-value (denoted as p).
The sample mean $\overline{x}$.
The sample standard deviation s.
The sample size n.

EXAMPLE

Going back to the first kiss example, let's try analyzing that problem but now using the TI-84. We wanted to see if the average age is less than 15. The data are the following:

$$15, 14, 16, 13, 16, 16, 19, 15, 14, 16, 9, 15, 13, 6, 14, 10, 14, 10, 15, 12$$

Type these numbers into a list (recall that to do this, press $\boxed{\text{STAT}}$, choose Option 1: $Edit$ ..., and type the twenty numbers into the L_1 column. Exit, then go to the Option 2: $T - Test$ to select your hypothesis testing. Select Data, a null mean of 15, the list L_1, and the alternative hypothesis $< \mu_0$. Choose Calculate, and you will see the following output:

$$t = -2.10055285$$
$$p = 0.0246302133$$
$$\bar{x} = 13.6$$

This matches what we obtained earlier. The p-value is below 0.05, so once again we reject the null hypothesis. We can also answer this question if instead we were given the summary statistics rather than the data:

$$\bar{x} = 13.6$$
$$s = 2.980639281$$
$$n = 20$$

Go to Option 2: $T - Test$, only this time select Stats. Type a null mean of 15, $\bar{x}$, s, n, and $< \mu_0$. Choose Calculate, and you will see the same output as above.

$$\Delta$$

Section 9.4 – Type I and Type II Errors

In Chapter 8, we discussed that a confidence interval most likely contains the population mean/proportion, but there is a very slight chance that the interval might miss the population mean/proportion. This is a small chance, but a chance nonetheless. This same possibility extends to hypothesis testing.

When we reject the null hypothesis and consequently have strong evidence for the alternative, we certainly hope that the alternative hypothesis is the correct statement. If it turns out that the null hypothesis was in fact correct, but we rejected it, we made a mistake in our conclusion. This can happen if we have an "unlucky" sample that leads to us making the wrong choice. Of course, we don't want such a mistake to happen, but unfortunately there will always be a slight chance of one occurring.

Similarly, if we do not reject the null hypothesis, but it turns out the alternative was the correct choice, this scenario is also a mistake, albeit a different type. Let's cover the four possible scenarios that can occur.

1) We reject the null hypothesis, and in fact the alternative hypothesis is true. This is a correct decision.
2) We reject the null hypothesis, but in fact the null hypothesis is true. This is an incorrect decision and is called a **Type I error**.
3) We don't reject the null hypothesis, and in fact the null hypothesis is true. This is a correct

decision.

4) We don't reject the null hypothesis, but in fact the alternative hypothesis is true. This is an incorrect decision and is called a **Type II error.**

These scenarios, including the error types, can be summarized in the following table.

	Reject H_0	Don't reject H_0
H_0 **was true**	Type I Error	Correct
H_A **was true**	Correct	Type II Error

DEFINITION

When we reject the null hypothesis, we are saying there is strong evidence for the alternative hypothesis. If it turns out the null hypothesis is in fact correct, we mistakenly rejected it. This is a **Type I error.**

When we fail to reject the null hypothesis, we are saying there is insufficient evidence for the alternative hypothesis. If it turns out the alternative hypothesis is in fact correct, we mistakenly failed to reject it. This is a **Type II error.**

The above chart also tells us that if we decide to reject the null hypothesis, we either made a correct choice or a Type I error. It is impossible to make a Type II error when rejecting the null. Similarly, if we don't reject the null hypothesis, we either made a correct choice or a Type II error, and so it is impossible to make a Type I error when failing to reject the null.

EXAMPLE

Suppose the average cost of admission to a castle in England used to be £20 (£ is the currency symbol for the pound sterling used in the United Kingdom). A curator believes the average price to tour a castle is now different. Set up the null and alternative hypotheses, and pick the applicable statements from the following list to describe what a Type I and Type II error would be in context.

A) The null hypothesis was rejected.
B) The null hypothesis was accepted.
C) The null hypothesis was not rejected.
D) The curator concluded that there was enough evidence to indicate a change in the average cost of admission to an English castle.
E) The curator concluded that there was insufficient evidence to indicate a change in the average cost of admission to an English castle.
F) The average cost of admission to an English castle has in fact not changed significantly.
G) The average cost of admission to an English castle has in fact changed significantly.

Solution: Let's first set up the hypotheses correctly.

$$H_0: \mu = 20$$
$$H_A: \mu \neq 20$$

A Type I error would be rejecting the null hypothesis when in fact the null hypothesis was correct. In doing so, we would conclude that the mean cost of admission has changed significantly from £20, but in reality the mean cost has not changed significantly. Thus, the corresponding choices are A, D, and F.

A Type II error would be failing to reject the null hypothesis when in fact the alternative hypothesis was correct. In doing so, we would conclude that the mean cost of admission has not changed significantly from £20, but in reality the mean cost has changed significantly. Thus, the corresponding choices are C, E, and G. (Remember, we do not accept the null hypothesis!)

Δ

Which error type is more serious? It really depends on the context of the situation being tested. The answer could come down to cost involved, time involved, safety and practical situations, or other reasons. Generally speaking, you will find that one of the errors could be somewhat serious to very serious, while the other might be a "better safe than sorry" situation, but you need to use your own judgment to decide which is which.

EXAMPLE

You have an appointment, and you want to decide what time to leave home to reach it on time. Your decision depends on how much traffic you think there will be on the roads. The hypotheses are as follows:

H_0: There will be little traffic (so you will not leave early).
H_A: There will be traffic (so you will leave early).

A Type I error would be when you reject the null hypothesis and decide there is evidence for the alternative, but in fact the null is true. In context, you would decide to leave early for your appointment thinking there will be traffic, but in fact there is little traffic, so you arrive too early.

A Type II error would be when you don't reject the null hypothesis and decide there is no evidence for the alternative, but in fact the alternative is true. In context, you would decide not to leave early for your appointment thinking there will be little traffic, but in fact there is a lot of traffic, so you arrive late. This is obviously a more serious situation – especially if your appointment is an interview or a date!.

Δ

EXAMPLE

You need to decide if it will rain later today. If you think it will rain, you will take an umbrella with you; otherwise you won't take one. The hypotheses are as follows:

H_0: It will not rain today (so you will not take an umbrella).
H_A: It will rain today (so you will take an umbrella).

A Type I error would be when you reject the null hypothesis and decide there is evidence for the alternative, but in fact the null is true. Here, you would decide to take an umbrella, but in fact it doesn't rain, so you are carrying an umbrella unnecessarily.

A Type II error would be when you don't reject the null hypothesis and decide there is no evidence for the alternative, but in fact the alternative is true. Here, you would decide not to take an umbrella, but in fact it ends up raining, so you get wet. Of course, this is the more serious error to make!

Δ

To be clear, I am not suggesting that a Type II error is always more serious based on these previous two examples. It depends on the context of the problem.

The other observation to make here concerns the Type I error. Recall that the interpretation of a p-value is the probability of getting a sample statistic of $\overline{x}$ or $\hat{p}$, or a more extreme result, if the null hypothesis were correct. If you reject the null hypothesis due to a low p-value, that p-value is the probability that the null was in fact correct after all. In other words, if you reject the null hypothesis, the probability of making a Type I error is equal to the p-value itself. (Finding the probability of making a Type II error is more complicated, so we shall not pursue that here.)

Section 9.5 – Connection Between Hypothesis Tests and Confidence Intervals

There is a direct connection between the outcomes of hypothesis testing and the outcomes of confidence intervals, so we now explore that topic here. In Chapter 8 we computed a confidence interval and then concluded that values inside were plausible values for the population mean, while values outside were unlikely. This is equivalent to saying that a sample mean is a plausible value for the population mean if we don't reject the null hypothesis, and it is not a plausible value if we do reject the null.

There is one catch, however –we can only make this connection if the hypothesis test is a two-tailed test.

Both confidence intervals and hypothesis testing give useful and equivalent conclusions, but they offer slightly different information along the way. In other words, they are two different ways of telling the same story. A confidence interval tells you a range of likely values at a specified confidence level, whereas a hypothesis test tells you to what extent a specific sample statistic is likely. Let's look at an example of how this works.

EXAMPLE

Consider the parasailing example from Chapter 8. To refresh your memory, 47 out of 162 students said that they had parasailed before, and we had built a 90% confidence interval that was (0.23148, 0.34877). This means we are 90% confident that the population proportion of students that have parasailed is between 0.23148 and 0.34877.

Now let's approach this problem from a hypothesis testing point of view. Suppose we want to test (at the 0.10 significance level) whether the population proportion of students who have parasailed is different from 0.20, so the hypotheses are

$$H_0: p = 0.20$$
$$H_A: p \neq 0.20$$

Going through the formulas, we have

$$\hat{p} = \frac{47}{162} = 0.2901234568$$

$$\text{standard error} = \sqrt{\frac{p_0(1 - p_0)}{n}} = \sqrt{\frac{0.20(1 - 0.20)}{162}} = 0.0314269681$$

$$Z = \frac{\hat{p} - p_0}{\text{standard error}} = \frac{0.2901234568 - 0.20}{0.0314269681} = 2.86771$$

Drawing the sketch, we need the probability above 2.86771 and also below −2.86771, so we can just find the probability above 2.86771 and double it.

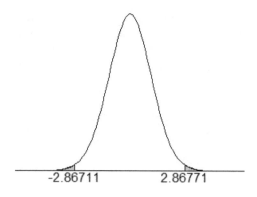

The lower limit is 2.86771 and the upper limit is 999999, so

$$2 \times normalcdf(2.86771, 999999) = 0.00413$$

The p-value is less than 0.10, so we reject the null hypothesis and conclude that the population proportion of parasailing students is different from 0.20. Now that we have established that conclusion, notice that 0.20 is not inside the 90% confidence interval of $(0.23148, 0.34877)$, which means it is an unlikely value for the population proportion. Thus, the confidence interval automatically tells us that 0.20 is an unlikely value, which is equivalent to rejecting the null hypothesis.

Both methods tell us different pieces of information. The hypothesis test shows that 0.20 is an unlikely value, and not only that, the degree of significance is very strong since the p-value is only 0.00413. This p-value is not only less than 0.10; it is much less. However, hypothesis testing does not indicate what the range of likely values is, but that is where the confidence interval comes into play. So the information that hypothesis testing does not report is covered by the confidence interval, and vice verse. Thus, hypothesis testing is the yin to the confidence interval's yang!

There is something else we should cover in this example. Notice we started with a 90% confidence interval and then switched to a hypothesis testing significance level of 0.10. There is a connection here: in loose terms, if you have a 90% confidence interval, then 10% is left over, and as a decimal that is 0.10. Similarly, a 95% confidence interval is equivalent to a two-tailed hypothesis test at the $\alpha = 0.05$ significance, while a test at the $\alpha = 0.01$ significance level is equivalent to a 99% confidence interval.

Δ

REVIEW: HYPOTHESIS TESTING AND CONFIDENCE INTERVALS

A two-tailed hypothesis test at the α significance level is equivalent to a $100(1 - \alpha)\%$ confidence interval. A confidence interval tells you a range of likely values at a specified confidence level, whereas a hypothesis test tells you to what extent a specific sample statistic is likely.

Rejecting the null hypothesis is equivalent to the assumed population null mean μ_0 (or null proportion p_0) falling outside the confidence interval.

Failing to reject the null hypothesis is equivalent to the assumed population null mean μ_0 (or null proportion p_0) falling inside the confidence interval.

You will notice we have specifically been mentioning two-tailed testing. Is a confidence interval equal to a left-tailed or right-tailed test? The answer is no, they are not equivalent (although in at least some cases the outcomes happen to be the same). One way to understand this intuitively is to recall that with confidence intervals, we drew a sketch and put, say, 0.95 in the middle and 0.025 on the left and right sides. However, when we do a two-tailed hypothesis test, we draw a normal sketch in a similar way, with two tails. (It is possible to make what are called one-sided confidence intervals that correspond to left-tailed and right-tailed tests, but this is covered in higher statistics classes.)

EXAMPLE
You want to test whether the population proportion of people in a city who enjoy gardening is different from 0.30. The resulting 95% confidence interval is $(0.28, 0.34)$. What is your conclusion, and at what significance level?

Solution: The hypotheses are

$$H_0: p = 0.30$$
$$H_A: p \neq 0.30$$

Since the confidence interval contains 0.30, that means that 0.30 is a likely value for the population proportion. This means that we do not reject the null hypothesis; there is insufficient evidence that the population proportion of people who enjoy gardening is different from 0.30. Since we have a 95% confidence interval, this would correspond to $\alpha = 0.05$ (because $100\% - 95\% = 5\%$). Failing to reject the null hypothesis means that the p-value is above 0.05.

Δ

EXAMPLE
The mean age at which women marry in a specific country used to be 25, but a sociologist believes the mean age has since changed. The sociologist takes a random sample of 40 recently married women and finds that their sample mean age is 27.3 with a standard deviation of 4.1.

A) Write the hypotheses for this test.
B) The 92% confidence interval is $(26.135, 28.465)$. Given this interval, would you reject the null hypothesis? What is our conclusion, and can we be more specific?
C) If our conclusion turns out to be an error, which type would it be?
D) We did not state what the level of significance was for this problem. What would it be? Is our p-value above or below α?
E) Without doing any calculations, what would our outcome be if we instead used the $\alpha = 0.10$ significance level?

Solution: For part A, the hypotheses are

$$H_0: \mu = 25$$
$$H_A: \mu \neq 25$$

Looking at the 92% confidence interval for part B, we want to see whether 25 is a likely value for the population mean. However, observe that it falls outside the interval, indicating that it is an unlikely value. That means that we would reject the null hypothesis and conclude that there is sufficient evidence that the mean age at which women marry is different from 25.

Can we be more specific? Notice that 25 falls below the confidence interval, so all plausible values are above 25. This means that not only can we say that the population mean is most likely different from 25, but it is most likely above 25.

For part C, since we rejected the null hypothesis, there is a slight chance that we made a mistake. This would be rejecting the null when in fact the null is correct, which would be a Type I error.

Part D gets into the significance level. Since we started with a 92% confidence interval, that means that $100\% - 92\% = 8\%$ is left over, and as a decimal that is $\alpha = 0.08$, the significance level. Since we rejected the null hypothesis, the p-value, whatever it is, is below 0.08.

We could easily answer part E by using the TI-84, but let's instead think about it conceptually. We just established that the p-value is below 0.08. That means that it is also below 0.10, so we would also reject the null hypothesis at the $\alpha = 0.10$ level.

Δ

EXAMPLE
Five years ago, a town held a "watermelon competition" in which citizens grew their own watermelons, picked the heaviest, and entered them into the contest, in which the winner was the person with the largest watermelon (in pounds). The overall average weight for these watermelons was 100 pounds. In this year's competition, a judge believes that the average weight of the watermelons has changed. Assume that the weight of the watermelons is normally distributed.

   A) Set up the hypotheses.
   B) Rather than examine all entries in the contest, the judge selects a random sample of the watermelons, and the resulting 94% confidence interval is $(114.8, 154.8)$. What is the sample average and margin of error from the judge's sample?
   C) Based on the confidence interval, what is your conclusion?
   D) Without doing the math, what can you say about the p-value? Is it above or below a certain number?
   E) What would our conclusion be if we instead started with a 91% confidence interval?

Solution: For part A, the hypotheses are

$$H_0: \mu = 100$$
$$H_A: \mu \neq 100$$

Part B simply calls upon skills from Chapter 8. The sample mean is the midpoint of the confidence interval, so

$$\bar{x} = \frac{114.8 + 154.8}{2} = 134.8$$

The margin of error is the distance from the middle of the interval to one of the endpoints, so

$$\text{margin of error} = \text{upper limit} - \text{middle} = 154.8 - 134.8 = 20$$

For part C, we want to see if the original mean of 100 is still a likely value based on the confidence interval. The whole interval is above 100, which shows that 100 is not a likely value for the population mean weight of the watermelons. Thus, this is equivalent to rejecting the null hypothesis and saying that there is strong evidence that the mean weight is different from 100 pounds.

For part D, let's get a bit more specific. Rejecting the null hypothesis means that the p-value must fall below α, but what is α? We have a 94% confidence interval, so $100\% - 94\% = 6\%$ is left over, meaning that $\alpha = 0.06$. Thus, the p-value is below 0.06.

Finally, for part E, we want to know what the results would be if we instead had a 91% confidence interval. There are two ways we can answer this. First, recall from Chapter 8 that the 91% interval is shorter than the 94% interval, which means that the lower limit would be greater than 114.8 and the upper limit would be smaller than 154.8. This new interval still does not contain 100, so our conclusion is still the same.

The second way we can solve this problem is to recognize that a 91% confidence interval is equivalent to a two-tailed hypothesis test using $\alpha = 0.09$ (because $100\% - 91\% = 9\%$). We already know that the p-value is below 0.06, and so it is also below 0.09, which means we would also reject the null hypothesis at $\alpha = 0.09$.

Δ

Section 9.6 – Hypothesis Tests and Confidence Intervals for Regression*

The last topic in this chapter deals with hypothesis tests and confidence intervals for linear regression equations, which you will recall from Chapter 3 are straight lines of best fit through two datasets x and y. We earlier fit the linear regression equation $\hat{y} = a + bx$ where a was the intercept and b was the slope. In that chapter we used the equation to predict the y-value $\hat{y}$ given a specific value for x, and we stated whether there was a strong linear relationship between x and y based on the correlation r.

In this section we learn a few more techniques to further study the relationship between x and y. We had to delay this material from Chapter 3 because it involves confidence intervals and hypothesis testing, but now we can successfully cover what we need. Your class may or may not teach some of these topics (especially since some of them are more advanced), in which case you can read the relevant ones and skip what you don't need.

For a start, while we learned earlier how to compute a and b both by hand and with the TI-84, the next step is to find the standard errors for a and b. The TI-84 won't directly find these for us, so we resort to using the formulas. In addition, each regression model has a third standard error called the residual standard error, which can be described as a standard deviation of all the residuals.

STANDARD ERRORS FOR REGRESSION EQUATION

Let $\hat{y} = a + bx$ be the regression equation, and let SE_a and SE_b be the standard errors for a and b, respectively. Also let $\hat{\sigma}$ be the residual standard error. If n is the sample size and s_x is the standard deviation of the x points, then the formulas for the three standard errors are

$$\hat{\sigma} = \sqrt{\frac{\sum(y_i - \hat{y}_i)^2}{n-2}}$$

$$SE_b = \frac{\hat{\sigma}}{s_x\sqrt{n-1}}$$

$$SE_a = SE_b\sqrt{\frac{\sum x_i^2}{n}}$$

The residual standard error $\hat{\sigma}$ is essentially the standard deviation of all residuals in the regression equation, while SE_a and SE_b are just the standard deviations of the intercept and the slope, respectively. Usually SE_b is the more important of the two to study.

EXAMPLE

Returning to the weight-lifting example from Section 3.3, we had the following dataset where x was the eight of a bar and y was the number of repetitions a specific person made with the given weight. The regression equation we computed was $\hat{y} = 37.08029197 - 0.3335766423x$ (using all available decimals). Find the residual standard error of the regression equation, as well as the standard errors of the intercept and the slope.

Weight (X)	30	50	55	80	65
Number of Reps (Y)	25	22	20	8	17

Solution: Let's first find the residual standard error, which means noting that $n = 5$ and that we need all five predicted y-values, the $\hat{y}_i$. We find them by first using the regression equation five times:

$$\hat{y}_1 = 37.08029197 - 0.3335766423(30) = 27.0729927$$
$$\hat{y}_2 = 37.08029197 - 0.3335766423(50) = 20.40145986$$
$$\hat{y}_3 = 37.08029197 - 0.3335766423(55) = 18.73357664$$
$$\hat{y}_4 = 37.08029197 - 0.3335766423(80) = 10.39416059$$
$$\hat{y}_5 = 37.08029197 - 0.3335766423(65) = 15.39781022$$

The sum of squared residuals is then

$$\sum (y_i - \hat{y}_i)^2 = (25 - 27.0729927)^2 + (22 - 20.40145986)^2 + (20 - 18.73357664)^2$$
$$+ (8 - 10.39416059)^2 + (17 - 15.39781022)^2$$
$$= 4.297298738 + 2.555330595 + 1.603828118 + 5.732004912 + 2.56701209$$
$$= 16.75547445$$

The residual standard error is

$$\hat{\sigma} = \sqrt{\frac{\sum (y_i - \hat{y}_\square)^2}{n - 2}} = \sqrt{\frac{16.75547445}{5 - 2}} = \sqrt{5.585158151} = 2.36329392$$

Noting that the standard deviation of the x values is $s_x = 18.50675552$ (which we can find using the $1 - Var\ Stats$ option), we can easily get the standard error for the slope:

$$SE_b = \frac{\hat{\sigma}}{s_x\sqrt{n - 1}} = \frac{2.36329392}{18.50675552\sqrt{5 - 1}} = 0.0638494932$$

Next, the sum of squared x_i values is

$$\sum x_i^2 = 30^2 + 50^2 + 55^2 + 80^2 + 65^2 = 17050$$

The standard error for the intercept is

$$SE_a = SE_b \sqrt{\frac{\sum x_i^2}{n}} = 0.0638494932 \sqrt{\frac{17050}{5}} = 3.72850426$$

Δ

The main topic of interest in this section, however, is hypothesis testing of the slope of the regression equation. The idea is to test whether the explanatory variable x has a significant effect on the response variable y – for instance, if an increase in x leads to a significant increase (or decrease) in y. Even though b represents the calculated slope from the sample, we denote the actual slope of the population by β (another Greek letter, pronounced "beta"). This type of hypothesis test will usually be two-tailed (except perhaps in some rare cases, so we cover all three possibilities for completeness).

Here's the general logic for hypothesis testing at the α significance level. If increasing x does not have a significant effect on y, then the slope must be $\beta = 0$. However, if increasing x results in a significant increase/decrease/difference in y, then we use the appropriate symbol. You can probably guess how we will state our hypotheses now!

$$H_0: \beta = 0$$
$$H_A: \beta > 0 \quad \text{or} \quad \beta < 0 \quad \text{or} \quad \beta \neq 0$$

There are some assumptions to check, but we will not explore them as they involve more advanced statistical topics. Instead, we go directly to the test statistic, a T-statistic, computed as

$$T = \frac{b - 0}{SE_b}$$

Why do we write 0 when mathematically we don't need to? We certainly don't need to include it, but it is written here just so you can more easily see the comparison to the test statistic formulas earlier in this chapter. You can see that it is a point estimate (b) minus the null value (0) all divided by a standard error (in this case, the standard error for the slope).

Next, we go to the T-distribution and find the appropriate probability. Unlike the hypothesis test for a mean earlier, here degrees of freedom is equal to $n - 2$ (the reason is because we have two numbers estimated in the regression equation, the intercept and the slope). Other than that one adjustment, we find the p-value the same way, as in the following sketches.

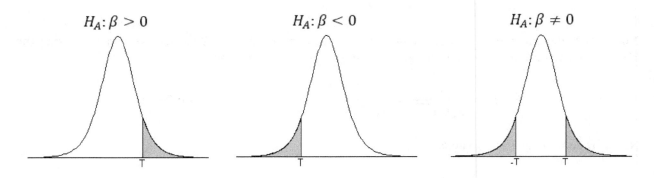

Finally, we compare the p-value to the significance level α and make our conclusion.

REVIEW: HYPOTHESIS TESTING FOR A REGRESSION EQUATION SLOPE

Step 1: Set up the hypotheses.

$$H_0: \beta = 0$$
$$H_A: \beta > 0 \qquad \text{or} \qquad H_A: \beta < 0 \qquad \text{or} \qquad H_A: \beta \neq 0$$

Step 2: (Assumptions are advanced; we won't pursue them here.)

Step 3: Compute the test statistic.

$$T = \frac{b - 0}{SE_b} \quad \text{where} \quad SE_b = \frac{\hat{\sigma}}{s_x \sqrt{n-1}} \quad \text{and} \quad \hat{\sigma} = \sqrt{\frac{\sum (y_i - \hat{y}_i)^2}{n-2}}$$

Step 4: Compute the p-value.

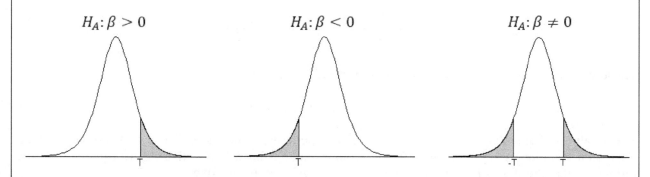

$$H_A: \beta > 0 \qquad\qquad H_A: \beta < 0 \qquad\qquad H_A: \beta \neq 0$$

Step 5: State the conclusion.

If the p-value is below the significance level (p-value $< \alpha$), then …
    1) We reject the null hypothesis.
    2) There is sufficient evidence against the null hypothesis.
    3) There is sufficient evidence that the slope is significantly positive/negative/different from 0.

If the p-value is above the significance level (p-value $> \alpha$), then…
    1) We fail to reject the null hypothesis.
    2) There is insufficient evidence against the null hypothesis.
    3) There is insufficient evidence that the slope is significantly positive/negative/different from 0.

EXAMPLE

Continuing the same weight-lifting example, conduct a hypothesis test at the $\alpha = 0.05$ level to see whether the weight of the bar has a significant effect on the number of repetitions made. That is, test whether the slope of the regression equation is significantly different from 0.

Solution: First, we are testing

$$H_0: \beta = 0$$
$$H_A: \beta \neq 0$$

The regression equation was $\hat{y} = 37.08029197 - 0.3335766423x$, so $b = -0.3335766423$ is the slope. We computed the slope standard error as $SE_b = 0.0638494932$. That means that the test statistic is

$$T = \frac{b - 0}{SE_b} = -\frac{0.3335766423}{0.0638494932} = -5.22442$$

Noting that $n = 5$ and therefore $DF = 5 - 2 = 3$, we draw a sketch of what we need:

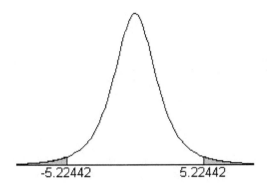

The lower limit is 5.22442 and the upper limit is 999999, and so

$$2tcdf(5.22442, 999999, 3) = 0.01364$$

The p-value is below 0.05, so we reject the null hypothesis. There is evidence that the slope of the regression equation is significantly different from 0. Noting that b is negative in the equation, we can further say that the slope of the regression equation is significantly negative.

Δ

You might recall that we studied the correlation coefficient (r) from linear regression, and that the sign of correlation is always the same as the sign of the slope (b). That means that we can actually conduct a hypothesis test for the population correlation coefficient, and doing so will give the same results as a test for the slope. Here comes another Greek letter: the population correlation coefficient is denoted as ρ (pronounced "rho"). The possible hypotheses are

$$H_0: \rho = 0$$
$$H_A: \rho > 0 \quad \text{or} \quad \rho < 0 \quad \text{or} \quad \rho \neq 0$$

There is a test statistic for correlation, and as luck would have it, it is also a T-statistic:

$$T = r\sqrt{\frac{n - 2}{1 - r^2}}$$

The good news gets better – although we won't show a proof of it, this test statistic gives the same calculation as the one we saw for the slope! That is,

$$T = \frac{b - 0}{SE_b} = r\sqrt{\frac{n - 2}{1 - r^2}}$$

The p-value is then computed the same way as earlier, again with $DF = n - 2$.

REVIEW: HYPOTHESIS TESTING FOR THE CORRELATION COEFFICIENT

Step 1: Set up the hypotheses.

$H_0: \rho = 0$

$H_A: \rho > 0$ or $H_A: \rho < 0$ or $H_A: \rho \neq 0$

Step 2: (Assumptions are advanced; we won't pursue them here.)

Step 3: Compute the test statistic.

$$T = r\sqrt{\frac{n - 2}{1 - r^2}}$$

Step 4: Compute the p-value.

$H_A: \rho > 0$	$H_A: \rho < 0$	$H_A: \rho \neq 0$
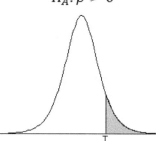	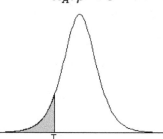	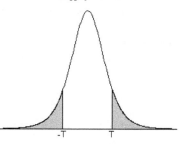

Step 5: State the conclusion.

If the p-value is below the significance level (p-value $< \alpha$), then …
    1) We reject the null hypothesis.
    2) There is sufficient evidence against the null hypothesis.
    3) There is sufficient evidence that the correlation coefficient is significantly positive/negative/ different from 0.

If the p-value is above the significance level (p-value $> \alpha$), then…
    1) We fail to reject the null hypothesis.
    2) There is insufficient evidence against the null hypothesis.
    3) There is insufficient evidence that the correlation coefficient is significantly positive/negative/ different from 0.

EXAMPLE

Continuing the same weight-lifting example, conduct a hypothesis test at the $\alpha = 0.05$ level on the correlation coefficient and whether it is significantly different from 0, given that $r = -0.9491956454$ and $n = 5$ (from an earlier example).

Solution: First, we are testing

$$H_0: \rho = 0$$
$$H_A: \rho \neq 0$$

The test statistic is

$$T = r\sqrt{\frac{n-2}{1-r^2}} = -0.9491956454 \times \sqrt{\frac{5-2}{1-(-0.9491956454)^2}}$$
$$= -0.9491956454 \times \sqrt{30.29457636}$$
$$= -5.22442$$

This is the same test statistic as we computed earlier! Thus, the p-value is the same one: 0.01364. As before, we conclude that the population correlation coefficient is significantly different from 0. Noting that r is negative, we can further say that the correlation coefficient is significantly negative ... which brings us to the next topic, confidence intervals!

Δ

We can also create a confidence interval for the slope of a regression equation. It is formed in the same way you would create one for a population mean, only using $DF = n - 2$.

DEFINITION
The general formula for a confidence interval for the slope of a regression equation is

$$b \pm T_{\alpha/2}(n-2) \times SE_b$$

The following parts are defined:

n is the sample size.
b is the slope of the regression equation.
SE_b is the standard error for the slope.
$T_{\alpha/2}(n-2)$ is a number that is determined by the confidence level and the degrees of freedom, using $DF = n - 2$.

The product $T_{\alpha/2}(n-2) \times SE_b$ is the margin of error.

If the confidence interval contains 0, then an increase in x does not lead to a significant increase (or decrease) in y. However, if the confidence interval does not contain 0, then an increase in x leads to a significant increase (or decrease) in y.

EXAMPLE
Continuing the same example, we already know that the slope is significantly negative, and so we would expect the 95% confidence interval to be entirely negative as well. To verify this, we know that $b = -0.3335766423$ and $SE_b = 0.0638494932$. To get the T-score, let's draw our sketch with $DF = 5 - 2 = 3$ and $\alpha/2 = 0.025$:

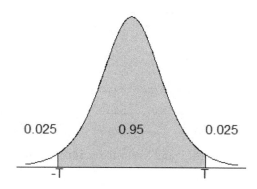

We see that $invT(0.025, 3) = -3.182446305$, so $T_{0.025}(3) = 3.182446305$. The 95% confidence interval for the slope is

$$b \pm T_{\alpha/2}(n-2) \times SE_b = -0.3335766423 \pm 3.182446305 \times 0.0638494932$$
$$= -0.3335766423 \pm 0.2031975837$$
$$= (-0.53678, -0.13038)$$

As expected, the confidence interval does not contain 0 and is entirely negative, resulting in the same conclusion as the equivalent hypothesis test.

Δ

We can also use the TI-84 to calculate the confidence interval and hypothesis testing.

TI-84 COMMAND: HYPOTHESIS TESTING FOR THE SLOPE / CORRELATION

To conduct a hypothesis test for the slope of a regression equation (or the correlation coefficient), first enter the explanatory variable into L_1 and the response variable into L_2. Now press $\boxed{\text{STAT}}$, scroll right to TESTS, and select Option F: $LinRegTTest$. Enter L_1 for Xlist, L_2 for Ylist, and select the appropriate symbol for the alternative (usually $\neq$). Choose Calculate, and the resulting output shows the following:

The regression equation format.
The alternative hypothesis selected.
The T-statistic.
The p-value (denoted as p).
The degrees of freedom DF.
The intercept a.
The slope b.
The residual standard error $\hat{\sigma}$ (denoted as s).
The squared correlation r^2 (we won't use this in these notes).
The correlation r.

TI-84 COMMAND: CONFIDENCE INTERVAL FOR THE SLOPE

To compute a $100(1-\alpha)\%$ confidence interval for the slope of a regression equation, first enter the explanatory variable into L_1 and the response variable into L_2. Now press $\boxed{\text{STAT}}$, scroll right to TESTS, and select Option G: $LinRegTInt$. Enter L_1 for Xlist, L_2 for Ylist, and the choice of confidence level (such as 0.95). Choose Calculate, and the resulting output shows the following:

The regression equation format.
The confidence interval for the slope.

The slope b.
The degrees of freedom DF.
The residual standard error $\hat{\sigma}$ (denoted as s).
The intercept a.
The squared correlation r^2 (we won't use this in these notes).
The correlation r.

EXAMPLE
Continuing with the same example, we enter the x numbers into L_1 and the y numbers into L_2. Going to Option F: $LinRegTTest$, the output is

$$t = -5.224421149$$
$$p = 0.0136410469$$
$$a = 37.08029197$$
$$b = -0.3335766423$$
$$s = 2.36329392$$

Now going to Option G: $LinRegTInt$, the confidence interval is $(-0.5368, -0.1304)$. All the output matches what we found by hand.

Δ

We have shown how to get the confidence interval for the slope, so the next question is how we find one for the correlation coefficient. This interval is more complicated to compute, but we show the steps anyway in case you ever need to find one (and there is no TI-84 command to find this interval, so we need to compute it by hand).

DEFINITION
To find the $100(1 - \alpha)\%$ confidence interval for the correlation coefficient, we need to perform the following steps. Note that unlike other formulas in introductory statistics, these formulas require using the ln( ) function (natural log) and the exp( ) function (exponential), both of which appear frequently in other math classes, especially calculus. Another way to write $\exp(x)$ is e^x where $e = 2.718281828\ldots$.

Step 1: Compute the sample correlation r.

Step 2: Compute the transformation $Z_r = \frac{1}{2}\ln\left(\frac{1+r}{1-r}\right)$.

Step 3: Compute the endpoint transformations $Z_L = Z_r - \frac{Z_{\alpha/2}}{\sqrt{n-3}}$ and $Z_U = Z_r + \frac{Z_{\alpha/2}}{\sqrt{n-3}}$, where $Z_{\alpha/2}$ is the usual Z-score that comes from the normal distribution with probability $\alpha/2$ to the right.

Step 4: Back-transform the endpoints to obtain the confidence interval limits

$$r_L = \frac{\exp(2Z_L) - 1}{\exp(2Z_L) + 1} \quad \text{and} \quad r_U = \frac{\exp(2Z_U) - 1}{\exp(2Z_U) + 1}$$

The $100(1 - \alpha)\%$ confidence interval for the correlation coefficient is (r_L, r_U). Unlike previous intervals we have seen, the sample correlation r will not always be right in the middle due to the transformations that took place.

If the confidence interval contains 0, then the correlation coefficient is not significantly different from 0. However, if the confidence interval does not contain 0, then correlation is significantly positive (or negative).

EXAMPLE

Continuing the same weight-lifting example, construct a 95% confidence interval for the correlation coefficient, given that $r = -0.9491956454$ and $n = 5$ (from an earlier example).

Solution: The first transformation is

$$Z_r = \frac{1}{2}\ln\left(\frac{1+r}{1-r}\right) = \frac{1}{2}\ln\left(\frac{1 + (-0.9491956454)}{1 - (-0.9491956454)}\right) = \frac{1}{2}\ln(0.0260642664)$$
$$= 0.5 \times -3.647190006$$
$$= -1.823595003$$

Next, recalling that $Z_{0.025} = 1.96$, we find the transformed endpoints by first computing

$$\frac{Z_{\alpha/2}}{\sqrt{n-3}} = \frac{1.96}{\sqrt{5-3}} = \frac{1.96}{\sqrt{2}} = 1.385929291$$

The transformed endpoints are

$$Z_L = Z_r - \frac{Z_{\alpha/2}}{\sqrt{n-3}} = -1.823595003 - 1.385929291 = -3.209524294$$
$$Z_U = Z_r + \frac{Z_{\alpha/2}}{\sqrt{n-3}} = -1.823595003 + 1.385929291 = -0.437665712$$

Back-transforming the endpoints, we get

$$r_L = \frac{\exp(2Z_L) - 1}{\exp(2Z_L) + 1} = \frac{\exp(2 \times -3.209524294) - 1}{\exp(2 \times -3.209524294) + 1} = \frac{0.0016302065 - 1}{0.0016302065 + 1} = -0.99674$$
$$r_U = \frac{\exp(2Z_U) - 1}{\exp(2Z_U) + 1} = \frac{\exp(2 \times -0.437665712) - 1}{\exp(2 \times -0.437665712) + 1} = \frac{0.4167238845 - 1}{0.4167238845 + 1} = -0.41171$$

Thus, the 95% confidence interval for the correlation coefficient is $(-0.99674, -0.41171)$. Observe that $r = -0.9491956454$ falls inside this interval, as it should, although it is clearly not in the center. Since the interval is entirely negative and does not contain 0, we conclude that the population correlation coefficient ρ is significantly lower than 0, indicating once again that the variables x and y are negatively correlated.

Δ

We have shown the formulas for confidence intervals for the slope of a regression equation, as well as the correlation coefficient. We can also create a confidence interval for the average (expected) value of y at a specific x value. The point estimate is $\hat{y} = a + bx$, as you would expect, but we can also find the appropriate T-score and a standard error, thereby producing a confidence interval.

DEFINITION

The general formula for a $100(1 - \alpha)\%$ confidence interval for the average value of y (or the expected value of y) at a specific value of x is

$$\hat{y} \pm T_{\alpha/2}(n-2) \times \hat{\sigma}\sqrt{\frac{1}{n} + \frac{(x - \overline{x})^2}{(n-1)s_x^2}}$$

The following parts are defined:

$\hat{y} = a + bx$ is the predicted value of y at the given x.
n is the sample size.
$\hat{\sigma}$ is the residual standard error.
x is the given x value of interest.
$\bar{x}$ is the mean of all the x values.
s_x is the standard deviation of all the x values.
b is the slope of the regression equation.
$T_{\alpha/2}(n - 2)$ is a number that is determined by the confidence level and the degrees of freedom, using $DF = n - 2$.

However, there is another type of interval we can construct with $\hat{y}$ as the point estimate. This is called a **prediction interval**. Unlike a confidence interval for y, which tells us a range of plausible values for the average value of y at a given x, a prediction interval tells us a range of plausible values for a specific value of y at a given x. In other words, if you want an interval for the average response of y, make a confidence interval, but if you want an interval for an individual response of y, make a prediction interval.

DEFINITION
The general formula for a $100(1 - \alpha)\%$ prediction interval for a specific value of y at a specific value of x is

$$\hat{y} \pm T_{\alpha/2}(n - 2) \times \hat{\sigma}\sqrt{1 + \frac{1}{n} + \frac{(x - \bar{x})^2}{(n - 1)s_x^2}}$$

Notice that this is the same formula as the preceding confidence interval, only with an extra 1 under the square root. The parts of the formula have the same meanings as those listed for the preceding confidence interval formula.

EXAMPLE
To illustrate these two new intervals on the everlasting weight-lifting example, we have $\hat{y} = 37.08029197 - 0.3335766423x$. Find a 95% confidence interval for the average number of repetitions made at 50 pounds, as well as a 95% prediction interval for a specific number of repetitions made at 50 pounds.

Solution: First, regarding the x values, the summary statistics show that $n = 5$, $\bar{x} = 56$, and $s_x = 18.50675552$. Earlier we computed the residual standard error as $\hat{\sigma} = 2.36329392$, and in the previous example we found the necessary T-score to be $T_{0.025}(3) = 3.182446305$.

The predicted value of y at $x = 50$ is

$$\hat{y} = 37.08029197 - 0.3335766423(50) = 20.40129197$$

To get the confidence interval, the square root piece is

$$\sqrt{\frac{1}{n} + \frac{(x - \overline{x})^2}{(n-1)s_x^2}} = \sqrt{\frac{1}{5} + \frac{(50 - 56)^2}{4 \times 18.50675552^2}} = \sqrt{0.2262773723} = 0.475686212$$

The margin of error is

$$T_{0.025}(3) \times \hat{\sigma} \sqrt{\frac{1}{n} + \frac{(x - \overline{x})^2}{(n-1)s_x^2}} = 3.182446305 \times 2.36329392 \times 0.475686212 = 3.57766264$$

Thus, the 95% confidence interval for an average value of y at $x = 50$ is

$$\hat{y} \pm \text{Margin of Error} = 20.40129197 \pm 3.57766264 = (16.82363, 23.97895)$$

Next, let's go for the prediction interval, so now we have the new square root piece:

$$\sqrt{1 + \frac{1}{n} + \frac{(x - \overline{x})^2}{(n-1)s_x^2}} = \sqrt{1 + \frac{1}{5} + \frac{(50 - 56)^2}{4 \times 18.50675552^2}} = \sqrt{1.226277372} = 1.107374089$$

The updated margin of error is

$$T_{0.025}(3) \times \hat{\sigma} \sqrt{1 + \frac{1}{n} + \frac{(x - \overline{x})^2}{(n-1)s_x^2}} = 3.182446305 \times 2.36329392 \times 1.107374089 = 8.328622538$$

Thus, the 95% prediction interval for an individual value of y at $x = 50$ is

$$\hat{y} \pm \text{Margin of Error} = 20.40129197 \pm 8.328622538 = (12.07267, 28.72991)$$

To be clear, the $(16.82363, 23.97895)$ interval is a 95% confidence interval for an average value of y at $x = 50$, whereas the $(12.07267, 28.72991)$ interval is a 95% prediction interval for a specific value of y at $x = 50$. Since the latter concerns one point rather than an average of points, there will be higher variability, which explains why the prediction interval is a lot wider than the confidence interval (this is always true about these two types of intervals).

$$\Delta$$

And now … for a joke! An engineer, a physicist, and a statistician go to a coffee shop to order drinks. The engineer is unfamiliar with this shop, so he orders orange juice. The physicist knows how much caffeine he needs to feel awake, so he orders a latte. The statistician has trouble deciding whether to order English Breakfast or Earl Grey … so to make up his mind, he does a Tea test!

Chapter 10 – Hypothesis Testing of Two Populations

In Chapter 9 we introduced hypothesis testing, concentrating on testing a population proportion and a population mean. In both cases we focused on just one population at a time. In this chapter we extend the testing techniques to the comparison of two population parameters. Whereas in Chapter 9 we tested to see if the population parameter was equal to a specified number, here we will test whether two population means (or proportions) are equal to each other. Put another way, we will test whether the difference in population means (or proportions) is equal to zero. The concepts are the same as in Chapter 9, but as you probably guessed, the formulas themselves change. We will also see how to create confidence intervals when two groups are involved.

First, let's define some basic notation for when there are two groups. When testing population means, let μ_1 denote the population mean for the first group and μ_2 the population mean for the second group. If we are testing population proportions, define them similarly as p_1 and p_2. The idea is to test whether μ_1 and μ_2 are the same, or equivalently whether $\mu_1 - \mu_2 = 0$ (and similarly, $p_1 - p_2 = 0$). This is how we will set up the hypotheses in this chapter.

Similarly to before, we will write down the hypotheses and check the assumptions, but this time we will collect data from two groups before computing the test statistic and p-value.

One other element that comes into play is whether the two groups are dependent or independent of each other. You must identify which one it is because this decision affects the subsequent formulas to use. In the first section, we start with the "easiest" case, matched pairs testing, where the two groups are dependent. We will then extend the ideas to the case where the two groups are independent, studying first proportions and later means.

Section 10.1 – Matched Pairs Hypothesis Testing

First, recall the following definition from Chapter 4.

DEFINITION

In some cases, the subjects across groups may be dependent. If we have two groups, and each person in Group A is somehow related to somebody in Group B, then the groups are dependent. In which case, it would be appropriate to "match up" the dependent subject pairs and compare their individual differences in response variable measurements. This is a **matched pairs** experiment.

How might subjects be dependent across groups? In most cases (and for the purposes of introductory statistics), the same subjects would participate in both groups on different occasions. If the subjects participate in both groups during the course of the experiment, then the two groups are obviously dependent since the same people are in both groups. Examples of this kind of study include the following:

1) 50 subjects have their cholesterol measured, and then they all test a new medicine that promises to lower it. Six months later, the same 50 people have their cholesterol checked, and the differences in measurements are recorded.

2) 15 people eat a cookie, record a rating of how much they liked it, and then the same 15 people eat another cookie of a different brand and record another rating for the second cookie. The difference in ratings is computed.

The key here is to notice that the same people participate in both groups during the experiment. That characteristic is what makes the two groups dependent. When this happens, a matched pairs design is most appropriate, so we need to conduct our hypothesis testing in the same way. We call this a hypothesis test of the matched pairs difference of means. This is actually an easy extension of what we learned in Chapter 9 because we will be analyzing the differences between the two groups, treating the differences as one group (so we have reduced two groups to just one). Here are the five steps to follow.

Step 1: Set up the hypotheses.
Let μ_1 and μ_2 denote the population mean for the first and second group, respectively. To test whether the two means are equal to each other is the same as testing whether their difference is equal to zero, as in $\mu_1 - \mu_2 = 0$. Actually, to make notation a little simpler, for matched pairs testing you will often see the difference in means written as $\mu_d = \mu_1 - \mu_2$. We will use this notation instead to indicate that we are dealing with dependent groups. The null hypothesis is

$$H_0: \mu_d = 0$$

The alternative hypothesis is one of the following:

$$H_A: \mu_d > 0 \qquad \text{(right-tailed test)}$$
$$H_A: \mu_d < 0 \qquad \text{(left-tailed test)}$$
$$H_A: \mu_d \neq 0 \qquad \text{(two-tailed test)}$$

Step 2: Check the assumptions.
For the hypothesis test to be valid, three assumptions need to be true, assuming a sample size n_d:

1) The data must be quantitative (meaning they are numbers that can be averaged).
2) The subjects must be randomly selected.
3) At least one of the following statements must be true:
   a. The population of differences is normal.
   b. $n_d > 30$.

These assumptions are essentially the same as those from one population mean. The difference is that normality is assumed for the population differences across the two groups, and n_d is the total number of differences in the sample. (For example, suppose a group of people have their cholesterol measured before and after taking a medicine. The differences in cholesterol scores are then recorded in this sample. The population would be the differences in the "before" and "after" scores if everybody in the whole population were to take this medicine. Of course, this is unrealistic, which is why we have a sample instead.)

Step 3: Compute the test statistic.
Recall that the general test statistic formula is

$$\text{test statistic} = \frac{(\text{sample statistic}) - (\text{null value})}{\text{standard error}}$$

For a hypothesis test of the difference of dependent means, the formula becomes

$$T = \frac{\overline{x}_d - 0}{\frac{s_d}{\sqrt{n_d}}}$$

Stated a simpler way, we can write

$$T = \frac{\overline{x}_d - 0}{\text{standard error}} \quad \text{where} \quad \text{standard error} = \frac{s_d}{\sqrt{n_d}}$$

Here $\overline{x}_d$ and s_d are the sample mean and sample standard deviation, respectively, of the computed differences across the two groups (this will become more clear in examples). Notice that since we are dealing with means, the test statistic is a T-statistic.

You may be wondering why we are writing "minus 0" in the numerator when mathematically there is no need to do so. The reason is because 0 is the assumed difference under the null hypothesis, so this is just a convenient notation to denote it as such. Of course, we can drop the 0 if we wish; it is there just to remind us that we are subtracting the null value from the computed sample mean difference. (We saw something similar in Section 9.6.)

Step 4: Compute the p-value.
Since we have a T-statistic, we must use the T-distribution to find the p-value. This will work just like in Chapter 9 for when our hypothesis test was on one population mean, so the degrees of freedom formula is still $DF = n - 1$. We still use the same techniques to find the p-value. For a right-tailed test, we find the probability to the right of T, as in the following graph.

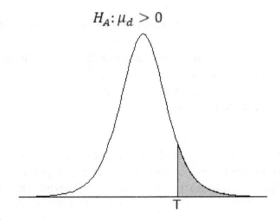

$$H_A: \mu_d > 0$$

For a left-tailed test, we find the probability to the left of T.

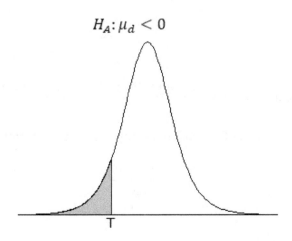

$$H_A: \mu_d < 0$$

For a two-tailed test, we first plot T and $-T$ on the T-distribution. We then find the probability to the right of T and add it to the probability to the left of $-T$. As before, these two probabilities are the same because the T-distribution is symmetric, so it suffices to find the right-tailed probability and double it.

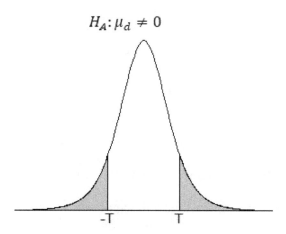

$$H_A: \mu_d \neq 0$$

Step 5: State the conclusion.

Finally, we compare the p-value to a predetermined significance level α. If the p-value is below the significance level (p-value $< \alpha$), then…

1) We reject the null hypothesis.
2) There is sufficient evidence against the null hypothesis.
3) There is sufficient evidence for the alternative hypothesis.

If the p-value is above the significance level (p-value $> \alpha$), then…

1) We fail to reject the null hypothesis.
2) There is insufficient evidence against the null hypothesis.
3) There is insufficient evidence for the alternative hypothesis.

REVIEW: HYPOTHESIS TESTING FOR DIFFERENCE OF DEPENDENT MEANS

Step 1: Set up the hypotheses.

$$H_0: \mu_d = 0$$
$$H_A: \mu_d > 0 \quad \text{or} \quad H_A: \mu_d < 0 \quad \text{or} \quad H_A: \mu_d \neq 0$$

Step 2: Check the assumptions.

1) Quantitative data
2) Random sample
3) Normal population of differences or $n_d > 30$

Step 3: Compute the test statistic.

$$T = \frac{\overline{x}_d - 0}{\text{standard error}} \quad \text{where} \quad \text{standard error} = \frac{s_d}{\sqrt{n_d}}$$

Step 4: Compute the p-value.

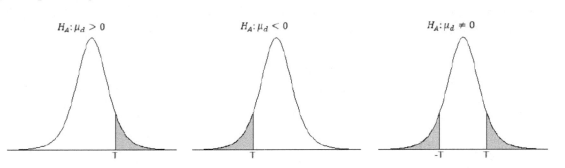

Step 5: State the conclusion.

If the p-value is below the significance level (p-value $< \alpha$), then …
      1) We reject the null hypothesis.
      2) There is sufficient evidence against the null hypothesis.
      3) There is sufficient evidence for the alternative hypothesis.

If the p-value is above the significance level (p-value $> \alpha$), then…
      1) We fail to reject the null hypothesis.
      2) There is insufficient evidence against the null hypothesis.
      3) There is insufficient evidence for the alternative hypothesis.

Let's go to some examples now!

EXAMPLE
We randomly sample five subjects and ask them for the sun protection factor (SPF) of their sunscreen of choice they use in April and the SPF they use in May. The following table lists the SPFs used in April and May for the same five subjects. We will assume that the differences between SPFs over the two months are normally distributed.

Subject	May SPF	April SPF
1	40	35
2	40	40
3	35	30
4	25	25
5	30	30

Let's test our claim that sunblock factors in May are significantly higher than in April at the $\alpha = 0.05$ significance level. Denote these differences with the letter d for comparing differences, so $d = $ May SPF $-$ April SPF.

Solution: To test whether May's mean SPF is higher than April's mean SPF, that would mean that the difference is positive. Thus, we have

$$H_0: \mu_d = 0$$
$$H_A: \mu_d > 0$$

Noting that the data are quantitative, the subjects were randomly selected, and the differences are assumed to be normal, we now compute the raw differences and note that they are generally equal to or just above 0.

Subject	May SPF	April SPF	d
1	40	35	5
2	40	40	0
3	35	30	5
4	25	25	0
5	30	30	0

Putting the numbers $5, 0, 5, 0, 0$ into L_1 on the TI-84, the summary statistics are

$$\overline{x}_d = 2$$
$$s_d = 2.738612788$$
$$n_d = 5$$

We compute the test statistic:

$$\text{standard error} = \frac{s_d}{\sqrt{n_d}} = \frac{2.738612788}{\sqrt{5}} = 1.224744872$$

$$T = \frac{\overline{x}_d - 0}{\text{standard error}} = \frac{2 - 0}{1.224744872} = 1.63299$$

To find the p-value, noting that this is a right-tailed test, we plot $T = 1.63299$ on the T-distribution with 4 degrees of freedom (because $DF = 5 - 1 = 4$) and find the probability to the right.

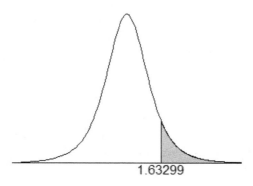

The lower limit is 1.63299 and the upper limit is 999999, so the p-value is

$$tcdf(1.63299, 999999, 4) = 0.08890$$

The p-value is above 0.05, so we don't reject the null hypothesis. There is insufficient evidence that the mean difference of sunscreen SPF used in May and April is greater from 0.

Δ

A second approach to hypothesis testing is to answer the question using a confidence interval instead.

CONFIDENCE INTERVAL FOR DIFFERENCE OF DEPENDENT MEANS

For a $100(1 - \alpha)\%$ confidence interval for the difference of two population means that are dependent, we have the following, which can be computed in the four steps outlined below:

$$\text{Point Estimate} = \overline{x}_d$$

$$\text{Standard Error} = \frac{s_d}{\sqrt{n_d}}$$

$$\text{Margin of Error} = T_{\alpha/2}(n - 1) \times \left(\frac{s_d}{\sqrt{n_d}}\right)$$

$$\text{Confidence Interval} = \overline{x}_d \pm T_{\alpha/2}(n - 1) \times \left(\frac{s_d}{\sqrt{n_d}}\right)$$

Remember, a confidence interval tells the equivalent results for a two-tailed hypothesis test, but the confidence interval can also shed some light as to whether the difference is positive or negative. If we first compute the raw differences, we go from two lists to one list, and then we can use the confidence interval formula above.

REVIEW: HYPOTHESIS TESTING AND CONFIDENCE INTERVALS

A two-tailed hypothesis test at the α significance level is equivalent to a $100(1 - \alpha)\%$ confidence interval. A confidence interval tells you a range of likely values at a specified confidence level, whereas a hypothesis test tells you to what extent a specific sample statistic is likely.

When there are two population parameters, if 0 falls inside the confidence interval (negative lower bound, positive upper bound), then 0 is a likely value for the population mean difference. This is equivalent to failing to reject the null hypothesis at the α significance (so the p-value is above α).

If 0 falls outside the confidence interval, then 0 is not a likely value for the population mean difference. This is equivalent to rejecting the null hypothesis at the α significance (so the p-value is below α). Further, if the interval is entirely positive, then $\mu_1 - \mu_2 > 0$, which means that $\mu_1 > \mu_2$. If the interval is entirely negative, then $\mu_1 - \mu_2 < 0$, which means that $\mu_1 < \mu_2$.

EXAMPLE

You want to see if a person's weight changes significantly before and after going on a cruise. You randomly sample 7 people who are going on the same seven-day cruise and record their weights (in pounds) before they leave. After they return from the cruise, you weigh them again. Assume that the difference in weight before and after a cruise is normally distributed. Build a 99% confidence interval and perform the equivalent hypothesis test given the data below.

Subject	After Cruise	Before Cruise
1	175	171
2	157	156
3	128	123
4	152	145
5	174	169
6	207	202
7	259	250

Solution: To test for a significant difference with this matched pairs design, we have

$$H_0: \mu_d = 0$$
$$H_A: \mu_d \neq 0$$

Noting the same assumptions as before, we now compute the raw differences and note that they are generally larger than the ones in the previous example. Define the difference to be the weight after the cruise minus the weight before the cruise.

Subject	After Cruise	Before Cruise	d
1	175	171	4
2	157	156	1
3	128	123	5
4	152	145	7
5	174	169	5
6	207	202	5
7	259	250	9

Putting the numbers $4, 1, 5, 7, 5, 5, 9$ into L_1 on the TI-84, the summary statistics are

$$\bar{x}_d = 5.142857143$$
$$s_d = 2.478478796$$
$$n_d = 7$$

To get the T-score $T_{\alpha/2}(n-1)$, note that we need a 99% confidence interval. Drawing our T-distribution, we put 0.99 in the middle, so 0.01 is left over, and half of that is 0.005. We therefore need the T with $DF = 7 - 1 = 6$ that has probability 0.005 above, as in the following sketch:

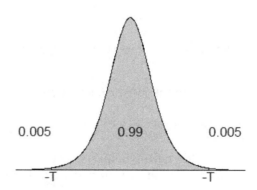

0.005 0.99 0.005

-T   -T

Next, $invT(0.005, 6) = -3.70742802$, which means that the T-score is $T_{0.005}(6) = 3.70742802$. We now have all four pieces to make the confidence interval:

$$\text{standard error} = \frac{s_d}{\sqrt{n_d}} = \frac{2.478478796}{\sqrt{7}} = 0.936776932$$
$$\text{margin of error} = T_{0.005}(6) \times (\text{standard error}) = 3.70742802 \times 0.936776932$$
$$= 3.473033047$$
$$\bar{x}_d \pm (\text{margin of error}) = 5.142857143 \pm 3.473033047$$
$$= (1.66982, 8.61589)$$

The 99% confidence interval does not contain 0 since it is entirely positive, which supports the alternative hypothesis that $\mu_d \neq 0$. This conclusion is equivalent to rejecting the null hypothesis. We can be a little more specific: since the confidence interval is positive, we can say the following:

$$\mu_{\text{After}} - \mu_{\text{Before}} > 0 \Rightarrow \mu_{\text{After}} > \mu_{\text{Before}}$$

In other words, not only is there a significant difference between weight after the cruise and weight before, the confidence interval tells us that the weight after the cruise is on average greater than the weight before the cruise, which is a more specific finding than simply declaring that they are different.

Now let's repeat this analysis for the hypothesis testing scenario. A 99% confidence interval corresponds to a two-tailed test at the $\alpha = 0.01$ significance level (because $100\% - 99\% = 1\%$). We compute the test statistic:

$$\text{standard error} = \frac{s_d}{\sqrt{n_d}} = \frac{2.478478796}{\sqrt{7}} = 0.936776932$$

$$T = \frac{\overline{x}_d - 0}{\text{standard error}} = \frac{5.142857143 - 0}{0.936776932} = 5.48995$$

To find the p-value, noting that this is a two-tailed test, we plot $T = 5.48995$ on the T-distribution with 6 degrees of freedom (because $DF = 7 - 1 = 6$) and find the probability to the right and double it.

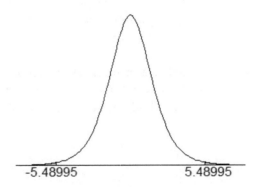

The lower limit is 5.48995 and the upper limit is 999999, so the p-value is

$$2 \times tcdf(5.48995, 999999, 6) = 0.00153$$

The p-value is below 0.01, so we reject the null hypothesis. There is sufficient evidence that the mean difference of weight after and before the cruise is different from 0. The hypothesis test tells us how significant the result is through the p-value, whereas the confidence interval tells us a range of likely values for the mean difference in weight.

Δ

It is now time to see how to do testing of two means of dependent groups on the TI-84. Since this matched pairs analysis is essentially the same as having one list of numbers, you can follow the same instructions as given in Chapters 8 and 9 for the mean confidence interval and hypothesis test. Nevertheless, we include them below. In both cases, assume that L_1 contains the computed differences.

TI-84 COMMAND: CONFIDENCE INTERVAL FOR DIFFERENCE OF DEPENDENT MEANS

To find the confidence interval for the population difference of dependent means, put the sample differences into a list by pressing $\boxed{\text{STAT}}$, choosing Option 1: Edit ..., and typing the numbers into the L_1 column.

From the home screen, press $\boxed{\text{STAT}}$, scroll right to TESTS, and choose Option 8: $TInterval$.

If you have your data typed into a list, choose Data for the input, L_1 for the List, select your desired confidence level, then scroll down to Calculate and press $\boxed{\text{ENTER}}$. On the other hand, if you are instead given $\overline{x}_d$, s_d, and n_d instead of the data values, choose Stats for the input. Type the values for $\overline{x}_d$, s_d, n_d, and the confidence level, then scroll down to Calculate and press $\boxed{\text{ENTER}}$. The output shows the confidence interval, the sample mean difference, the sample standard deviation of the differences, and the sample size.

TI-84 COMMAND: HYPOTHESIS TESTING FOR DIFFERENCE OF DEPENDENT MEANS

To conduct a hypothesis test for the population mean difference of dependent means, press $\boxed{\text{STAT}}$, scroll right to TESTS, and select Option 2: $T - Test$. For input, if your data are already stored in a list, select Data, but if you instead have the sample mean, standard deviation, and size of the differences, select Stats.

If you chose Data, type the null hypothesis value (this will be 0) and your list name (in our example, L_1). If you chose Stats, type the null hypothesis value of 0, the sample mean difference ($\overline{x}_d$), the sample standard deviation of the differences (s_d), and the sample size (n_d). After these necessary inputs, select the appropriate symbol for the alternative hypothesis ($\neq \mu_0, < \mu_0, > \mu_0$). Choose Calculate, and the resulting output shows the following:

The alternative hypothesis selected.
The T-statistic.
The p-value (denoted as p).
The sample mean difference (denoted as $\overline{x}$).
The sample standard deviation of the differences (denoted as s).
The sample size (denoted as n).

EXAMPLE

Repeating the previous example, let's get the 99% confidence interval. Choosing Option 8: $TInterval$, we either enter L_1 (already with the data), or we can enter $\overline{x}_d = 5.142857143$, $s_d = 2.478478796$, $n_d = 7$, and a confidence level of 0.99. Pressing Calculate, we get $(1.6698, 8.6159)$, which matches our earlier result.

To do the hypothesis test, we choose Option 2: $T - Test$. We enter the same numbers and choose a two-tailed test with a null value of 0. Pressing Calculate, we get $T = 5.489948532$ and a p-value of 0.0015291382, both of which match our earlier results.

Δ

Section 10.2 – Hypothesis Testing of Two Independent Proportions

The next topic to explore is hypothesis testing for when we have two groups, each of which has its own proportion, but this time the two groups are independent of each other. This means that the outcomes of one group have no impact on the outcomes of the other group. In contrast, the matched pairs scenario involved two dependent groups. Thus, when you are faced with two groups and need to do hypothesis testing or a confidence interval, in addition to deciding whether the problem involves means or proportions, you also need to decide whether they are dependent or independent.

The easiest way to see whether two groups are independent is to see if the subjects in the first group are different from the subjects in the second group. (Of course, we also require that there are no familial ties between the groups such as twins.) On that note, if the two sample sizes happen to be different from each other, then the two groups cannot involve the same people and therefore must be independent.

To generate a confidence interval and hypothesis testing for the difference of two proportions, note that we will be using the normal distribution because the test statistic will be a Z. The general process of forming a confidence interval and hypothesis test is the same as what we have already seen, but the formulas expand in ways we haven't seen before, especially for the standard error.

To begin, let p_1 and p_2 denote the population proportion for the first and second group, respectively, which are assumed to be independent of each other. The first group has n_1 subjects, x_1 of which are successes, while the second group has n_2 subjects, x_2 of which are successes. Thus, the sample proportions are $\hat{p}_1 = x_1/n_1$ and $\hat{p}_2 = x_2/n_2$.

Since we are interested in testing whether there is a difference between the two group proportions, the hypotheses would be written as follows. (You could also do a left-tailed or right-tailed test if necessary.)

$$H_0: p_1 - p_2 = 0$$
$$H_A: p_1 - p_2 \neq 0$$

Let's start with the confidence interval formula.

CONFIDENCE INTERVAL FOR DIFFERENCE OF INDEPENDENT PROPORTIONS

For a confidence interval for the difference of two population proportions, we have the following, which can be computed in the four steps outlined below:

$$\text{Point Estimate} = \hat{p}_1 - \hat{p}_2$$

$$\text{Standard Error} = \sqrt{\frac{\hat{p}_1(1 - \hat{p}_1)}{n_1} + \frac{\hat{p}_2(1 - \hat{p}_2)}{n_2}}$$

$$\text{Margin of Error} = Z_{\alpha/2}\sqrt{\frac{\hat{p}_1(1 - \hat{p}_1)}{n_1} + \frac{\hat{p}_2(1 - \hat{p}_2)}{n_2}}$$

$$\text{Confidence Interval} = (\hat{p}_1 - \hat{p}_2) \pm Z_{\alpha/2}\sqrt{\frac{\hat{p}_1(1 - \hat{p}_1)}{n_1} + \frac{\hat{p}_2(1 - \hat{p}_2)}{n_2}}$$

Although this formula might look a little scarier than what we are used to seeing, it is just an extension of the formula from Section 8.2. To use it, we check to see whether 0 is inside the interval. If 0 is outside the interval, this is equivalent to rejecting the null hypothesis, which brings us to the steps for conducting the hypothesis test:

Step 1: Set up the hypotheses.
The null hypothesis is

$$H_0: p_1 - p_2 = 0$$

The alternative hypothesis is one of the following:

$$H_A: p_1 - p_2 > 0 \qquad \text{(right-tailed test)}$$
$$H_A: p_1 - p_2 < 0 \qquad \text{(left-tailed test)}$$
$$H_A: p_1 - p_2 \neq 0 \qquad \text{(two-tailed test)}$$

Step 2: Check the assumptions.
For the hypothesis test to be valid, four assumptions need to be true:

1) The data must be categorical (meaning a characteristic is either true or is not).
2) The subjects must be randomly selected.
3) The two groups of subjects must be independent of each other.
4) Both samples must include at least 15 successes and 15 failures.

Step 3: Compute the test statistic.
Recall that the general test statistic formula is

$$\text{test statistic} = \frac{(\text{sample statistic}) - (\text{null value})}{\text{standard error}}$$

For a hypothesis test of the difference of two proportions, we first need to define the pooled sample proportion, which is just the sum of the successes per group divided by the sum of the sample sizes:

$$\hat{p} = \frac{x_1 + x_2}{n_1 + n_2}$$

The test statistic is

$$Z = \frac{\hat{p} - p_0}{\sqrt{\hat{p}(1 - \hat{p})\left(\frac{1}{n_1} + \frac{1}{n_2}\right)}}$$

Stated a simpler way, we can write

$$Z = \frac{(\hat{p}_1 - \hat{p}_2) - 0}{\text{standard error}} \quad \text{where} \quad \text{standard error} = \sqrt{\hat{p}(1 - \hat{p})\left(\frac{1}{n_1} + \frac{1}{n_2}\right)} \quad \text{and} \quad \hat{p} = \frac{x_1 + x_2}{n_1 + n_2}$$

Notice the test statistic is a Z-statistic because we are dealing with proportions. The reason we use a pooled sample proportion in the standard error is because under the null hypothesis, the proportions are equal to each other (analogous to Chapter 9, when we used p_0 in the test statistic standard error since this was the assumed proportion).

Step 4: Compute the p-value.
Since we have a Z-statistic, we must use the standard normal distribution to find the p-value. For a right-tailed test, we find the probability to the right of Z, as in the following graph.

$$H_A: p_1 - p_2 > 0$$

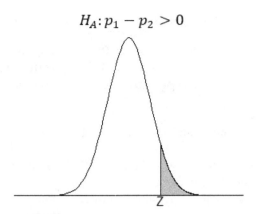

For a left-tailed test, we find the probability to the left of Z.

$$H_A: p_1 - p_2 < 0$$

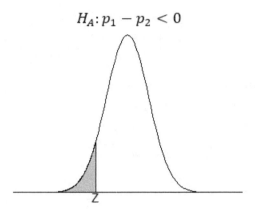

For a two-tailed test, we first plot Z and $-Z$ on the standard normal distribution. We then find the probability to the right of Z and double it.

$$H_A: p_1 - p_2 \neq 0$$

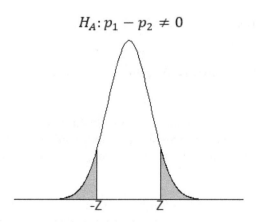

Step 5: State the conclusion.
Finally, we compare the p-value to a predetermined significance level α. If the p-value is below the significance level (p-value $< \alpha$), then...

1) We reject the null hypothesis.
2) There is sufficient evidence against the null hypothesis.
3) There is sufficient evidence for the alternative hypothesis.

If the p-value is above the significance level (p-value $> \alpha$), then…

1) We fail to reject the null hypothesis.
2) There is insufficient evidence against the null hypothesis.
3) There is insufficient evidence for the alternative hypothesis.

REVIEW: HYPOTHESIS TESTING FOR DIFFERENCE OF INDEPENDENT PROPORTIONS

Step 1: Set up the hypotheses.

$$H_0: p_1 - p_2 = 0$$
$$H_A: p_1 - p_2 > 0 \quad \text{or} \quad H_A: p_1 - p_2 < 0 \quad \text{or} \quad H_A: p_1 - p_2 \neq 0$$

Step 2: Check the assumptions.

1) Categorical data
2) Random samples
3) Two groups are independent of each other
4) At least 15 successes and 15 failures in both groups

Step 3: Compute the test statistic.

$$Z = \frac{(\hat{p}_1 - \hat{p}_2) - 0}{\text{standard error}} \quad \text{where} \quad \text{standard error} = \sqrt{\hat{p}(1 - \hat{p})\left(\frac{1}{n_1} + \frac{1}{n_2}\right)} \quad \text{and} \quad \hat{p} = \frac{x_1 + x_2}{n_1 + n_2}$$

Step 4: Compute the p-value.

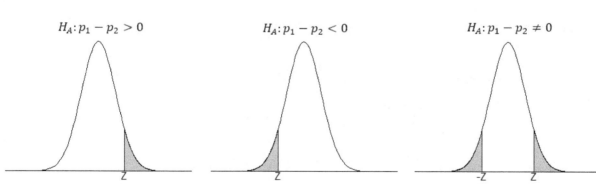

Step 5: State the conclusion.

If the p-value is below the significance level (p-value $< \alpha$), then …
1) We reject the null hypothesis.
2) There is sufficient evidence against the null hypothesis.
3) There is sufficient evidence for the alternative hypothesis.

If the p-value is above the significance level (p-value $> \alpha$), then...
1) We fail to reject the null hypothesis.
2) There is insufficient evidence against the null hypothesis.
3) There is insufficient evidence for the alternative hypothesis.

EXAMPLE

A researcher wants to see if there is a significant difference between the proportion of men and the proportion of women who play golf. He selects a random sample of 125 men and 138 women and finds that 67 men and 55 women play golf. Construct a 95% confidence interval and perform a hypothesis test at the $\alpha = 0.05$ significance level.

Solution: First, this is a proportion problem because a person either plays golf or does not. We have two groups, and they are independent because the two groups are separate from each other (no subject falls into both groups at once). Let's take Group 1 to be men and Group 2 to be women, and testing for a difference, our hypotheses are

$$H_0: p_1 - p_2 = 0$$
$$H_A: p_1 - p_2 \neq 0$$

There are more numbers than what we are used to seeing, so let's go ahead and label them. For the men, we have $x_1 = 67$ and $n_1 = 125$, and for the women, $x_2 = 55$ and $n_2 = 138$. This means that

$$\hat{p}_1 = \frac{x_1}{n_1} = \frac{67}{125} = 0.536$$
$$\hat{p}_2 = \frac{x_2}{n_2} = \frac{55}{138} = 0.3985507246$$

To make the confidence interval, the point estimate is

$$\hat{p}_1 - \hat{p}_2 = 0.536 - 0.3985507246 = 0.1374492754$$

The standard error is

$$\text{Standard Error} = \sqrt{\frac{\hat{p}_1(1 - \hat{p}_1)}{n_1} + \frac{\hat{p}_2(1 - \hat{p}_2)}{n_2}}$$
$$= \sqrt{\frac{0.536(1 - 0.536)}{125} + \frac{0.3985507246\,(1 - 0.3985507246\,)}{138}}$$
$$= \sqrt{0.001989632 + 0.0017370148}$$
$$= 0.0610462677$$

The margin of error for a 95% confidence interval is

$$\text{Margin of Error} = Z_{0.025}\sqrt{\frac{\hat{p}_1(1 - \hat{p}_1)}{n_1} + \frac{\hat{p}_2(1 - \hat{p}_2)}{n_2}} = 1.96 \times 0.0610462677$$
$$= 0.1196506847$$

The confidence interval is therefore

$$\text{Confidence Interval} = (\hat{p}_1 - \hat{p}_2) \pm Z_{0.025} \times \sqrt{\frac{\hat{p}_1(1-\hat{p}_1)}{n_1} + \frac{\hat{p}_2(1-\hat{p}_2)}{n_2}}$$

$$= 0.1374492754 \pm 0.1196506847$$

$$= (0.01780, 0.25710)$$

Notice that the confidence interval is entirely positive, so 0 is not inside. That means that there is a significant difference between the two group proportions (and in fact, the first proportion is significantly higher than the second), which means we will reject the null hypothesis. Now let's repeat the analysis using a two-tailed hypothesis test. To compute the test statistic, we will need the pooled sample proportion and the resulting standard error (which is different from the confidence interval standard error).

$$\hat{p} = \frac{67 + 55}{125 + 138} = \frac{122}{263} = 0.463878327$$

$$\text{standard error} = \sqrt{\hat{p}(1-\hat{p})\left(\frac{1}{n_1} + \frac{1}{n_2}\right)} = \sqrt{0.463878327(1 - 0.463878327)\left(\frac{1}{125} + \frac{1}{138}\right)}$$

$$= \sqrt{0.2486952247 \times 0.0152463768} = \sqrt{0.0037917011}$$

$$= 0.0615767903$$

$$Z = \frac{(\hat{p}_1 - \hat{p}_2) - 0}{\text{standard error}} = \frac{0.1374492754 - 0}{0.0615767903}$$

$$= 2.23216$$

Thus, the test statistic is $Z = 2.23216$. The two-tailed p-value is found by finding the probability above $Z = 2.23216$ and doubling it:

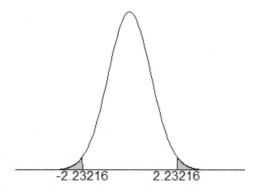

The lower limit is 2.23216 and the upper limit is 999999, so

$$2 \times normalcdf(2.23216, 999999) = 0.02560$$

Noting that the p-value is below 0.05, we reject the null hypothesis (as expected from the confidence interval), and we conclude that there is a significant difference between the proportions of men and women who play golf.

Δ

Luckily, the TI-84 will do these computations for us.

TI-84 COMMAND: CONFIDENCE INTERVAL FOR DIFFERENCE OF INDEPENDENT PROPORTIONS

To find the confidence interval for the difference of two independent proportions, press $\boxed{\text{STAT}}$, scroll right to TESTS, and choose Option B: $2 - propZInt$. Enter x_1 (the number of successes in Group 1), n_1 (the Group 1 sample size), x_2 (the number of successes in Group 2), n_2 (the Group 2 sample size), the desired confidence level, then scroll down to Calculate and press $\boxed{\text{ENTER}}$. The output shows the confidence interval, the two sample proportions, and the two sample sizes.

TI-84 COMMAND: HYPOTHESIS TESTING FOR DIFFERENCE OF INDEPENDENT PROPORTIONS

To conduct a hypothesis test for the difference of two independent proportions, press $\boxed{\text{STAT}}$, scroll right to TESTS, and select Option 6: $2 - PropZTest$. On the next screen, type x_1 (the number of successes in Group 1), n_1 (the Group 1 sample size), x_2 (the number of successes in Group 2), n_2 (the Group 2 sample size), the appropriate symbol for the alternative hypothesis ($\neq p_2, < p_2, > p_2$), then scroll down to Calculate and press $\boxed{\text{ENTER}}$. The resulting output shows the following:

The alternative hypothesis selected.
The Z-statistic.
The p-value (denoted as p).
The sample proportions $\hat{p}_1$ and $\hat{p}_2$, as well as the pooled sample proportion $\hat{p}$.
The sample sizes n_1 and n_2.

EXAMPLE

Repeating the previous example, let's get the 95% confidence interval. Choosing Option B: $2 - propZInt$, we enter $x_1 = 67$, $n_1 = 125$, $x_2 = 55$, $n_2 = 138$, and a confidence level of 0.95. Pressing Calculate, we get $(0.0178, 0.2571)$, which matches our earlier result.

To do the hypothesis test, we choose Option 6: $2 - PropZTest$. We enter the same numbers and choose a two-tailed test. Pressing Calculate, we get $Z = 2.232160439$ and a p-value of 0.0256042756, both of which match our earlier results (with more decimals).

Δ

Section 10.3 – Hypothesis Testing of Two Independent Means

The last topic in this chapter is hypothesis testing for when we have two independent groups, each of which has its own mean. Thus, we will build a confidence interval and hypothesis test for the difference of independent means. The process is different from that in Section 10.1 because previously the means were dependent, but now when they are independent, they must be analyzed differently. Again, you first must decide whether the two groups are independent or dependent, and if the latter, you instead need to use the matched pairs analysis.

To generate a confidence interval and hypothesis testing for the difference of two independent means, we go back to using the T-distribution and get a T-statistic. The general process of forming a confidence interval and hypothesis test is the same as what we have already seen, but once again the formulas expand in ways we haven't seen before. In addition, a new wrinkle is that the TI-84 will ask us whether we want the standard deviations pooled together. Generally speaking, the answer will be no, which affects the way the problem is analyzed. This approach is typically more realistic, which is why we will pursue it, but the only drawback is that the degrees of freedom formula becomes horrendous. This is because we now have two samples rather than just one. Fortunately, the TI-84 will compute it for us!

To begin, let $\overline{x}_1$, s_1, and n_1 denote the sample mean, sample standard deviation, and sample size of Group 1, and let $\overline{x}_2$, s_2, and n_2 denote the sample mean, sample standard deviation, and sample size of Group 2. These numbers will either be told to us, or we will be given the raw data for both groups and asked to compute the six summary numbers.

Since we are interested in testing whether there is a difference between the two group means, the hypotheses would be written as follows. (You could also do a left-tailed or right-tailed test if necessary.)

$$H_0: \mu_1 - \mu_2 = 0$$
$$H_A: \mu_1 - \mu_2 \neq 0$$

Let's start with the confidence interval formula.

CONFIDENCE INTERVAL FOR DIFFERENCE OF INDEPENDENT MEANS

For a confidence interval for the difference of two population means that are independent, we have the following, which can be computed in the four steps outlined below:

$$\text{Point Estimate} = \overline{x}_1 - \overline{x}_2$$

$$\text{Standard Error} = \sqrt{\frac{s_1^2}{n_1} + \frac{s_2^2}{n_2}}$$

$$\text{Margin of Error} = T_{\alpha/2}(DF)\sqrt{\frac{s_1^2}{n_1} + \frac{s_2^2}{n_2}}$$

$$\text{Confidence Interval} = (\overline{x}_1 - \overline{x}_2) \pm T_{\alpha/2}(DF)\sqrt{\frac{s_1^2}{n_1} + \frac{s_2^2}{n_2}}$$

This process is straightforward…until you see what to use for the degrees of freedom. Previously we had just one sample, but now that there are two, the formula gets a little…complicated, to put it mildly!

DEGREES OF FREEDOM FOR DIFFERENCE OF INDEPENDENT MEANS

To use the T-distribution correctly for the difference of two population means that are independent, the formula for degrees of freedom is given by

$$DF = \frac{\left(\frac{s_1^2}{n_1} + \frac{s_2^2}{n_2}\right)^2}{\frac{s_1^4}{n_1^2(n_1 - 1)} + \frac{s_2^4}{n_2^2(n_2 - 1)}}$$

Although we will practice using this formula once, realize that the TI-84 will compute the degrees of freedom for you, and hopefully the homework problem will be so kind as to just give it to you for this type of problem.

The above formulas are the ones to use if we cannot assume that the population variances are the same for both groups (remember variance is standard deviation squared). This will usually be the case, which is why we focus on it here. There are alternative formulas to use if you are assuming that the population variances are equal, but we delay that discussion until the end of this section (and even then, we will not dwell on it).

Once again, to use the confidence interval formula, we check to see whether 0 is inside the interval. If 0 is outside the interval, this is equivalent to rejecting the null hypothesis, and on that note, here are the steps for conducting the hypothesis test:

Step 1: Set up the hypotheses.
The null hypothesis is

$$H_0: \mu_1 - \mu_2 = 0$$

The alternative hypothesis is one of the following:

$$H_A: \mu_1 - \mu_2 > 0 \qquad \text{(right-tailed test)}$$
$$H_A: \mu_1 - \mu_2 < 0 \qquad \text{(left-tailed test)}$$
$$H_A: \mu_1 - \mu_2 \neq 0 \qquad \text{(two-tailed test)}$$

Step 2: Check the assumptions.
For the hypothesis test to be valid, four assumptions need to be true:

1) The data must be quantitative (meaning they are numbers that can be averaged).
2) The subjects must be randomly selected.
3) The two groups of subjects must be independent of each other.
4) At least one of the following statements must be true for both groups:
   a. The population is normal.
   b. The sample size is greater than 30.

Step 3: Compute the test statistic.
Recall that the general test statistic formula is

$$\text{test statistic} = \frac{(\text{sample statistic}) - (\text{null value})}{\text{standard error}}$$

For a hypothesis test of the difference of two independent means, the test statistic is

$$T = \frac{(\bar{x}_1 - \bar{x}_2) - 0}{\sqrt{\dfrac{s_1^2}{n_1} + \dfrac{s_2^2}{n_2}}}$$

Stated a simpler way, we can write

$$T = \frac{(\bar{x}_1 - \bar{x}_2) - 0}{\text{standard error}} \quad \text{where} \quad \text{standard error} = \sqrt{\frac{s_1^2}{n_1} + \frac{s_2^2}{n_2}}$$

Notice the test statistic is a T-statistic because we are dealing with means.

Step 4: Compute the p-value.
Since we have a T-statistic, we must use the T-distribution to find the p-value. For a right-tailed test, we find the probability to the right of T, as in the following graph.

$$H_A: \mu_1 - \mu_2 > 0$$

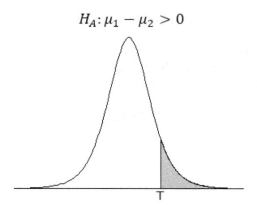

For a left-tailed test, we find the probability to the left of T.

$$H_A: \mu_1 - \mu_2 < 0$$

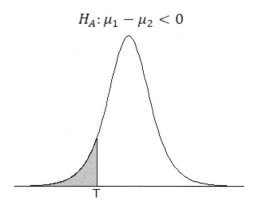

For a two-tailed test, we first plot T and $-T$ on the T-distribution. We then find the probability to the right of T and double it.

$$H_A: \mu_1 - \mu_2 \neq 0$$

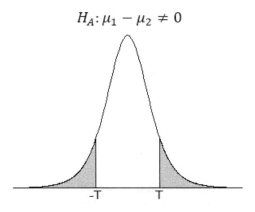

Step 5: State the conclusion.
Finally, we compare the p-value to a predetermined significance level α. If the p-value is below the significance level (p-value $< \alpha$), then...

1) We reject the null hypothesis.
2) There is sufficient evidence against the null hypothesis.
3) There is sufficient evidence for the alternative hypothesis.

If the p-value is above the significance level (p-value $> \alpha$), then…

    1)   We fail to reject the null hypothesis.
    2)   There is insufficient evidence against the null hypothesis.
    3)   There is insufficient evidence for the alternative hypothesis.

REVIEW: HYPOTHESIS TESTING FOR DIFFERENCE OF INDEPENDENT MEANS

<u>Step 1</u>: Set up the hypotheses.

$$H_0: \mu_1 - \mu_2 = 0$$
$$H_A: \mu_1 - \mu_2 > 0 \qquad \text{or} \qquad H_A: \mu_1 - \mu_2 < 0 \qquad \text{or} \qquad H_A: \mu_1 - \mu_2 \neq 0$$

<u>Step 2</u>: Check the assumptions.

    1) Quantitative data
    2) Random samples
    3) Two groups are independent of each other
    4) Normal population or sample size greater than 30 for both groups

<u>Step 3</u>: Compute the test statistic.

$$T = \frac{(\overline{x}_1 - \overline{x}_2) - 0}{\text{standard error}} \quad \text{where} \quad \text{standard error} = \sqrt{\frac{s_1^2}{n_1} + \frac{s_2^2}{n_2}}$$

<u>Step 4</u>: Compute the p-value.

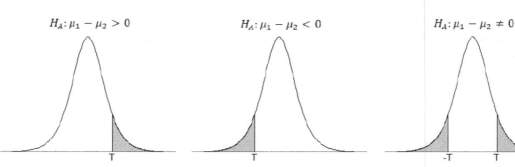

$$H_A: \mu_1 - \mu_2 > 0 \qquad\qquad H_A: \mu_1 - \mu_2 < 0 \qquad\qquad H_A: \mu_1 - \mu_2 \neq 0$$

<u>Step 5</u>: State the conclusion.

If the p-value is below the significance level (p-value $< \alpha$), then …
    1) We reject the null hypothesis.
    2) There is sufficient evidence against the null hypothesis.
    3) There is sufficient evidence for the alternative hypothesis.

If the p-value is above the significance level (p-value $> \alpha$), then…
    1) We fail to reject the null hypothesis.
    2) There is insufficient evidence against the null hypothesis.
    3) There is insufficient evidence for the alternative hypothesis.

EXAMPLE

To study whether the average GPAs of seniors from two different colleges are significantly different from each other, a researcher selects a random sample of 6 seniors from College A and 8 seniors from College B and asks them for their current GPAs. The responses are below. Build a 92% confidence interval and the equivalent two-tailed hypothesis test. You may assume that GPAs at both colleges are normally distributed.

College A: 3.42, 3.56, 3.81, 2.95, 3.14, 3.98
College B: 3.51, 4.00, 3.24, 2.71, 3.16, 3.12, 3.55, 3.75

Solution: Let's first state the hypotheses of interest. We are dealing with a means problem (because GPA is a number), and the two population means are independent because students fall into exactly one of the two groups (we can assume that no student attends both colleges at once). Since we are testing for a difference, we have (taking College A to be Group 1 and College B to be Group 2)

$$H_0: \mu_1 - \mu_2 = 0$$
$$H_A: \mu_1 - \mu_2 \neq 0$$

Let's go ahead and find the summary statistics by putting the above numbers into two lists L_1 and L_2:

$$\bar{x}_1 = 3.476666667$$
$$s_1 = 0.3912373534$$
$$n_1 = 6$$
$$\bar{x}_2 = 3.38$$
$$s_2 = 0.4056036066$$
$$n_2 = 8$$

To make the confidence interval, the point estimate is

$$\bar{x}_1 - \bar{x}_2 = 3.476666667 - 3.38 = 0.096666667$$

The standard error is

$$\text{Standard Error} = \sqrt{\frac{s_1^2}{n_1} + \frac{s_2^2}{n_2}} = \sqrt{\frac{0.3912373534^2}{6} + \frac{0.4056036066^2}{8}}$$
$$= \sqrt{0.0255111111 + 0.0205642857}$$
$$= 0.2146518037$$

I will be kind and tell you that the degrees of freedom for this problem is $DF = 11.1395981$ (yes, degrees of freedom can be a decimal). However, for the sake of practice, let's compute DF to make sure we can do it:

$$DF = \frac{\left(\frac{s_1^2}{n_1} + \frac{s_2^2}{n_2}\right)^2}{\frac{s_1^4}{n_1^2(n_1 - 1)} + \frac{s_2^4}{n_2^2(n_2 - 1)}} = \frac{\left(\frac{0.3912373534^2}{6} + \frac{0.4056036066^2}{8}\right)^2}{\frac{0.3912373534^4}{6^2(6 - 1)} + \frac{0.4056036066^4}{8^2(8 - 1)}}$$

Simplifying the numerator first (and pieces of the denominator),

$$DF = \frac{(0.0255111111 + 0.0205642857)^2}{\dfrac{0.3912373534^4}{6^2(6-1)} + \dfrac{0.4056036066^4}{8^2(8-1)}} = \frac{0.0021229422}{\dfrac{0.3912373534^4}{36(5)} + \dfrac{0.4056036066^4}{64(7)}}$$

Simplifying the denominator now, we get

$$DF = \frac{0.0021229422}{0.0001301633581 + 0.00006041283526} = 11.1395981$$

Now that we have the degrees of freedom, let's find the correct $T_{\alpha/2}(DF)$ for a 92% confidence interval. We draw 0.92 in the middle, so 0.08 is left over, and half of that is 0.04.

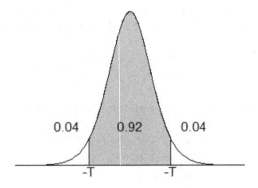

Next, $invT(0.04, 11.1395981) = -1.925987509$, so $T_{0.04}(11.1395981) = 1.925987509$ is the T-score. That means that the margin of error is

$$\text{Margin of Error} = T_{0.04}(11.1395981)\sqrt{\frac{s_1^2}{n_1} + \frac{s_2^2}{n_2}} = 1.925987509 \times 0.2146518037$$
$$= 0.4134166927$$

The confidence interval is therefore

$$\text{Confidence Interval} = (\overline{x}_1 - \overline{x}_2) \pm T_{0.04}(11.1395981)\sqrt{\frac{s_1^2}{n_1} + \frac{s_2^2}{n_2}}$$
$$= 0.096666667 \pm 0.4134166927$$
$$= (-0.31675, 0.51008)$$

Notice that the confidence interval contains 0 since the lower limit is negative and the upper limit is positive. That means that there is no significant difference between the college mean GPAs, and this is equivalent to failing to reject the null hypothesis. Now let's repeat the analysis using a two-tailed hypothesis test. To compute the test statistic, we can use the same standard error and degrees of freedom, and note that $\alpha = 0.08$.

$$\text{standard error} = \sqrt{\frac{s_1^2}{n_1} + \frac{s_2^2}{n_2}} = \sqrt{\frac{0.3912373534^2}{6} + \frac{0.4056036066^2}{8}}$$
$$= 0.2146518037$$

$$T = \frac{(\overline{x}_1 - \overline{x}_2) - 0}{\text{standard error}} = \frac{0.096666667 - 0}{0.2146518037}$$
$$= 0.45034$$

Thus, the test statistic is $T = 0.45034$. The two-tailed p-value is found by finding the probability above $T = 0.45034$ and doubling it:

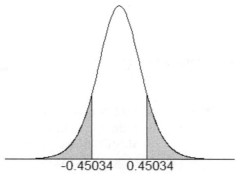

The lower limit is 0.45034 and the upper limit is 999999, so

$$2 \times tcdf(0.45034, 999999, 11.1395981) = 0.66110$$

Noting that the p-value is above 0.08, we don't reject the null hypothesis (as expected from the confidence interval), and we conclude that there is no significant difference between the mean GPAs of seniors from the two colleges.

Δ

Now let's see how the TI-84 can come to the rescue.

TI-84 COMMAND: CONFIDENCE INTERVAL FOR DIFFERENCE OF INDEPENDENT MEANS

To find the confidence interval for the difference of two population means that are independent, if the data numbers are provided, first put them into two lists by pressing $\boxed{\text{STAT}}$, choosing Option 1: Edit ..., and typing in the numbers into the L_1 and L_2 columns.

From the home screen, press $\boxed{\text{STAT}}$, scroll right to TESTS, and choose Option 0: $2 - SampTInt$.

If you have your data typed into L_1 and L_2, choose Data for the input, L_1 for List1, L_2 for List2, select your desired confidence level, choose No for Pooled, then scroll down to Calculate and press $\boxed{\text{ENTER}}$. On the other hand, if you are instead given $\overline{x}_1, s_1, n_1, \overline{x}_2, s_2$, and n_2 instead of the data values, choose Stats for the input. Type these six values and the confidence level, choose No for Pooled, then scroll down to Calculate and press $\boxed{\text{ENTER}}$. The output shows the confidence interval, the degrees of freedom, the two sample means, the two sample standard deviations, and the two sample sizes.

TI-84 COMMAND: HYPOTHESIS TESTING FOR DIFFERENCE OF INDEPENDENT MEANS

To conduct a hypothesis test for the difference of two population means that are independent, press $\boxed{\text{STAT}}$, scroll right to TESTS, and select Option 4: $2 - SampTTest$. For input, if your data are already stored in a list (say L_1 and L_2), select Data, but if you instead have the sample means, standard deviations, and sizes, select Stats.

If you chose Data, type L_1 for List1 and L_2 for List2, but if you chose Stats, type the numbers for $\overline{x}_1$, s_1, n_1, $\overline{x}_2$, s_2, and n_2. Select the appropriate symbol for the alternative hypothesis ($\neq \mu_2$, $< \mu_2$, $> \mu_2$), choose No for Pooled, then scroll down to Calculate and press $\boxed{\text{ENTER}}$. The resulting output shows the following:

The alternative hypothesis selected.
The T-statistic.
The p-value (denoted as p).
The degrees of freedom.
The two sample means, standard deviations, and sample sizes.

EXAMPLE

Repeating the previous example, let's get the 92% confidence interval. Choosing Option 0: $2 - SampTInt$, we either enter L_1 and L_2 (already with the data), or we can enter $\overline{x}_1 = 3.476666667$, $s_1 = 0.3912373534$, $n_1 = 6$, $\overline{x}_2 = 3.38$, $s_2 = 0.4056036066$, and $n_2 = 8$, and a confidence level of 0.92 with No for Pooled. Pressing Calculate, we get $(-0.3168, 0.51008)$, which matches our earlier result.

To do the hypothesis test, we choose Option 4: $2 - SampTTest$. We enter the same numbers and choose a two-tailed test (again, with No for Pooled). Pressing Calculate, we get $T = 0.4503417395$ and a p-value of 0.6611026444, both of which match our earlier results.

Δ

What is this question in the TI-84 commands about pooled? Some textbooks teach an alternative way of analyzing tests of two independent means by introducing a new assumption, that the two population variances are equal. If this is known to be true, then when you find the standard error used in the confidence interval and the hypothesis test, you can select Yes for Pooled. This means that the standard error uses a pooled standard deviation (rather like the hypothesis test standard error does for two proportions). In practice, this situation is less likely as it is generally unclear whether the population variances could be equal to each other.

Nevertheless, we state the updated formulas in the unlikely event you need to use them. The confidence interval and T-statistic are still

$$\text{Confidence Interval} = (\overline{x}_1 - \overline{x}_2) \pm T_{\alpha/2}(DF) \times (\text{standard error})$$

$$T = \frac{(\overline{x}_1 - \overline{x}_2) - 0}{\text{standard error}}$$

The standard error for the typical situation (when standard deviation is not pooled, which is what we have been using) is

$$\text{standard error} = \sqrt{\frac{s_1^2}{n_1} + \frac{s_2^2}{n_2}}$$

If we are instead going to assume that the two population variances are equal, then the standard error with pooled standard deviation becomes

$$\text{standard error} = s_p \sqrt{\frac{1}{n_1} + \frac{1}{n_2}} \quad \text{where} \quad s_p = \sqrt{\frac{(n_1 - 1)s_1^2 + (n_2 - 1)s_2^2}{n_1 + n_2 - 2}}$$

The other change is that if we pool the standard deviations, then $DF = n_1 + n_2 - 2$.

EXAMPLE

In the previous example, if we instead assume equal population variances, then

$$s_p = \sqrt{\frac{(n_1 - 1)s_1^2 + (n_2 - 1)s_2^2}{n_1 + n_2 - 2}} = \sqrt{\frac{(6 - 1)0.3912373534^2 + (8 - 1)0.4056036066^2}{6 + 8 - 2}}$$

$$= \sqrt{\frac{0.7653333335 + 1.1516}{12}} = \sqrt{0.1597444444}$$

$$= 0.3996804279$$

This means that

$$\text{standard error} = s_p\sqrt{\frac{1}{n_1} + \frac{1}{n_2}} = 0.3996804279\sqrt{\frac{1}{6} + \frac{1}{8}} = 0.3996804279 \times 0.5400617249$$

$$= 0.2158521013$$

The degrees of freedom is now

$$DF = n_1 + n_2 - 2 = 6 + 8 - 2 = 12$$

Noting that $tinv(0.04, 12) = -1.912313304$, $T_{0.04}(12) = 1.912313304$ is the confidence interval T-score, so

$$\text{Margin of Error} = T_{0.04}(12) \times (\text{standard error}) = 1.912313304 \times 0.2158521013 = 0.4127768449$$

Thus, the updated confidence interval is

$$\text{Confidence Interval} = (0.096666667 \pm 0.4127768449) = (-0.31611, 0.50944)$$

The updated test statistic for hypothesis testing is

$$T = \frac{(\overline{x}_1 - \overline{x}_2) - 0}{\text{standard error}} = \frac{0.096666667 - 0}{0.2158521013} = 0.44784$$

This results in an updated two-tailed p-value of

$$2 \times tcdf(0.44784, 999999, 12) = 0.66225$$

There are some slight differences between these results and the earlier ones without pooled standard deviations, but the overall conclusions are the same. The confidence interval still contains 0, and the p-value is still above $\alpha = 0.08$.

Δ

Once again, unless your textbook wants you to do otherwise, usually it is better not to pool the standard deviations; generally you should use the techniques earlier in this section.

Chapter 11 – Chi-Square Tests and F-Tests

In this final chapter we present the last few topics that may or may not be covered in a typical introductory statistics class. The topics in the first three sections cover applications of the chi-square distribution, including a goodness of fit test and a test for independence. The chapter moves on to hypothesis testing of a population variance, which uses the same distribution. The last two sections cover hypothesis testing of two population variances as well as ANOVA testing, both of which use the F-distribution. Some of the tests cannot be implemented easily on the TI-84, so when this happens, we need to resort to using statistical tables. As mentioned, some of these last few topics might not be covered in your class, in which case you can skip them (or if you are up to the challenge, by all means you can tackle them!).

Section 11.1 – Chi-Square Goodness of Fit Test

In Chapter 9 we saw how to use hypothesis testing to test whether a proportion is equal to a specific value (for instance, $p = 0.40$). In Chapter 10 we extended this idea to see if two different proportions are equal, as in $p_1 = p_2$. In the first section of this final chapter, we learn how to test many proportions at once. We can test whether they all equal one another, or if they are all equal to predetermined values. This is called a goodness of fit test.

DEFINITION

A **goodness of fit test** is a statistical procedure that tests whether a group of proportions are all equal to specific values, or alternatively whether they are all equal to one another. For instance, given three proportions, we could test the statement that $p_1 = 0.20$, $p_2 = 0.30$, and $p_3 = 0.50$. Alternatively, given four proportions, we could test whether they are all equal, as in $p_1 = p_2 = p_3 = p_4 = 0.25$.

As an example, a coffee shop claims to sell coffee drinks in the following percentages:

Regular	French Vanilla	Caramel	Pumpkin	Peppermint	Gingerbread
10%	24%	33%	16%	5%	12%

We can test all these percentages in one test using the goodness of fit test by taking a random sample of customers to this coffee shop and asking them which flavor of coffee they bought. Then we compute the sample percentages of the six possible flavors and see how close they are to the claimed percentages. Over the next few pages, we will perform the goodness of fit test on this example.

Suppose we randomly select 140 customers and obtain the following counts: 12 regular, 30 French vanilla, 42 caramel, 27 pumpkin, 12 peppermint, and 17 gingerbread. These are the observed values.

To conduct the test, we need to compare these observed values to the values that we would expect to see from a sample of 140 customers, assuming the stated percentages are correct. Such counts are called the expected counts, and each is computed by multiplying the sample size by the expected proportion.

DEFINITION

Given a sample of size n, the **observed counts** are the counts that are seen in the sample broken down by the categories of interest. The **expected counts** are the counts that we expect to see in the sample if the assumed population proportions are correct. The first expected count is computed as $n \times p_1$, the second expected count is $n \times p_2$, and so on.

For instance, if the percentage of regular coffee drinks really is 10%, then given 140 customers, we would expect about $140 \times 0.10 = 14$ of them to choose a regular drink.

Returning to our example, here is a table comparing the observed counts to the expected counts, the latter of which is computed as $n \times$(expected proportion).

Coffee Flavor	Observed Counts	Assumed Proportions	Expected Counts
Regular	12	0.10	140 X 0.10 = 14
French Vanilla	30	0.24	140 X 0.24 = 33.6
Caramel	42	0.33	140 X 0.33 = 46.2
Pumpkin	27	0.16	140 X 0.16 = 22.4
Peppermint	12	0.05	140 X 0.05 = 7
Gingerbread	17	0.12	140 X 0.12 = 16.8
Total	140	1.00	140

To interpret this table for, say, gingerbread-flavored coffee, a sample of 140 customers on average is expected to contain 16.8 gingerbread-flavored coffees if the true percentage were 12%. In this particular sample, there were actually 17 coffees of this flavor, which is almost right on par with the expected amount. On the other hand, we expect to see on average 46.2 caramel coffee drinks, whereas we actually saw 42, a little lower than expected.

Just as with hypothesis testing, some small amounts of differences between observed and expected are to be expected (pun intended!). The question is how much is too much to the point where we cast doubt on the claimed percentages. This is where goodness of fit testing comes to the rescue. This kind of test checks how far away our observed counts are from the expected counts.

Before we state the testing steps, we first need to introduce a new distribution. We have seen the binomial, normal, and T-distributions. It is now time to make your acquaintance with the fourth one in these notes, the chi-square distribution.

PROPERTIES OF THE CHI-SQUARE DISTRIBUTION

Property 1: The total area under the curve for the chi-square distribution is 1.

Property 2: The chi-square distribution is skewed right, which means the right tail is longer than the left tail.

Property 3: The notation for a chi-square test statistic is X^2, while the name of the distribution is often denoted in mathematical notation as the χ^2 distribution, with the Greek letter χ (pronounced "kai") with the "squared" notation.

Property 4: The chi-square distribution takes a degrees of freedom value and takes on different shapes (and consequently different probabilities) for different values of degrees of freedom.

Property 5: The lowest possible value the chi-square distribution can take is 0.

Let's discuss these points further.

Property 1: Just like the previous distributions, the total area under the chi-square distribution curve is 1, so the same techniques of finding the area of one side given the other side still apply here.

Property 2: Unlike the normal and T-distributions, the chi-square distribution is skewed right, so the right tail is longer than the left. This means that the chi-square distribution is not symmetric.

Property 3: In 1900, the English mathematician Karl Pearson introduced the chi-square test. The notation he used for it was χ^2, partly because of a theoretical connection to the normal distribution full formula involving the square of a normally distributed variable. However, Friedrich Robert Helmert, a German geodesist, had earlier introduced the chi-square distribution itself in 1876 (whereas Pearson created a statistical test based on the distribution).

Property 4: The shape of the chi-square distribution is different depending on the degrees of freedom. This is similar to how the T-distribution works with different sample sizes. The following graph shows what the distribution looks like for $DF = 4$ and $DF = 5$.

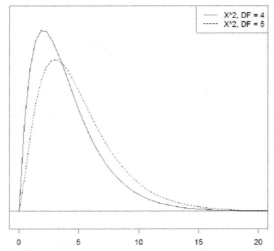

This skewed-right image usually describes the chi-square distribution. However, it should be noted that the distribution does not look like that when $DF = 1$ or 2. For those two values, the distribution instead looks like a steep curve that is declining the further right we go, as in the following graph. (We will see these cases later in this chapter.)

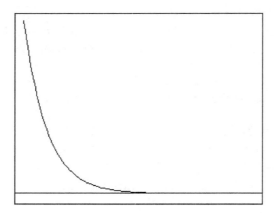

Property 5: Unlike the normal and T-distributions, the lowest value the chi-square distribution can take is 0. (With the normal and T-distributions, the distribution can go to negative infinity). However, the upper limit can still be positive infinity. These facts can be seen in the above graph.

Just like with the T-distribution, when using the chi-square distribution, we need to enter a quantity called degrees of freedom.

DEFINITION

The **degrees of freedom** (abbreviated DF) is a quantity that influences the overall shape of the chi-square distribution. For a goodness of fit test, $DF = c - 1$ where c is the number of categories in a table, so here degrees of freedom is equal to the number of categories minus one.

Remember not to use $n - 1$ here because that was for hypothesis testing of a mean.

We also need to discuss how to use the chi-square distribution on the TI-84.

TI-84 COMMAND: CHI-SQUARE DISTRIBUTION

To find the probability between a lower limit and an upper limit given a specified DF, press $\boxed{\text{2nd}}$, $\boxed{\text{VARS}}$, and choose Option 8: $\chi^2 cdf$(. The command is

$$\chi^2 cdf(\text{lower limit}, \text{upper limit}, DF)$$

If there is no upper limit, use 999999.

EXAMPLE

Let's find the probability above $X^2 = 12.5$ for a table with 8 categories. A sketch looks like the following:

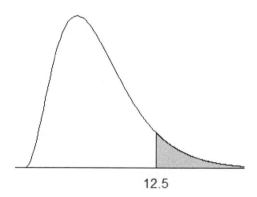

12.5

The lower limit is $X^2 = 12.5$, and since there is no upper limit, we can say $X^2 = 999999$. Since $c = 8$, $DF = 7$ and therefore

$$\chi^2 cdf(12.5, 999999, 7) = 0.08527$$

Δ

Now that we have seen the chi-square distribution, the following is a description of the goodness of fit test.

CHI-SQUARE GOODNESS OF FIT TEST

Assume that we have a table containing c categories and that each of the categories is believed to have proportions $p_1, p_2, \ldots, p_c$ (where all proportions add to 1). A random sample of size n is drawn, and the subjects are classified into one of the c categories.

Step 1: State the null and alternative hypotheses.
H_0: The proportions as stated are correct.
H_A: At least one of the stated proportions is incorrect.

Step 2: Create a table of the observed counts and the expected counts. The expected count is computed as $n \times$ (stated proportion) in each category.

Step 3: There are two assumptions to check for the test to be valid.
Assumption 1: The sample must be randomly chosen.
Assumption 2: The **expected** counts per category all need to be at least 5.

Step 4: Compute the chi-square test statistic across all categories using the formula

$$X^2 = \sum \frac{(\text{Observed} - \text{Expected})^2}{\text{Expected}}$$

Step 5: Compute the p-value by finding the probability above X^2 on the chi-square distribution with degrees of freedom equal to $DF = c - 1$. This is always a right-tailed p-value.

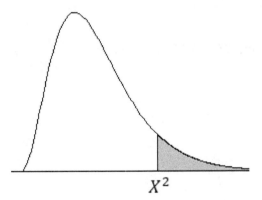

X^2

Step 6: State the conclusion:
If the p-value is below the significance level α, we reject the null hypothesis.
There is evidence that at least one of the stated proportions is incorrect

If the p-value is above the significance level α, we fail to reject the null hypothesis.
There is no evidence that the stated proportions are incorrect.

To further clarify, we could also write out the null hypothesis using the provided assumed proportion numbers. For instance, given three categories, we might write $H_0: p_1 = 0.20, p_2 = 0.30, p_3 = 0.50$, or we could write H_0: The three stated proportions are correct. Similarly, for the alternative hypothesis, we could write H_A: The stated proportions are incorrect, or we could write H_A: At least one of the three stated proportions is incorrect.

For the second assumption listed, note that we require all expected counts in the tables to be at least 5. If there is an observed count less than 5, that is not a concern, as long as all expected counts are at least 5.

Regarding the chi-square test statistic, in each of the c categories you compute the quantity stated, and then you add up all c calculations.

EXAMPLE

Let's return to our coffee flavor example and use the goodness of fit test to see if the six stated proportions are correct. Here is the problem again. A coffee shop claims to sell coffee drinks in the following percentages:

Regular	French Vanilla	Caramel	Pumpkin	Peppermint	Gingerbread
10%	24%	33%	16%	5%	12%

Suppose we randomly select 140 customers and obtain the following counts: 12 regular, 30 French vanilla, 42 caramel, 27 pumpkin, 12 peppermint, and 17 gingerbread. We need to conduct a chi-square goodness of fit test to see if the six stated percentages are correct at the 5% significance level.

Solution: First, let's state the null and alternative hypotheses.

H_0: The six stated proportions are correct.
H_A: At least one of the six stated proportions is incorrect.

Alternatively, we could state them as follows:

H_0: $p_1 = 0.10$, $p_2 = 0.24$, $p_3 = 0.33$, $p_4 = 0.16$, $p_5 = 0.05$, $p_6 = 0.12$
H_A: At least one of the six stated proportions is incorrect.

The second step is to check the assumptions. The sample was randomly selected, and for the second assumption we need to compute the expected counts per coffee flavor. We computed them earlier, so the table is repeated below.

Coffee Flavor	Observed Counts	Assumed Proportions	Expected Counts
Regular	12	0.10	140 X 0.10 = 14
French Vanilla	30	0.24	140 X 0.24 = 33.6
Caramel	42	0.33	140 X 0.33 = 46.2
Pumpkin	27	0.16	140 X 0.16 = 22.4
Peppermint	12	0.05	140 X 0.05 = 7
Gingerbread	17	0.12	140 X 0.12 = 16.8
Total	140	1.00	140

Note that all the expected counts $(14, 33.6, 46.2, 22.4, 7, 16.8)$ are at least 5, so both assumptions are satisfied.

The third step is to compute the chi-square test statistic. We need to compute a total of six calculations and add them up. For the regular category, we have

$$\frac{(\text{Observed} - \text{Expected})^2}{\text{Expected}} = \frac{(12 - 14)^2}{14} = \frac{(-2)^2}{14} = \frac{4}{14} = 0.2857142857$$

As another example, for the French vanilla category,

$$\frac{(\text{Observed} - \text{Expected})^2}{\text{Expected}} = \frac{(30 - 33.6)^2}{33.6} = \frac{(-3.6)^2}{33.6} = \frac{12.96}{33.6} = 0.3857142857$$

Continuing, we compute this quantity for all six categories and then add them:

$$
\begin{aligned}
X^2 &= \sum \frac{(\text{Observed} - \text{Expected})^2}{\text{Expected}} \\
&= \frac{(12 - 14)^2}{14} + \frac{(30 - 33.6)^2}{33.6} + \frac{(42 - 46.2)^2}{46.2} + \frac{(27 - 22.4)^2}{22.4} + \frac{(12 - 7)^2}{7} + \frac{(17 - 16.8)^2}{16.8} \\
&= 0.2857142857 + 0.3857142857 + 0.3818181818 + 0.9446428571 + 3.571428571 \\
&\quad + 0.0023809524 \\
&= 5.57170
\end{aligned}
$$

The fourth step is to compute the p-value by finding the probability above $X^2 = 5.57170$. The following sketch illustrates this region of the chi-square distribution:

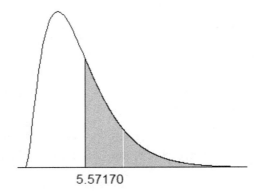

5.57170

Since there are $c = 6$ categories (flavors of coffee), $DF = 6 - 1 = 5$. The p-value is

$$\chi^2 cdf(5.57170, 999999, 5) = 0.35015$$

Noting that the p-value is above $\alpha = 0.05$, we fail to reject the null hypothesis. There is no evidence that the six stated proportions are incorrect. Put another way, based on our sample, there is no reason to doubt the coffee shop's claims of the six proportions of coffee flavors that the customers choose.

Δ

As we saw with earlier calculations, we can also use the TI-84 to calculate the goodness of fit test. Here are the steps for doing so.

TI-84 COMMAND: CHI-SQUARE GOODNESS OF FIT TEST

To conduct a chi-square goodness of fit test, first put the observed and expected counts into two separate lists by pressing $\boxed{\text{STAT}}$, choosing Option 1: Edit ..., and typing the observed counts into the L_1 column and the expected counts into the L_2 column.

From the home screen, press $\boxed{\text{STAT}}$, scroll right to TESTS, and choose Option D: $\chi^2 GOF - Test$. Choose L_1 for Observed and L_2 for Expected, enter the correct degrees of freedom, then scroll down to Calculate and press $\boxed{\text{ENTER}}$. The output shows the chi-square test statistic and the p-value.

EXAMPLE
To illustrate this procedure using the previous example, enter the observed counts $12, 30, 42, 27, 12,$ and 17 into L_1. Next, enter the expected counts $14, 33.6, 46.2, 22.4, 7,$ and 16.8 into L_2. By pressing $\boxed{\text{STAT}}$, scrolling right to TESTS, and choosing Option D: $\chi^2 GOF - Test$, we obtain $X^2 = 5.571699134$ and a p-value of 0.3501478475, which match what we computed by hand.

Δ

EXAMPLE
Suppose we interview a randomly selected group of 200 students asking them which method of exercise was their favorite when they visit the gym. The following summarizes their responses.

Treadmill	Elliptical	Weights	Swimming
34	54	65	47

Is there enough evidence to indicate that the proportions favoring each category are significantly different from each other at the 0.05 significance level?

Solution: This question is quite different because we have not been directly told what proportions to test. However, notice we are testing to see if the category proportions are equal to one another. Since there are 4 categories, under the null hypothesis each should have proportion 1/4, or 0.25.

This means that in general, when we have c categories and we are testing for equal proportions, under the null hypothesis each category proportion is $1/c$.
The hypotheses are as follows.

H_0: The four proportions are equal to one another, or $p_1 = p_2 = p_3 = p_4 = 0.25$.
H_A: At least one of the four proportions is not equal to the others.

The table of observed and expected counts is shown below.

Exercise	Observed Counts	Assumed Proportions	Expected Counts
Treadmill	34	0.25	200 X 0.25 = 50
Elliptical	54	0.25	200 X 0.25 = 50
Weights	65	0.25	200 X 0.25 = 50
Swimming	47	0.25	200 X 0.25 = 50
Total	200	1.00	200

Regarding the two assumptions, the sample was randomly selected, and each of the expected counts is equal to 50, above the minimum requirement of 5. So this problem is going to "work out" for us!

Let's solve this problem by hand first and then repeat the calculations using the TI-84. The chi-square test statistic is

$$X^2 = \sum \frac{(\text{Observed} - \text{Expected})^2}{\text{Expected}}$$
$$= \frac{(34 - 50)^2}{50} + \frac{(54 - 50)^2}{50} + \frac{(65 - 50)^2}{50} + \frac{(47 - 50)^2}{50}$$

$$= 5.12 + 0.32 + 4.5 + 0.18$$
$$= 10.12$$

The next step is to compute the p-value by finding the probability above $X^2 = 10.12$. The following sketch illustrates this region of the chi-square distribution:

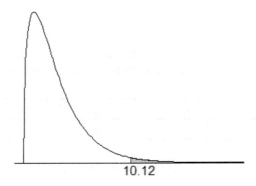

10.12

Since there are $c = 4$ categories (exercise methods), $DF = 4 - 1 = 3$. The p-value is

$$\chi^2 cdf(10.12, 999999, 3) = 0.01757$$

Noting that the p-value is below $\alpha = 0.05$, we reject the null hypothesis and conclude that at least one of the four category proportions is different from the others. The goodness of fit test does not tell us specifically which categories are different (there are additional statistical tests we could use that we will not discuss here), but looking at the observed counts, it appears that treadmill and weights might be the "offending" categories.

Repeating the calculations on the TI-84, enter the observed counts $34, 54, 65$, and 47 into L_1. Next, enter the expected counts $50, 50, 50$, and 50 into L_2. By pressing $\boxed{\text{STAT}}$, scrolling right to TESTS, and choosing Option D: $\chi^2 GOF - Test$, we obtain $X^2 = 10.12$ and a p-value of 0.0175731552, which match what we computed by hand.

Δ

EXAMPLE
We are interested in the breakdown of 1st, 2nd, 3rd, 4th, and 5th year college students taking a literature class, and we want to investigate whether the proportions are equal to one another. The following table contains the observed and expected counts per year based on a survey from 130 randomly selected students.

	1st-Year	2nd-Year	3rd-Year	4th-Year	5th-Year
Observed	60	37	18	15	0
Expected	26	26	26	26	26

A) State the null and alternative hypotheses.
B) One of the observed counts is 0. Can the goodness of fit test still be performed?
C) True/False: In general, the sum of the expected counts is equal to the total sample size.
D) True/False: In general, the further away the observed counts are from the corresponding expected counts, the larger the chi-square statistic.

E) Given that the test statistic is $X^2 = 82.23077$, find the p-value and state your conclusion at the $\alpha = 0.01$ significance level.

F) Would it be a good idea to look at the observed counts before choosing a set of assumed category proportions so that we can force a "fail to reject the null" conclusion?

Solution: For part A, the hypotheses are as follows.

H_0: The five proportions are equal to one another.
H_A: At least one of the five proportions is not equal to the others.

For part B, note that the sample was randomly selected and that each expected category count is $130 \times 0.20 = 26$, where the 0.20 is equal to $1/5$ since there are 5 categories. The expected counts are all greater than 5, so the assumptions have been met. The fact that there are no 5th year students taking the class does not cause a problem since that is an observed count.

Regarding part C, the sum of the expected counts is always equal to the total sample size n. Obviously the sum of the observed counts is equal to n, but you can check the preceding examples to verify that the expected counts also add to n. For instance, here $26 + 26 + 26 + 26 + 26 = 130$, and using the expected count formula for 5 categories, notice that

$$(n \times p_1) + (n \times p_2) + (n \times p_3) + (n \times p_4) + (n \times p_5) = n \times (p_1 + p_2 + p_3 + p_4 + p_5)$$
$$= n \times 1$$
$$= n$$

For part D, notice that the calculation per category is

$$\frac{(\text{Observed} - \text{Expected})^2}{\text{Expected}}$$

This calculation generally gets larger when the observed and expected counts are far from each other since this creates a larger numerator. Thus, the further away the observed counts are from the corresponding expected counts, the larger the chi-square statistic and therefore the smaller the p-value. (By a similar argument, when the observed and expected counts are close together, the chi-square statistic is smaller, resulting in a larger p-value.)

Part E says that $X^2 = 82.23077$, and the following sketch illustrates this region of the chi-square distribution. Note that since the test statistic is so high, the X^2 is far to the right on the sketch, much higher than the main part of the distribution.

82.23077

Since there are $c = 5$ categories (student years), $DF = 5 - 1 = 4$. The p-value is

$$\chi^2 cdf(82.23077, 4) = 5.86 \times 10^{-17}$$

Once again, we encounter scientific notation, which tells us that the p-value most certainly is below 0.01. (To be more precise, it is 0.0000000000000000586 – that is 586 preceded by sixteen 0s!) We reject the null hypothesis and conclude that at least one of the five category proportions is different from the others. It certainly appears that "1st year" and "5th year" are among the "offending" categories.

As for part F, should we look at the observed counts before choosing a set of assumed category proportions, thereby forcing a small chi-square statistic and a "pass?" The answer is no – as we discussed with hypothesis testing, this is cheating since we would be peeking at the data before making our guesses about the category proportions. As I mentioned back in Chapter 9, this is like opening a Christmas present early!

$$\Delta$$

Section 11.2 – Chi-Square Independence Test

Back in Chapter 3, when we were learning about relative risk, we looked at the following table:

	Left-Handed	Right-Handed	Total
Male	260	620	880
Female	240	580	820
Total	500	1200	1700

We talked about looking at the conditional proportions, and based on how different they were, we could predict if there was an association between gender and whether someone was left-handed or right-handed. However, we had stopped there because we did not yet have the skills needed to formally test for an association. Now we will learn a procedure that tests if there is an association between these two variables. It is called the chi-square independence test.

DEFINITION
An **independence test** is a statistical procedure that tests whether there is an association between the explanatory variable (the row categories) and the response variable (the column categories) in a table. That is, an independence test checks if two variables are independent of each other or if there is an association between them, and if so, how strong the association is.

Using the above table as an example, we can do an independence test by taking a random sample of people, dividing them by gender, and asking each person whether they are left-handed or right-handed. Then we compute the observed counts and see how close they are to the expected counts (which also need to be computed). Over the next few pages, we will perform the independence test on this example.

DEFINITION
Given a sample of size n (the grand total number of subjects), the **observed counts** are the counts that are seen in the sample broken down by the rows and columns in the contingency table of interest. The **expected counts** are the counts that we expect to see in each cell in the table if there is no association between the explanatory and response variables. Unlike the goodness of fit test, the expected count for a given cell in the table is computed as

$$\text{Expected Count} = \frac{(\text{Row Total})(\text{Column Total})}{\text{Grand Total}}$$

When we calculate these expected counts, these are the counts we would expect to get if there really is no association between these two variables.

Returning to the table, here are the observed counts, the data we actually collected:

	Left-Handed	Right-Handed	Total
Male	260	620	880
Female	240	580	820
Total	500	1200	1700

To compute the expected count for left-handed males, the top left cell, we need the row total and column totals for that cell. The row total (total males) is 880, while the column total (total left-handed people) is 500. The grand total number of subjects is 1700, and so the expected count for left-handed males is

$$\text{Expected Count} = \frac{(\text{Row Total})(\text{Column Total})}{\text{Grand Total}} = \frac{880 \times 500}{1700} = 258.8235294$$

This means that if there were no association in this table, we would expect to see, on average, 258.8235294 left-handed males. In fact we observed 260, very close but slightly higher than expected.

As another example, let's compute the expected count for left-handed females, the bottom left cell. The row total (total females) is 820, while the column total (total left-handed people) is 500. The grand total number of subjects is 1700, and so the expected count for left-handed females is

$$\text{Expected Count} = \frac{(\text{Row Total})(\text{Column Total})}{\text{Grand Total}} = \frac{820 \times 500}{1700} = 241.1764706$$

This means that if there were no association in this table, we would expect to see, on average, 241.1764706 left-handed females. In fact we observed 240, very close but slightly lower than expected. Continuing in this fashion, the table of expected counts is the following:

	Left-Handed	Right-Handed	Total
Male	$\dfrac{880 \times 500}{1700} = 258.8235294$	$\dfrac{880 \times 1200}{1700} = 621.1764706$	880
Female	$\dfrac{820 \times 500}{1700} = 241.1764706$	$\dfrac{820 \times 1200}{1700} = 578.8235294$	820
Total	500	1200	1700

Looking at the above tables, the observed counts are very close to the counts we would expect to get if there is no association between gender and whether someone is left-handed or right-handed. The following is a description of the independence test.

CHI-SQUARE INDEPENDENCE TEST

Assume that we have a table containing r rows for the explanatory variable and c columns for the response variable (and therefore $r \times c$ cells in the table). A random sample of size n is drawn, and the subjects are classified into one of the cells.

Step 1: State the null and alternative hypotheses.

H_0: There is no association between the explanatory and response variables.

H_A: There is an association between the explanatory and response variables.

Step 2: Create a table of the observed counts and the expected counts. In each cell of the table, the expected count is computed as

$$\text{Expected Count} = \frac{(\text{Row Total})(\text{Column Total})}{\text{Grand Total}}$$

Step 3: There are two assumptions to check for the test to be valid.

Assumption 1: The sample must be randomly chosen.

Assumption 2: The **expected** counts per category all need to be at least 5.

Step 4: Compute the chi-square test statistic across all rows and columns using the formula

$$X^2 = \sum \frac{(\text{Observed} - \text{Expected})^2}{\text{Expected}}$$

Step 5: Compute the p-value by finding the probability above X^2 on the chi-square distribution with degrees of freedom equal to $DF = (r-1)(c-1)$. This is always a right-tailed p-value. Here r is the number of rows and c is the number of columns (in both cases, not counting the last row and column with the total counts).

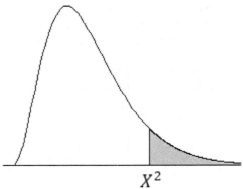

X^2

Step 6: State the conclusion:

If the p-value is below the significance level α, we reject the null hypothesis.
There is evidence of association between the explanatory and response variables.

If the p-value is above the significance level α, we fail to reject the null hypothesis.
There is no evidence of association between the explanatory and response variables.

As before, for the second assumption listed, note that we require all expected counts in the tables to be at least 5. If there is an observed count less than 5, that is not a concern, as long as all expected counts are at least 5. Regarding the chi-square test statistic, in each of the $r \times c$ categories you compute the quantity stated, and then you add up all $r \times c$ calculations. Finally, notice that the DF formula has changed from $(c - 1)$ to $(r - 1)(c - 1)$.

EXAMPLE

Let's return to our left/right-handed example and use the independence test to see if there is an association between gender and hand preference. Here are the observed counts again, and let's assume that the subjects were randomly selected.

	Left-Handed	Right-Handed	Total
Male	260	620	880
Female	240	580	820
Total	500	1200	1700

Solution: First, let's state the null and alternative hypotheses.

H_0: There is no association between the explanatory and response variables.
H_A: There is an association between the explanatory and response variables.

The second step is to check the assumptions. The sample was randomly selected, and for the second assumption we need to compute the expected counts per cell. We computed them earlier, so the table is repeated below.

	Left-Handed	Right-Handed	Total
Male	258.8235294	621.1764706	880
Female	241.1764706	578.8235294	400
Total	500	780	1280

Note that all the expected counts are at least 5, so both assumptions are satisfied.

The third step is to compute the chi-square test statistic. We need to compute a total of four calculations and add them up. For the left-handed males cell, we have

$$\frac{(\text{Observed} - \text{Expected})^2}{\text{Expected}} = \frac{(260 - 258.8235294)^2}{258.8235294} = \frac{(1.1764706)^2}{258.8235294} = \frac{1.384083073}{258.8235294}$$
$$= 0.0053475937$$

As another example, for the left-handed females cell,

$$\frac{(\text{Observed} - \text{Expected})^2}{\text{Expected}} = \frac{(240 - 241.1764706)^2}{241.1764706} = \frac{(-1.1764706)^2}{241.1764706} = \frac{1.384083073}{241.1764706}$$
$$= 0.005738881$$

Continuing, we compute this quantity for all $2 \times 2 = 4$ cells and then add them:

$$X^2 = \sum \frac{(\text{Observed} - \text{Expected})^2}{\text{Expected}}$$

$$= \frac{(260 - 258.8235294)^2}{258.8235294} + \frac{(240 - 241.1764706)^2}{241.1764706} + \frac{(620 - 621.1764706)^2}{621.1764706}$$
$$+ \frac{(580 - 578.8235294)^2}{578.8235294}$$
$$= 0.0053475937 + 0.005738881 + 0.002228164 + 0.0023912004$$
$$= 0.015706$$

The fourth step is to compute the p-value by finding the probability above $X^2 = 0.015706$. The following sketch illustrates this region of the chi-square distribution. (The strange shape is because $DF = 1$.)

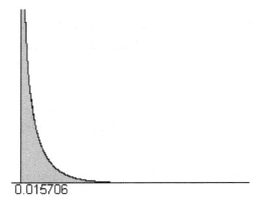

Since there are $r = 2$ rows and $c = 2$ columns in the table, $DF = (2 - 1)(2 - 1) = 1$. The p-value is

$$\chi^2 cdf(0.015706, 999999, 1) = 0.90027$$

Noting that the p-value is above $\alpha = 0.05$ (well above!), we fail to reject the null hypothesis. There is no evidence of association in the table. Put another way, based on our sample, there is no reason to say that there is an association between gender and whether a person is left-handed or right-handed.

Δ

We can also use the TI-84 to calculate the independence test (but be warned – these steps are a bit messier than what you are used to seeing!). Here are the steps for doing so.

TI-84 COMMAND: CHI-SQUARE INDEPENDENCE TEST

To conduct a chi-square independence test, we first need to create what is known as a matrix of the observed counts, followed by a second matrix of the expected counts. To do this, press [2nd] and [x^{-1}] to access the matrix menu. Scroll right to Edit, and select Option 1: [A]. Type in the dimensions of the table (number of rows followed by number of columns), and then in the resulting matrix type the observed counts. When finished, press [2nd] and [MODE] to quit and return to the home screen.

We then repeat these steps to build the second matrix. Again, press [2nd] and [x^{-1}] to access the matrix menu. Scroll right to Edit, and select Option 2: [B]. Type in the dimensions of the table (number of rows followed by number of columns), and then in the resulting matrix type the expected counts. When finished, press [2nd] and [MODE] to quit and return to the home screen.

Next, press $\boxed{\text{STAT}}$, scroll right to TESTS, and choose Option C: $\chi^2 - Test$. Here we need to enter the correct matrices (plural of matrix). For observed, press $\boxed{\text{2nd}}$ and $\boxed{x^{-1}}$ to access the matrix menu, and under the Names menu, choose Option 1: [A]. For expected, press $\boxed{\text{2nd}}$ and $\boxed{x^{-1}}$ to access the matrix menu again, and under the Names menu, choose Option 1: [B]. Finally, press Calculate, and the output will show you the chi-square test statistic, the p-value, and the degrees of freedom.

EXAMPLE

To illustrate this procedure using the previous example, enter the observed counts $260, 240, 620$, and 580 into matrix [A], specifying it to be a 2×2 matrix. Next, define the 2×2 matrix [B] and enter the expected counts $258.8235294, 241.1764706, 621.1764706$, and 578.8235294. Pressing $\boxed{\text{STAT}}$, scrolling right to TESTS, and choosing Option C: $\chi^2 - Test$, we obtain $X^2 = 0.0.0157058389$ and a p-value of 0.9002678932, which match what we computed by hand except with more decimals.

Δ

REVIEW: DEGREES OF FREEDOM

Be careful not to use $DF = n - 1$ or $DF = c - 1$ for the independence test since they were the degrees of freedom formulas for the T-distribution and the goodness of fit test, respectively.

For a confidence interval or hypothesis test for the population mean, $DF = n - 1$ where n is the sample size. (This is also used for a matched pairs difference of means.)

For a confidence interval or hypothesis test for the slope of a regression equation, $DF = n - 2$.

For a confidence interval or hypothesis test for the different of two independent population means, DF is the ugly formula (to coin a nifty technical term!) we saw in Chapter 10.

For a chi-square goodness of fit test, $DF = c - 1$ where c is the number of categories in a table.

For a chi-square independence test, $DF = (r - 1)(c - 1)$ where r is the number of rows and c is the number of columns in a table.

EXAMPLE

We survey a random selection of 300 people and ask them where they would rather go on holiday and in which season. The choice is between the mountains and the beach, and the seasons in question are winter, spring, and summer. That is, the subjects were asked, "Would you rather go on holiday in winter, spring, or summer? And would you prefer the mountains or the beach in your season of choice?" The results are shown below. Is there an association between the holiday location and the season of choice at the $\alpha = 0.05$ significance level?

	Winter	Spring	Summer	Total
Mountains	51	67	43	161
Beach	22	38	79	139
Total	73	105	122	300

Solution: We will first go through this problem by hand, then later using the TI-84 test. First, the hypotheses are as follows.

H_0: There is no association between holiday location and season of choice.

H_A: There is an association between holiday location and season of choice.

The second step is to compute the expected counts for the six cells. For the mountains and winter cell, note that the row total is 161 and the column total is 73, so the expected count is

$$\text{Expected Count} = \frac{161 \times 73}{300} = 39.17666667$$

This means that under the null hypothesis that there is no association between the two variables, one would expect to see, on average, 39. 17666667subjects responding that their choice would be to go to the mountains in the winter. In fact, there are 51 subjects, so the expected count is somewhat lower than what was observed. Repeating these calculations for the remaining cells, we get the table of expected counts.

	Winter	Spring	Summer	Total
Mountains	$\frac{161 \times 73}{300} = 39.17666667$	$\frac{161 \times 105}{300} = 56.35$	$\frac{161 \times 122}{300} = 65.47333333$	161
Beach	$\frac{139 \times 73}{300} = 33.82333333$	$\frac{139 \times 105}{300} = 48.65$	$\frac{139 \times 122}{300} = 56.52666667$	139
Total	73	105	122	300

Note that the subjects were randomly selected and that all six expected counts are greater than 5, so the assumptions are satisfied. The fourth step is to compute the test statistic:

$$
\begin{aligned}
X^2 &= \sum \frac{(\text{Observed} - \text{Expected})^2}{\text{Expected}} \\
&= \frac{(51 - 39.17666667)^2}{39.17666667} + \frac{(67 - 56.35)^2}{56.35} + \frac{(43 - 65.47333333)^2}{65.47333333} + \frac{(22 - 33.82333333)^2}{33.82333333} \\
&\quad + \frac{(38 - 48.65)^2}{48.65} + \frac{(79 - 56.52666667)^2}{56.52666667} \\
&= 3.568226266 + 2.01282165 + 7.713838372 + 4.132981503 + 2.331397739 + 8.934733653 \\
&= 28.693999
\end{aligned}
$$

The next step is to compute the p-value by finding the probability above $X^2 = 28.693999$. The following sketch illustrates this region of the chi-square distribution. (The strange shape is because $DF = 2$.)

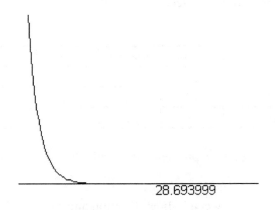

28.693999

There are $r = 2$ rows (holiday locations) and $c = 3$ columns (seasons), and again we do not count the row and column with the totals. That means

$$DF = (r - 1)(c - 1) = (2 - 1)(3 - 1) = 1 \times 2 = 2$$

The p-value is

$$\chi^2 cdf(28.69399, 999999, 2) = 5.88 \times 10^{-7}$$

Noting that the p-value (which is in scientific notation) is below $\alpha = 0.05$, we reject the null hypothesis and conclude that there is an association between holiday location and the season in which to go on holiday. (Writing out the p-value in decimals, it would be 0.000000588 – that's six zeros after the decimal – which as you can see is well below 0.05.)

Repeating the calculations on the TI-84, enter the observed counts $51, 67, 43$, $22, 38$, and 79 into matrix $[A]$, specifying it to be a 2×3 matrix. Next, create the 2×3 matrix $[B]$ and enter the expected counts $39.17666667, 56.35, 65.47333333, 33.82333333, 48.65$, and 56.52666667. Press $\boxed{\text{STAT}}$, scroll right to Tests, and choose Option C: $\chi^2 - Test$, and we obtain $\chi^2 = 28.69399919$ and a p-value of 5.88×10^{-7}, which match what we computed by hand but with more decimals.

Δ

EXAMPLE
Suppose we have another table of r rows and c columns. Answer the following questions:

A) True/False: In general, the sum of the expected counts always equals the sample size.
B) Given that $DF = 6$, which of the following is a possible number of rows and columns in this table (not including the row and column with total counts)? The choices are 2×2, 2×3, 5×4, and 3×4.

Solution: For part A, just like with the goodness of fit test, this statement is true. We are simply taking the total sample size and reallocating it into the cells based on what counts are expected to occur if the null hypothesis were correct.

Part B is a little different since we do not have the number of rows and columns given to us, only the degrees of freedom. What we can do is compute the degrees of freedom for each of the four choices and then pick the table dimension that produces $DF = 6$:

1) For a 2×2 table, $DF = (2 - 1)(2 - 1) = 1 \times 1 = 1$.
2) For a 2×3 table, $DF = (2 - 1)(3 - 1) = 1 \times 2 = 2$.
3) For a 5×4 table, $DF = (5 - 1)(4 - 1) = 4 \times 3 = 12$.
4) For a 3×4 table, $DF = (3 - 1)(4 - 1) = 2 \times 3 = 6$.

Given the four choices, the only possible table would have 3 rows and 4 columns. (Note that there are other possible dimensions here as well. For instance, we could also have a table with 4 rows and 3 columns. In addition, a 7×2 table would work since then $DF = (7 - 1)(2 - 1) = 6$, and consequently so would a 2×7 table.)

Δ

MNEMONIC
Here is a funny mnemonic that helps you remember that the chi-square distribution is skewed right. Imagine you are presented with a big bowl of chocolate squares, and you eat as many as you can. Chocolate and chi both begin with "ch," so let's describe the "chocolate-square" distribution. The horizontal axis is the number of chocolate squares you eat, and the vertical axis is your "enjoyment" level of them.

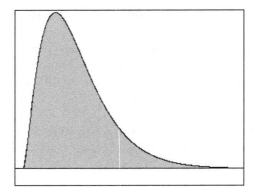

When you only eat a few chocolate squares, you enjoy them, so your enjoyment level is high. However, there quickly comes a point when the more you eat, the more disgusting you feel, and consequently your enjoyment level quickly declines, just like the long right tail in the graph!

Section 11.3 – Confidence Interval and Hypothesis Testing of a Variance*

Next, we turn our attention to another application of the chi-square distribution. In Chapters 8, 9, and 10, we built confidence intervals and conducted hypothesis testing for population means and population proportions, but we never studied another parameter seen in these notes – the population standard deviation. Now the time has come to extend our testing to the population standard deviation and whether it is greater than, less than, or not equal to a specified value. Actually, in this section and the next one, we will instead concentrate on the population variance since statistical theory is built on the variance (although the results can be extended to the standard deviation). We begin with a quick review from Section 2.3. (Note that not all introductory classes will cover this topic.)

REVIEW: VARIANCE AND STANDARD DEVIATION
The **sample variance** is a measure of how spread apart the data values are. The higher the variance, the more the data are spread apart. The lower the variance, the closer together the data. To compute it, you square all the individual deviations, add them, and divide by $n - 1$. Sample variance is denoted by s^2, and the formula is

$$s^2 = \frac{\sum(x_i - \overline{x})^2}{n - 1}$$

The **sample standard deviation** is also a measure of how spread apart the data values are. The higher the standard deviation, the more the data are spread apart. The lower the standard deviation, the closer together the data. Standard deviation is easier to see on a graph of data than variance is, which is why we have focused on it in these notes. To compute it, you first find the sample variance and then take the positive square root. Sample standard deviation is denoted by s, and the formula is

$$s = \sqrt{\frac{\sum(x_i - \overline{x})^2}{n-1}}$$

The population standard deviation is a parameter and is denoted by σ (pronounced "sigma"), and so the population variance is denoted by σ^2.

Recall that a sample mean is approximately normally distributed if its population is normal or if the sample size is large enough (using the T-distribution for confidence intervals and hypothesis testing). Similarly, a sample proportion is approximately normally distributed if the sample size is large enough in such a way that np and $n(1-p)$ are both large enough (using $\hat{p}$ or p_0 appropriately for confidence intervals and hypothesis testing, respectively). It can be shown that the sample variance also approximately follows a distribution, but instead of the normal or T, we use the chi-square distribution that we have been using in this chapter.

DISTRIBUTION OF THE SAMPLE VARIANCE
Let's assume that the quantitative data come from a normal distribution and that they were randomly selected. Suppose the population variance is σ^2 and that there are n data values. Then the following statement is true:

$\frac{(n-1)s^2}{\sigma^2}$ follows a chi-square distribution with $n-1$ degrees of freedom.

Although we deliberately avoided using it earlier in Chapter 11, we now need to introduce some statistical notation as it will come into play in some of the formulas. A chi-square distribution with $n-1$ degrees of freedom is denoted as $\chi^2(n-1)$, and we use the tilde symbol $\sim$ to say that a computation "follows" a specific distribution. Thus, the above statement can be written as

$$\frac{(n-1)s^2}{\sigma^2} \sim \chi^2(n-1)$$

Of course, in practice the population variance σ^2 is usually unknown, but there are ways around this little dilemma when we conduct the tests. Unfortunately the TI-84 is not equipped with computing the necessary values for the chi-square distribution. If you recall, when we made confidence intervals previously, we used the $invNorm(\ )$ and the $invT(\ )$ functions, but there is no $inv\chi^2(\ )$ function that will look up the values to use for, say, probability 0.025 above a point.

Instead, without introducing new technology, we have to use a chi-square table to look up values. You will find this table in Appendix E, a section of which is included below for illustrative purposes. (Actually, it is not impossible to use the TI-84 to get the necessary values, but it is quite an unpleasant task, so we will not study that here.)

DF	Probability to the Right of x^2									
	0.995	0.99	0.975	0.95	0.9	0.1	0.05	0.025	0.01	0.005
1	0.00004	0.00016	0.00098	0.00393	0.01579	2.70554	3.84146	5.02389	6.63490	7.87944
2	0.01003	0.02010	0.05064	0.10259	0.21072	4.60517	5.99146	7.37776	9.21034	10.59663
3	0.07172	0.11483	0.21580	0.35185	0.58437	6.25139	7.81473	9.34840	11.34487	12.83816
4	0.20699	0.29711	0.48442	0.71072	1.06362	7.77944	9.48773	11.14329	13.27670	14.86026
5	0.41174	0.55430	0.83121	1.14548	1.61031	9.23636	11.07050	12.83250	15.08627	16.74960
6	0.67573	0.87209	1.23734	1.63538	2.20413	10.64464	12.59159	14.44938	16.81189	18.54758
7	0.98926	1.23904	1.68987	2.16735	2.83311	12.01704	14.06714	16.01276	18.47531	20.27774
8	1.34441	1.64650	2.17973	2.73264	3.48954	13.36157	15.50731	17.53455	20.09024	21.95495
9	1.73493	2.08790	2.70039	3.32511	4.16816	14.68366	16.91898	19.02277	21.66599	23.58935
10	2.15586	2.55821	3.24697	3.94030	4.86518	15.98718	18.30704	20.48318	23.20925	25.18818

We first need to discuss how to use the table. Suppose we need to find the lower and upper chi-square values to use for a 95% confidence interval with a sample of size 10. Unlike the normal and T-distributions, the chi-square distribution is not symmetric, so we cannot use the same tricks as before. Instead, we need to look up two different values on the chi-square table.

First, the two values will always come from the same row. The row number equals the degrees of freedom to use. In this example, with a sample of size 10, $DF = 10 - 1 = 9$, so our two values will come from row 9.

DF	Probability to the Right of x^2									
	0.995	0.99	0.975	0.95	0.9	0.1	0.05	0.025	0.01	0.005
1	0.00004	0.00016	0.00098	0.00393	0.01579	2.70554	3.84146	5.02389	6.63490	7.87944
2	0.01003	0.02010	0.05064	0.10259	0.21072	4.60517	5.99146	7.37776	9.21034	10.59663
3	0.07172	0.11483	0.21580	0.35185	0.58437	6.25139	7.81473	9.34840	11.34487	12.83816
4	0.20699	0.29711	0.48442	0.71072	1.06362	7.77944	9.48773	11.14329	13.27670	14.86026
5	0.41174	0.55430	0.83121	1.14548	1.61031	9.23636	11.07050	12.83250	15.08627	16.74960
6	0.67573	0.87209	1.23734	1.63538	2.20413	10.64464	12.59159	14.44938	16.81189	18.54758
7	0.98926	1.23904	1.68987	2.16735	2.83311	12.01704	14.06714	16.01276	18.47531	20.27774
8	1.34441	1.64650	2.17973	2.73264	3.48954	13.36157	15.50731	17.53455	20.09024	21.95495
9	1.73493	2.08790	2.70039	3.32511	4.16816	14.68366	16.91898	19.02277	21.66599	23.58935
10	2.15586	2.55821	3.24697	3.94030	4.86518	15.98718	18.30704	20.48318	23.20925	25.18818

The next step is to choose the two appropriate columns. For a 95% confidence interval, we draw the chi-square sketch as follows. We put 0.95 in the middle, which means 0.05 is left over, and half of that is 0.025. Thus, we need the value that gives probability 0.025 above (U for Upper) and probability 0.025 below (L for Lower).

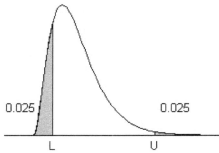

Let's introduce some notation here.

NOTATION: CHI-SQUARE TABLE VALUES

Recall that a $100(1 - \alpha)\%$ confidence interval corresponds to a two-tailed hypothesis test with significance level α. That means we need to look up the upper value (U) that gives probability $\alpha/2$ above it, and the lower value (L) that gives probability $\alpha/2$ below it. However, realize that L is also the point that gives probability $1 - \alpha/2$ above it (this is necessary to understand the table, which deals with probabilities to the right). Assuming a sample of size n, we denote these quantities using the following notation.

$$L = \chi^2_{1-\alpha/2}(n - 1)$$
$$U = \chi^2_{\alpha/2}(n - 1)$$

For 99% confidence, we would use $\chi^2_{0.995}(n - 1)$ and $\chi^2_{0.005}(n - 1)$.
For 95% confidence, we would use $\chi^2_{0.975}(n - 1)$ and $\chi^2_{0.025}(n - 1)$.
For 90% confidence, we would use $\chi^2_{0.95}(n - 1)$ and $\chi^2_{0.05}(n - 1)$.

As an example, the subscripts for 95% confidence come from the following calculation: we have $\alpha = 0.05$, so $\alpha/2 = 0.025$ and $1 - \alpha/2 = 1 - 0.025 = 0.975$.

Continuing the example with $DF = 9$ and 95% confidence, we look on row 9 of the table and in the two columns labeled 0.975 and 0.025. In the following image, the row and two columns are highlighted, with the chosen cells in black with white font.

DF	0.995	0.99	0.975	0.95	0.9	0.1	0.05	0.025	0.01	0.005
				Probability to the Right of X^2						
1	0.00004	0.00016	0.00098	0.00393	0.01579	2.70554	3.84146	5.02389	6.63490	7.87944
2	0.01003	0.02010	0.05064	0.10259	0.21072	4.60517	5.99146	7.37776	9.21034	10.59663
3	0.07172	0.11483	0.21580	0.35185	0.58437	6.25139	7.81473	9.34840	11.34487	12.83816
4	0.20699	0.29711	0.48442	0.71072	1.06362	7.77944	9.48773	11.14329	13.27670	14.86026
5	0.41174	0.55430	0.83121	1.14548	1.61031	9.23636	11.07050	12.83250	15.08627	16.74960
6	0.67573	0.87209	1.23734	1.63538	2.20413	10.64464	12.59159	14.44938	16.81189	18.54758
7	0.98926	1.23904	1.68987	2.16735	2.83311	12.01704	14.06714	16.01276	18.47531	20.27774
8	1.34441	1.64650	2.17973	2.73264	3.48954	13.36157	15.50731	17.53455	20.09024	21.95495
9	1.73493	2.08790	2.70039	3.32511	4.16816	14.68366	16.91898	19.02277	21.66599	23.58935
10	2.15586	2.55821	3.24697	3.94030	4.86518	15.98718	18.30704	20.48318	23.20925	25.18818

This tells us that for this problem, $L = \chi^2_{0.975}(9) = 2.70039$ and $U = \chi^2_{0.025}(9) = 19.02277$. We can create our sketch:

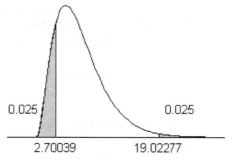

EXAMPLE

As one more example, let's find the lower and upper chi-square values to be used in a 90% confidence interval for a sample of size 15.

Solution: First, note that $DF = 15 - 1 = 14$. We consult row 14 in the chi-square table:

DF	\multicolumn{10}{c}{Probability to the Right of X^2}
	0.995	0.99	0.975	0.95	0.9	0.1	0.05	0.025	0.01	0.005
1	0.00004	0.00016	0.00098	0.00393	0.01579	2.70554	3.84146	5.02389	6.63490	7.87944
2	0.01003	0.02010	0.05064	0.10259	0.21072	4.60517	5.99146	7.37776	9.21034	10.59663
3	0.07172	0.11483	0.21580	0.35185	0.58437	6.25139	7.81473	9.34840	11.34487	12.83816
4	0.20699	0.29711	0.48442	0.71072	1.06362	7.77944	9.48773	11.14329	13.27670	14.86026
5	0.41174	0.55430	0.83121	1.14548	1.61031	9.23636	11.07050	12.83250	15.08627	16.74960
6	0.67573	0.87209	1.23734	1.63538	2.20413	10.64464	12.59159	14.44938	16.81189	18.54758
7	0.98926	1.23904	1.68987	2.16735	2.83311	12.01704	14.06714	16.01276	18.47531	20.27774
8	1.34441	1.64650	2.17973	2.73264	3.48954	13.36157	15.50731	17.53455	20.09024	21.95495
9	1.73493	2.08790	2.70039	3.32511	4.16816	14.68366	16.91898	19.02277	21.66599	23.58935
10	2.15586	2.55821	3.24697	3.94030	4.86518	15.98718	18.30704	20.48318	23.20925	25.18818
11	2.60322	3.05348	3.81575	4.57481	5.57778	17.27501	19.67514	21.92005	24.72497	26.75685
12	3.07382	3.57057	4.40379	5.22603	6.30380	18.54935	21.02607	23.33666	26.21697	28.29952
13	3.56503	4.10692	5.00875	5.89186	7.04150	19.81193	22.36203	24.73560	27.68825	29.81947
14	4.07467	4.66043	5.62873	6.57063	7.78953	21.06414	23.68479	26.11895	29.14124	31.31935
15	4.60092	5.22935	6.26214	7.26094	8.54676	22.30713	24.99579	27.48839	30.57791	32.80132

For 90% confidence, that means $\alpha = 0.10$, which means $\alpha/2 = 0.05$ and $1 - \alpha/2 = 0.95$. We look in those two columns in row 14:

DF	\multicolumn{10}{c}{Probability to the Right of X^2}
	0.995	0.99	0.975	0.95	0.9	0.1	0.05	0.025	0.01	0.005
1	0.00004	0.00016	0.00098	0.00393	0.01579	2.70554	3.84146	5.02389	6.63490	7.87944
2	0.01003	0.02010	0.05064	0.10259	0.21072	4.60517	5.99146	7.37776	9.21034	10.59663
3	0.07172	0.11483	0.21580	0.35185	0.58437	6.25139	7.81473	9.34840	11.34487	12.83816
4	0.20699	0.29711	0.48442	0.71072	1.06362	7.77944	9.48773	11.14329	13.27670	14.86026
5	0.41174	0.55430	0.83121	1.14548	1.61031	9.23636	11.07050	12.83250	15.08627	16.74960
6	0.67573	0.87209	1.23734	1.63538	2.20413	10.64464	12.59159	14.44938	16.81189	18.54758
7	0.98926	1.23904	1.68987	2.16735	2.83311	12.01704	14.06714	16.01276	18.47531	20.27774
8	1.34441	1.64650	2.17973	2.73264	3.48954	13.36157	15.50731	17.53455	20.09024	21.95495
9	1.73493	2.08790	2.70039	3.32511	4.16816	14.68366	16.91898	19.02277	21.66599	23.58935
10	2.15586	2.55821	3.24697	3.94030	4.86518	15.98718	18.30704	20.48318	23.20925	25.18818
11	2.60322	3.05348	3.81575	4.57481	5.57778	17.27501	19.67514	21.92005	24.72497	26.75685
12	3.07382	3.57057	4.40379	5.22603	6.30380	18.54935	21.02607	23.33666	26.21697	28.29952
13	3.56503	4.10692	5.00875	5.89186	7.04150	19.81193	22.36203	24.73560	27.68825	29.81947
14	4.07467	4.66043	5.62873	6.57063	7.78953	21.06414	23.68479	26.11895	29.14124	31.31935
15	4.60092	5.22935	6.26214	7.26094	8.54676	22.30713	24.99579	27.48839	30.57791	32.80132

Therefore $L = \chi^2_{0.95}(14) = 6.57063$ and $U = \chi^2_{0.05}(14) = 23.68479$.

Δ

Now that we have covered how to use the chi-square table, we need to use it in the formulas for the confidence interval and the hypothesis test. Let's start with the confidence interval. Unlike many of the previous formulas, we don't compute a standard error and margin of error; instead we just compute a lower and upper limit.

CONFIDENCE INTERVAL FOR A VARIANCE

Without giving a mathematical proof of it, the $100(1 - \alpha)\%$ confidence interval for the population variance σ^2 is

$$\left(\frac{(n-1)s^2}{\chi^2_{\alpha/2}(n-1)}, \frac{(n-1)s^2}{\chi^2_{1-\alpha/2}(n-1)} \right)$$

As an extension, the $100(1 - \alpha)\%$ confidence interval for the population standard deviation σ is

$$\left(\sqrt{\frac{(n-1)s^2}{\chi^2_{\alpha/2}(n-1)}}, \sqrt{\frac{(n-1)s^2}{\chi^2_{1-\alpha/2}(n-1)}} \right)$$

(Caution: Some textbooks will reverse the $\chi^2_{\alpha/2}(n-1)$ and $\chi^2_{1-\alpha/2}(n-1)$ notation, depending how the chi-square table is set up in the appendix.)

EXAMPLE

An electronics store provides the prices for twelve laptops that were sold on the same day. Assuming the prices are normally distributed and represent a random sample of laptops sold, create a 99% confidence interval for the population variance of prices of sold laptops in one day. The prices are as follows:

$$220, 240, 240, 240, 250, 270, 280, 310, 350, 380, 390, 400$$

Solution: First, putting the numbers into L_1, we see that $s = 66.07502623$ and $n = 12$. (We don't need the sample mean here.) This means the sample variance is $s^2 = 4365.909091$.

Next, we need the two chi-square values from the table. Since we need 99% confidence, $\alpha/2 = 0.005$ and $1 - \alpha/2 = 0.995$. Noting that $DF = 12 - 1 = 11$, we go to the table and discover that $L = \chi^2_{0.995}(11) = 2.60322$ and $U = \chi^2_{0.005}(11) = 26.75685$.

DF	\multicolumn{10}{c}{Probability to the Right of X^2}
	0.995	0.99	0.975	0.95	0.9	0.1	0.05	0.025	0.01	0.005
1	0.00004	0.00016	0.00098	0.00393	0.01579	2.70554	3.84146	5.02389	6.63490	7.87944
2	0.01003	0.02010	0.05064	0.10259	0.21072	4.60517	5.99146	7.37776	9.21034	10.59663
3	0.07172	0.11483	0.21580	0.35185	0.58437	6.25139	7.81473	9.34840	11.34487	12.83816
4	0.20699	0.29711	0.48442	0.71072	1.06362	7.77944	9.48773	11.14329	13.27670	14.86026
5	0.41174	0.55430	0.83121	1.14548	1.61031	9.23636	11.07050	12.83250	15.08627	16.74960
6	0.67573	0.87209	1.23734	1.63538	2.20413	10.64464	12.59159	14.44938	16.81189	18.54758
7	0.98926	1.23904	1.68987	2.16735	2.83311	12.01704	14.06714	16.01276	18.47531	20.27774
8	1.34441	1.64650	2.17973	2.73264	3.48954	13.36157	15.50731	17.53455	20.09024	21.95495
9	1.73493	2.08790	2.70039	3.32511	4.16816	14.68366	16.91898	19.02277	21.66599	23.58935
10	2.15586	2.55821	3.24697	3.94030	4.86518	15.98718	18.30704	20.48318	23.20925	25.18818
11	2.60322	3.05348	3.81575	4.57481	5.57778	17.27501	19.67514	21.92005	24.72497	26.75685
12	3.07382	3.57057	4.40379	5.22603	6.30380	18.54935	21.02607	23.33666	26.21697	28.29952
13	3.56503	4.10692	5.00875	5.89186	7.04150	19.81193	22.36203	24.73560	27.68825	29.81947
14	4.07467	4.66043	5.62873	6.57063	7.78953	21.06414	23.68479	26.11895	29.14124	31.31935
15	4.60092	5.22935	6.26214	7.26094	8.54676	22.30713	24.99579	27.48839	30.57791	32.80132

Putting all the values into the formula, the 99% confidence interval is

$$\left(\frac{(n-1)s^2}{\chi^2_{\alpha/2}(n-1)}, \frac{(n-1)s^2}{\chi^2_{1-\alpha/2}(n-1)}\right) = \left(\frac{11\times 4365.909091}{\chi^2_{0.005}(11)}, \frac{11\times 4365.909091}{\chi^2_{0.995}(11)}\right)$$

$$= \left(\frac{48025}{26.75685}, \frac{48025}{2.60322}\right)$$

$$= (1794.867483, 18448.30633)$$

Notice that this interval should make sense because the sample variance 4365.909091 is inside the interval, although it is not at the center of the interval (because the chi-square distribution is not symmetric). If you instead need a 99% confidence interval for the population standard deviation, then square root both sides to get

$$\left(\sqrt{1794.867483}, \sqrt{18448.30633}\right) = (42.36588, 135.82454)$$

Δ

Although the formula is different than what you are used to seeing, the interpretation of the confidence interval is still the same. In the previous example, we are 99% confident that the population variance is between 1794.867483 and 18448.30633. This means that 2000, 5000, and 15000 are all likely values for the population variance, but 1500 is not a likely value. (Note that if you use a statistical program to find the confidence interval, you might get slightly different answers because they would be more precise than any that come from a table. However, the interpretation of the answer would still be the same.)

We now turn our attention to hypothesis testing. The steps are similar to what we have used before, except in Step 4 we will not find a p-value. Instead, we will create what is known as a **rejection region** that will help determine the conclusion to the problem. (Actually the TI-84 can find the p-value for a left-tailed or right-tailed test, but the two-tailed p-value is harder to do although not impossible. For that reason, we stick to using rejection regions here. However, different computer programs will find the p-values.)

Here are the five steps to follow for hypothesis testing.

Step 1: Set up the hypotheses.
Suppose we want to test whether the population variance is equal to a specific number, and call it σ_0^2. This is the assumed population variance. The null hypothesis is

$$H_0: \sigma^2 = \sigma_0^2$$

The alternative hypothesis is one of the following:

$$H_A: \sigma^2 > \sigma_0^2 \quad \text{(right-tailed test)}$$
$$H_A: \sigma^2 < \sigma_0^2 \quad \text{(left-tailed test)}$$
$$H_A: \sigma^2 \neq \sigma_0^2 \quad \text{(two-tailed test)}$$

Note that alternatively, we could write the hypotheses using standard deviations instead of variances. If you do that, the following would be an example of how to write it:

$$H_0: \sigma = \sigma_0$$
$$H_A: \sigma > \sigma_0$$

However, I recommend you stick with variance notation for consistency.

Step 2: Check the assumptions.
For the hypothesis test to be valid, three assumptions need to be true, assuming a sample size n:

1) The data must be quantitative (meaning they are numbers that can be averaged).
2) The subjects must be randomly selected.
3) The data must come from a normally distributed population.

Step 3: Compute the test statistic.
The test statistic for a population variance is

$$X^2 = \frac{(n-1)s^2}{\sigma_0^2}$$

Simply stated, you find the sample variance, multiply it by $(n-1)$, and divide it by the assumed population variance under the null hypothesis.

Step 4: Determine the rejection region.
In simple terms, a rejection region is the part of the chi-square distribution that is the extreme upper (and/or lower side). If the test statistic falls inside this region, then we reject the null hypothesis. If the test statistic falls outside this region, we do not reject the null hypothesis. As you probably guessed, there are three ways of sketching the rejection region, and they all depend on the choice of alternative hypothesis.

For a right-tailed test, we find the chi-square value from the Appendix E table that gives probability α to the right. That means we need $\chi_\alpha^2(n-1)$. If X^2 lies above this value, we reject the null hypothesis, and if it lies below, we don't reject it.

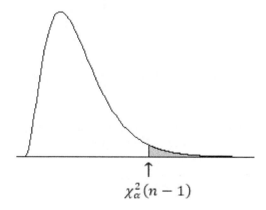

$$\chi_\alpha^2(n-1)$$

For a left-tailed test, we find the chi-square value from the Appendix E table that gives probability α to the left (and therefore $1-\alpha$ to the right). That means we need $\chi_{1-\alpha}^2(n-1)$. If X^2 lies below this value, we reject the null hypothesis, and if it lies above, we don't reject it.

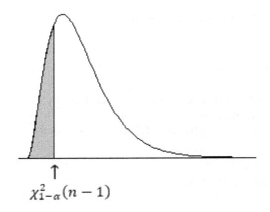

$$\chi^2_{1-\alpha}(n-1)$$

For a two-tailed test, we find the chi-square value from the Appendix E table that gives probability $\alpha/2$ to the right, which is $\chi^2_{\alpha/2}(n-1)$. We also need the value that gives probability $\alpha/2$ to the left (and therefore $1 - \alpha/2$ to the right), which is $\chi^2_{1-\alpha/2}(n-1)$. If X^2 lies below the lower value or above the upper value, we reject the null hypothesis, and if it lies in between, we don't reject it.

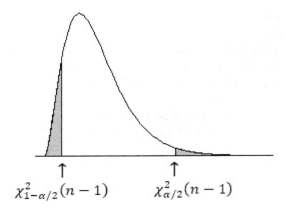

$$\chi^2_{1-\alpha/2}(n-1) \qquad \chi^2_{\alpha/2}(n-1)$$

Step 5: State the conclusion.
Finally, we determine the outcome. If the test statistic falls inside the rejection region, then…

1) We reject the null hypothesis.
2) There is sufficient evidence against the null hypothesis.
3) There is sufficient evidence for the alternative hypothesis.

If the test statistic falls outside the rejection region, then…

1) We fail to reject the null hypothesis.
2) There is insufficient evidence against the null hypothesis.
3) There is insufficient evidence for the alternative hypothesis.

REVIEW: HYPOTHESIS TESTING FOR A POPULATION VARIANCE
Step 1: Set up the hypotheses.

$$H_0: \sigma^2 = \sigma_0^2$$
$$H_A: \sigma^2 > \sigma_0^2 \quad \text{or} \quad H_A: \sigma^2 < \sigma_0^2 \quad \text{or} \quad H_A: \sigma^2 \neq \sigma_0^2$$

Step 2: Check the assumptions.

    1) Quantitative data
    2) Random sample
    3) Data come from normal population

Step 3: Compute the test statistic.

$$X^2 = \frac{(n-1)s^2}{\sigma_0^2}$$

Step 4: Determine the rejection region.

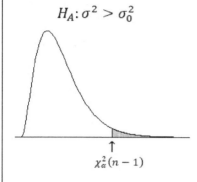

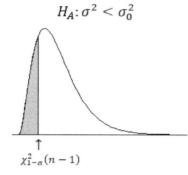

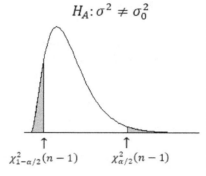

Step 5: State the conclusion.

If the test statistic falls inside the rejection region, then…
    1) We reject the null hypothesis.
    2) There is sufficient evidence against the null hypothesis.
    3) There is sufficient evidence for the alternative hypothesis.

If the test statistic falls outside the rejection region, then…
    1) We fail to reject the null hypothesis.
    2) There is insufficient evidence against the null hypothesis.
    3) There is insufficient evidence for the alternative hypothesis.

Let's tackle some examples!

EXAMPLE

Let's continue the laptop selling prices example, recalling that $s^2 = 4365.909091$ and $n = 12$. Test whether the population variance is greater than 2000, then whether it is different from 2000, both at the $\alpha = 0.01$ significance level.

Solution: First, here are the hypotheses for a right-tailed test.

$$H_0: \sigma^2 = 2000$$
$$H_A: \sigma^2 > 2000$$

Remember we assumed that the prices represented a random selection and that they were from a normal population. The test statistic is

$$X^2 = \frac{(n-1)s^2}{\sigma_0^2} = \frac{11 \times 4365.909091}{2000} = 24.0125$$

Next comes the new part; we need the rejection region. First, drawing a sketch of the situation, we see that since this is a right-tailed test, we need the chi-square value with $DF = 12 - 1 = 11$ that has probability 0.01 to the right.

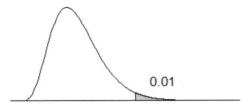

That means we need to find $\chi_{0.01}^2(11)$. Consulting the table, we discover that it is 24.72497. Now let's redraw our sketch but with the rejection region and the computed X^2:

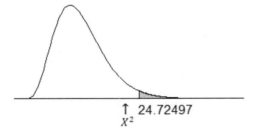

The null hypothesis is rejected if X^2 falls above 24.72497. However, we see that the test statistic ($X^2 = 24.0125$) is below the rejection region (not inside it). That means that we do not reject the null hypothesis; there is insufficient evidence that the population variance is greater than 2000.

Next, let's repeat this exercise for a two-tailed test. The hypotheses are

$$H_0: \sigma^2 = 2000$$
$$H_A: \sigma^2 \neq 2000$$

The test statistic is still the same: $X^2 = 24.0125$. However, we need to redraw our rejection region so that probability $\alpha/2$ is in the lower tail and another probability $\alpha/2$ is in the upper tail.

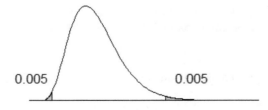

Since $\alpha = 0.01$, we need the chi-square values at $1 - \alpha/2 = 0.995$ and $\alpha/2 = 0.005$ for $DF = 11$. From the earlier example, we had already computed these values as $\chi_{0.995}^2(11) = 2.60322$ and $\chi_{0.005}^2(11) = 26.75685$. Let's add everything to our sketch:

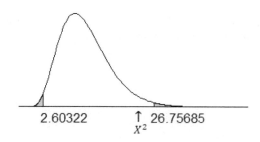

The null hypothesis is rejected if X^2 falls below 2.60322 or above 26.75685. However, we see that the test statistic $(X^2 = 24.0125)$ is between these values. That means that we do not reject the null hypothesis; there is insufficient evidence that the population variance is difference than 2000.

As a side note, if we actually did compute the p-values in this problem, we would have discovered that they are both greater than $\alpha = 0.01$, which again would lead to failing to reject the null hypothesis. Although we won't show the work here, the p-value for the right-tailed test is 0.01268, while the p-value for the two-tailed test is 0.01459 (and note that it is not double the right-tailed p-value, which again is because the chi-square distribution is not symmetric).

Δ

To recap our point here, if the test statistic is outside the rejection region, then this is equivalent to the p-value being greater than α and therefore failing to reject the null hypothesis. If the test statistic is inside the rejection region, then this is equivalent to the p-value being less than α and therefore rejecting the null hypothesis.

EXAMPLE
A shop wants to see if the weight (in pounds) of bags of birdseed sold has a variance significantly less than 3. A random sample of 17 birdseed bags that were sold produced a sample standard deviation of 1.04929. Assuming the weights of the bags are normally distributed, conduct the appropriate hypothesis test at the $\alpha = 0.05$ significance level.

Solution: First, the hypotheses are

$$H_0: \sigma^2 = 3$$
$$H_A: \sigma^2 < 3$$

Noting that $n = 17$ and $s = 1.04929$ (and therefore $s^2 = 1.101009504$), the test statistic is

$$X^2 = \frac{(n-1)s^2}{\sigma_0^2} = \frac{16 \times 1.101009504}{3} = 5.87205$$

Next comes the rejection region. First, drawing a sketch of the situation, we see that since this is a left-tailed test, we need the chi-square value with $DF = 17 - 1 = 16$ that has probability 0.05 to the left (and therefore probability 0.95 to the right).

That means we need to find $\chi^2_{0.95}(16)$ (because $1 - \alpha = 0.95$). Consulting the table, we discover that it is 7.96165. Now let's redraw our sketch but with the rejection region and the computed X^2:

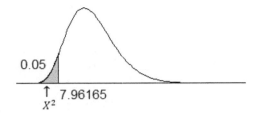

The null hypothesis is rejected if X^2 falls below 7.96165. We see that the test statistic is indeed inside the rejection region. That means that we reject the null hypothesis; there is sufficient evidence that the population variance is less than 3. (If you in fact compute the left-tailed p-value, you will see that it is 0.01058, which is less than $\alpha = 0.05$, as expected.)

Δ

Section 11.4 – Confidence Interval and Hypothesis Testing of Two Variances*

Having covered the confidence interval and hypothesis testing for one population variance, the next step is to present them for the case of two population variances. In Chapter 10 we studied the difference of two proportions and the difference of two means, in both cases seeing whether the difference was significantly different from 0.

When we study two population variances, it is more convenient to look at their ratio instead, namely σ_1^2/σ_2^2, and see whether it is significantly different from 1 (because if two numbers are the same, then their ratio is 1). The reason is due to statistical theory, which we won't explore as it is a little complicated – which brings us to a brand new distribution to use. Just as the sample variance is connected to the chi-square distribution, the ratio of sample variances in fact is connected to the fifth and final distribution you will see in these notes – the F-distribution. (This is another topic that may or may not be covered in an introductory statistics class.)

PROPERTIES OF THE F-DISTRIBUTION
Property 1: The total area under the curve for the F-distribution is 1.
Property 2: The F-distribution is skewed right, which means the right tail is longer than the left tail.
Property 3: The notation for an F-statistic is just F.
Property 4: The F-distribution takes two different degrees of freedom values (called numerator and denominator degrees of freedom). This means that it takes on different shapes (and consequently different probabilities) for different values of both sets of degrees of freedom. In addition, the distribution changes shapes if the degrees of freedom are swapped.
Property 5: The lowest possible value the F-distribution can take is 0.

Let's discuss these points further.

Property 1: Just like the previous distributions, the total area under the F-distribution curve is 1, so the same techniques of finding the area of one side given the other side still apply here.

Property 2: Like the chi-square distribution, the F-distribution is skewed right, so the right tail is longer than the left. This means that the F-distribution is not symmetric.

Property 3: Sir Ronald Aylmer Fisher (another English statistician!) and George W. Snedecor (from Memphis) introduced the F-distribution. The choice of letter F comes from Fisher's name.

Property 4: The shape of the F-distribution is different depending on the numerator degrees of freedom and denominator degrees of freedom. This is similar to how the T-distribution and chi-square distribution work with different sample sizes, only this time there are two sample sizes in play. The following graph shows what the distribution looks like for $DF_1 = 4$ and $DF_2 = 8$, as well as for $DF_1 = 8$ and $DF_2 = 4$, illustrating that the shape changes even when we interchange the degrees of freedom.

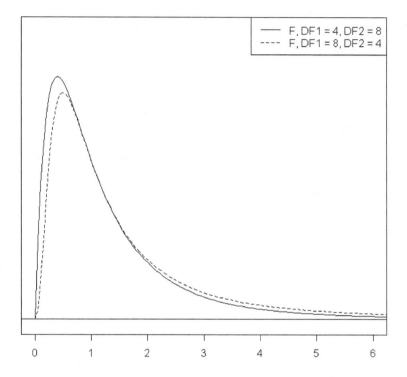

This skewed-right image usually describes the F-distribution. However, it should be noted that the distribution does not look like that when $DF_1 = 1$ or when $DF_1 = 2$. For those scenarios, the distribution instead looks like a steep curve that is declining the further right we go, as in the following graph.

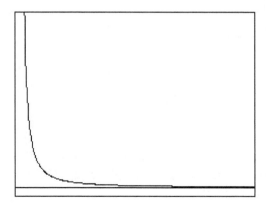

Property 5: Like the chi-square distribution, the lowest value the F-distribution can take is 0.

Just like the T-distribution and the chi-square distribution, we need to enter degrees of freedom.

DEFINITION

The **degrees of freedom** is a quantity that influences the overall shape of the F-distribution. There are actually two of them: the numerator degrees of freedom (DF_1) and the denominator degrees of freedom (DF_2). With two different sample sizes n_1 and n_2, we use $DF_1 = n_1 - 1$ and $DF_2 = n_2 - 1$.

Again, the TI-84 is lacking a function we need to look up specific values. As before, although we used the $invNorm(\ )$ and $invT(\ )$ functions, we don't have an $invX^2(\ )$ or $invF(\ )$ function, so we need to use another statistical table instead (see Appendix F – which, appropriately, contains the F-tables!). However, the TI-84 will at least produce probabilities between two values, so we state how to do that in case you are interested.

TI-84 COMMAND: F-DISTRIBUTION

To find the probability between a lower limit and an upper limit given two specified DF values, press $\boxed{\text{2nd}}$, $\boxed{\text{VARS}}$, and choose Option 0: $Fcdf($. The command is

$$Fcdf(\text{lower limit, upper limit}, DF_1, DF_2)$$

If there is no upper limit, use 999999.

EXAMPLE

Let's find the probability above $F = 2$ given that Group 1 has 4 subjects and Group 2 has 9 subjects. A sketch looks like the following:

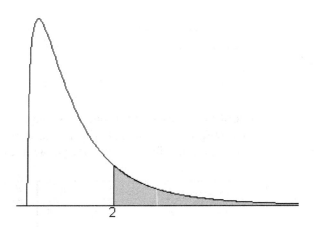

The lower limit is $F = 2$, and since there is no upper limit, we can say $F = 999999$. Since $n_1 = 4$ and $n_2 = 9$, we have $DF_1 = 3$ and $DF_2 = 8$, and therefore

$$Fcdf(2, 999999, 3, 8) = 0.1926574285$$

Note that the order in which we specify the groups matters since it affects the ratio of the sample variances. In this example, if we instead compute $Fcdf(2, 999999, 8, 3)$, the probability becomes 0.3073751315.

Δ

Now that we have seen the F-distribution, we turn our attention to using the F-tables in Appendix F. Once again, the TI-84 does not perform the necessary function we need, so we need to consult the F-tables. (Again, it is not impossible to use the TI-84 to get the necessary values, but it takes quite a long time to do so.) Unlike the chi-square table, there is an F-table for each choice of probability $0.05, 0.01, 0.025, 0.05, 0.10, 0.90, 0.95, 0.975, 0.99$, and 0.995. The reason for this is because the rows and columns are used for the two different degrees of freedom, so it is necessary to split the table into multiple tables, one for each probability.

Let's first discuss how to use the F-tables. Suppose we need to find the lower and upper F-values to use for a 95% confidence interval where the first sample is size 7 and the second sample is size 8. This means that $DF_1 = 7 - 1 = 6$ and $DF_2 = 8 - 1 = 7$. Just as with the chi-square table, we need to look up two different values, only this time they will come from two different tables. To decide which two, we first draw a sketch of what we are after. For a 95% confidence interval, we put 0.95 in the middle, which means 0.05 is left over, and half of that is 0.025. Thus, we need the value that gives probability 0.025 above (U for Upper) and probability 0.025 below and therefore probability 0.975 above (L for Lower).

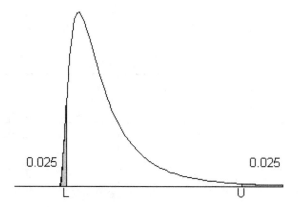

Let's introduce some notation here.

NOTATION: *F*-TABLE VALUES

For a $100(1 - \alpha)\%$ confidence interval, we need to choose the F-table that corresponds to $\alpha/2$ and the F-table that corresponds to $1 - \alpha/2$. The tables reveal the F-value that had the probability of interest above (to the right). Assuming Group 1 has n_1 subjects and Group 2 has n_2 subjects, we need the following two quantities, one per table:

$$L = F_{1-\alpha/2}(n_1 - 1, n_2 - 1)$$
$$U = F_{\alpha/2}(n_1 - 1, n_2 - 1)$$

For 99% confidence, we would use $\chi^2_{0.995}(n_1 - 1, n_2 - 1)$ and $\chi^2_{0.005}(n_1 - 1, n_2 - 1)$.
For 95% confidence, we would use $\chi^2_{0.975}(n_1 - 1, n_2 - 1)$ and $\chi^2_{0.025}(n_1 - 1, n_2 - 1)$.
For 90% confidence, we would use $\chi^2_{0.95}(n_1 - 1, n_2 - 1)$ and $\chi^2_{0.05}(n_1 - 1, n_2 - 1)$.

As an example, the subscripts for 95% confidence come from the following calculation: we have $\alpha = 0.05$, so $\alpha/2 = 0.025$.

Continuing our example, our degrees of freedom are $DF_1 = 6$ and $DF_2 = 7$. For a 95% confidence interval, we need the $1 - \alpha/2 = 0.975$ table, a section of which is included below for illustrative purposes.

0.975 F Table	Numerator DF									
Denom. DF	1	2	3	4	5	6	7	8	9	10
1	0.00154	0.02597	0.05733	0.08185	0.09993	0.11347	0.12387	0.13209	0.13871	0.14416
2	0.00125	0.02564	0.06233	0.09390	0.11857	0.13774	0.15287	0.16503	0.17499	0.18327
3	0.00116	0.02553	0.06477	0.10021	0.12881	0.15154	0.16978	0.18464	0.19692	0.20723
4	0.00111	0.02548	0.06622	0.10412	0.13536	0.16059	0.18107	0.19792	0.21195	0.22380
5	0.00108	0.02545	0.06718	0.10679	0.13993	0.16701	0.18921	0.20759	0.22299	0.23607
6	0.00107	0.02542	0.06787	0.10873	0.14331	0.17183	0.19537	0.21498	0.23150	0.24557
7	0.00105	0.02541	0.06838	0.11020	0.14592	0.17558	0.20020	0.22082	0.23826	0.25318
8	0.00105	0.02540	0.06878	0.11136	0.14799	0.17858	0.20411	0.22557	0.24379	0.25941
9	0.00104	0.02539	0.06909	0.11230	0.14968	0.18105	0.20733	0.22950	0.24839	0.26462
10	0.00103	0.02538	0.06935	0.11307	0.15108	0.18311	0.21003	0.23282	0.25228	0.26905

To use the table, the numerator degrees of freedom is selected from the column headers (left to right), while the denominator degrees of freedom is selected from the row headers (top to bottom). To find $F_{1-\alpha/2}(n_1 - 1, n_2 - 1) = F_{0.975}(6, 7)$, we need to select 6 from the column headers and 7 from the row headers, then find the cell that overlaps the chosen row and column. In the following image, the row and two columns are highlighted, with the chosen cells in black with white font.

0.975 F Table	Numerator DF									
Denom. DF	1	2	3	4	5	6	7	8	9	10
1	0.00154	0.02597	0.05733	0.08185	0.09993	0.11347	0.12387	0.13209	0.13871	0.14416
2	0.00125	0.02564	0.06233	0.09390	0.11857	0.13774	0.15287	0.16503	0.17499	0.18327
3	0.00116	0.02553	0.06477	0.10021	0.12881	0.15154	0.16978	0.18464	0.19692	0.20723
4	0.00111	0.02548	0.06622	0.10412	0.13536	0.16059	0.18107	0.19792	0.21195	0.22380
5	0.00108	0.02545	0.06718	0.10679	0.13993	0.16701	0.18921	0.20759	0.22299	0.23607
6	0.00107	0.02542	0.06787	0.10873	0.14331	0.17183	0.19537	0.21498	0.23150	0.24557
7	0.00105	0.02541	0.06838	0.11020	0.14592	0.17558	0.20020	0.22082	0.23826	0.25318
8	0.00105	0.02540	0.06878	0.11136	0.14799	0.17858	0.20411	0.22557	0.24379	0.25941
9	0.00104	0.02539	0.06909	0.11230	0.14968	0.18105	0.20733	0.22950	0.24839	0.26462
10	0.00103	0.02538	0.06935	0.11307	0.15108	0.18311	0.21003	0.23282	0.25228	0.26905

This tells us that for this problem, $F_{0.975}(6, 7) = 0.17558$.

Next, we need to find $F_{\alpha/2}(n_1 - 1, n_2 - 1) = F_{0.025}(6, 7)$. Using the 0.025 table this time, we again select 6 from the column headers and 7 from the row headers, and once again find the cell that overlaps the chosen row and column.

0.025 F Table	Numerator DF									
Denom. DF	1	2	3	4	5	6	7	8	9	10
1	647.78901	799.50000	864.16297	899.58331	921.84790	937.11108	948.21689	956.65622	963.28458	968.62744
2	38.50633	39.00000	39.16549	39.24842	39.29823	39.33146	39.35521	39.37302	39.38688	39.39797
3	17.44344	16.04411	15.43918	15.10098	14.88482	14.73472	14.62440	14.53989	14.47308	14.41894
4	12.21786	10.64911	9.97920	9.60453	9.36447	9.19731	9.07414	8.97958	8.90468	8.84388
5	10.00698	8.43362	7.76359	7.38789	7.14638	6.97770	6.85308	6.75717	6.68105	6.61915
6	8.81310	7.25986	6.59880	6.22716	5.98757	5.81976	5.69547	5.59962	5.52341	5.46132
7	8.07267	6.54152	5.88982	5.52259	5.28524	5.11860	4.99491	4.89934	4.82322	4.76112
8	7.57088	6.05947	5.41596	5.05263	4.81728	4.65170	4.52856	4.43326	4.35723	4.29513
9	7.20928	5.71471	5.07812	4.71808	4.48441	4.31972	4.19705	4.10196	4.02599	3.96387
10	6.93673	5.45640	4.82562	4.46834	4.23609	4.07213	3.94982	3.85489	3.77896	3.71679

Thus, we have $F_{0.025}(6, 7) = 5.11860$.

EXAMPLE

As one more example, let's find the two values to be used in a 90% confidence interval when Group 1 has 5 subjects and Group 2 has 9 subjects.

Solution: First, note that for 90% confidence, $\alpha/2 = 0.05$ and $1 - \alpha/2 = 0.95$, and we have $DF_1 = 5 - 1 = 4$ and $DF_2 = 9 - 1 = 8$. To find $F_{1-\alpha/2}(n_1 - 1, n_2 - 1) = F_{0.95}(4, 8)$, we need to select 4 from the column headers and 8 from the row headers, then find the cell that overlaps the chosen row and column. In the following image, the row and two columns are highlighted, with the chosen cells in black with white font.

0.95 F Table	Numerator DF									
Denom. DF	1	2	3	4	5	6	7	8	9	10
1	0.00619	0.05402	0.09874	0.12972	0.15133	0.16702	0.17884	0.18805	0.19541	0.20143
2	0.00501	0.05263	0.10469	0.14400	0.17283	0.19443	0.21109	0.22427	0.23494	0.24373
3	0.00464	0.05218	0.10780	0.15171	0.18486	0.21021	0.23005	0.24593	0.25890	0.26967
4	0.00445	0.05196	0.10968	0.15654	0.19260	0.22057	0.24270	0.26056	0.27525	0.28752
5	0.00434	0.05182	0.11095	0.15985	0.19801	0.22793	0.25179	0.27119	0.28722	0.30068
6	0.00427	0.05173	0.11185	0.16226	0.20201	0.23343	0.25867	0.27928	0.29641	0.31083
7	0.00422	0.05167	0.11253	0.16409	0.20509	0.23772	0.26406	0.28568	0.30370	0.31893
8	0.00419	0.05162	0.11306	0.16553	0.20754	0.24115	0.26840	0.29086	0.30964	0.32556
9	0.00416	0.05159	0.11348	0.16670	0.20954	0.24396	0.27198	0.29515	0.31457	0.33108
10	0.00413	0.05156	0.11382	0.16766	0.21119	0.24631	0.27499	0.29876	0.31875	0.33577

This tells us that for this problem, $F_{0.95}(4, 8) = 0.16553$.

Next, we need to find $F_{\alpha/2}(n_1 - 1, n_2 - 1) = F_{0.05}(4, 8)$. Using the same table, we again select 4 from the column headers and 8 from the row headers, and once again find the cell that overlaps the chosen row and column.

0.05 F Table	Numerator DF									
Denom. DF	1	2	3	4	5	6	7	8	9	10
1	161.44764	199.50000	215.70735	224.58324	230.16188	233.98600	236.76840	238.88269	240.54325	241.88175
2	18.51282	19.00000	19.16429	19.24679	19.29641	19.32953	19.35322	19.37099	19.38483	19.39590
3	10.12796	9.55209	9.27663	9.11718	9.01346	8.94065	8.88674	8.84524	8.81230	8.78552
4	7.70865	6.94427	6.59138	6.38823	6.25606	6.16313	6.09421	6.04104	5.99878	5.96437
5	6.60789	5.78614	5.40945	5.19217	5.05033	4.95029	4.87587	4.81832	4.77247	4.73506
6	5.98738	5.14325	4.75706	4.53368	4.38737	4.28387	4.20666	4.14680	4.09902	4.05996
7	5.59145	4.73741	4.34683	4.12031	3.97152	3.86597	3.78704	3.72573	3.67667	3.63652
8	5.31766	4.45897	4.06618	3.83785	3.68750	3.58058	3.50046	3.43810	3.38813	3.34716
9	5.11736	4.25649	3.86255	3.63309	3.48166	3.37375	3.29275	3.22958	3.17889	3.13728
10	4.96460	4.10282	3.70826	3.47805	3.32583	3.21717	3.13546	3.07166	3.02038	2.97824

Thus, we have $F_{0.05}(4, 8) = 3.83785$.

Δ

Now that we have covered how to use the F-tables, we need to use them in the formulas for the confidence interval and the hypothesis test. Let's start with the confidence interval. Just as with the single variance confidence interval, we don't compute a standard error and margin of error; instead we just compute a lower and upper limit.

CONFIDENCE INTERVAL FOR THE RATIO OF TWO VARIANCES

Suppose we have two populations with variances σ_1^2 and σ_2^2. Without giving a mathematical proof of it, the $100(1 - \alpha)\%$ confidence interval for the variance ratio σ_1^2/σ_2^2 is

$$\left(\frac{s_1^2}{s_2^2 F_{\alpha/2}(n_1 - 1, n_2 - 1)}, \frac{s_1^2}{s_2^2 F_{1-\alpha/2}(n_1 - 1, n_2 - 1)} \right)$$

As an extension, the $100(1 - \alpha)\%$ confidence interval for the standard deviation ratio σ_1/σ_2 is

$$\left(\sqrt{\frac{s_1^2}{s_2^2 F_{\alpha/2}(n_1 - 1, n_2 - 1)}}, \sqrt{\frac{s_1^2}{s_2^2 F_{1-\alpha/2}(n_1 - 1, n_2 - 1)}} \right)$$

When we get to hypothesis testing, we test whether $\sigma_1^2 = \sigma_2^2$. If the two population variances are equal, then their ratio is 1. Thus, if the confidence interval contains 1, then we cannot rule out the possibility that the variances are equal, which is equivalent to failing to reject the null hypothesis. However, if the confidence interval does not contain 1, then the variances most likely are not equal, which is equivalent to rejecting the null hypothesis.

Caution: Some textbooks present alternative formulas for the confidence interval formula where at least one of the Fs is on the numerator with degrees of freedom reversed. This is in fact the same formula rearranged due to some statistical theory going on behind the scenes. We present the above formula to make it easy to compare the confidence interval to that of the chi-square formula for the one-variance case (and also to avoid additional computations needed to manipulate the table values).

EXAMPLE

You want to see if the variances of heights (in inches) of fifth-graders at a school are equal to each other for boys and girls. A random sample of 7 boys yields a sample standard deviation of 4.68, while a random sample of 9 girls results in a sample standard deviation of 1.71. Assuming that heights of boys and girls in these two populations are normally distributed. Construct a 95% confidence interval for the ratio of population variances of boys to girls.

Solution: First, let's label our numbers as $s_1 = 4.68$, $n_1 = 7$, $s_2 = 1.71$, and $n_2 = 9$. That means that $s_1^2 = 21.9024$ and $s_2^2 = 2.9241$, while the corresponding degrees of freedom are $DF_1 = 7 - 1 = 6$ and $DF_2 = 9 - 1 = 8$.

Since 95% confidence corresponds to $\alpha/2 = 0.025$, we need the two F-values

$$F_{1-\alpha/2}(n_1 - 1, n_2 - 1) = F_{0.975}(6, 8)$$
$$F_{\alpha/2}(n_1 - 1, n_2 - 1) = F_{0.025}(6, 8)$$

Going to the 0.975 F-table, we need to select 6 from the column headers and 8 from the row headers, then find the cell that overlaps the chosen row and column. In the following image, the rows and columns are highlighted, with the chosen cell in black with white font.

0.975 F Table	Numerator DF									
Denom. DF	1	2	3	4	5	6	7	8	9	10
1	0.00154	0.02597	0.05733	0.08185	0.09993	0.11347	0.12387	0.13209	0.13871	0.14416
2	0.00125	0.02564	0.06233	0.09390	0.11857	0.13774	0.15287	0.16503	0.17499	0.18327
3	0.00116	0.02553	0.06477	0.10021	0.12881	0.15154	0.16978	0.18464	0.19692	0.20723
4	0.00111	0.02548	0.06622	0.10412	0.13536	0.16059	0.18107	0.19792	0.21195	0.22380
5	0.00108	0.02545	0.06718	0.10679	0.13993	0.16701	0.18921	0.20759	0.22299	0.23607
6	0.00107	0.02542	0.06787	0.10873	0.14331	0.17183	0.19537	0.21498	0.23150	0.24557
7	0.00105	0.02541	0.06838	0.11020	0.14592	0.17558	0.20020	0.22082	0.23826	0.25318
8	0.00105	0.02540	0.06878	0.11136	0.14799	0.17858	0.20411	0.22557	0.24379	0.25941
9	0.00104	0.02539	0.06909	0.11230	0.14968	0.18105	0.20733	0.22950	0.24839	0.26462
10	0.00103	0.02538	0.06935	0.11307	0.15108	0.18311	0.21003	0.23282	0.25228	0.26905

We see that $F_{0.975}(6, 8) = 0.17858$. Next, going to the 0.025 F-table, we select 6 from the column headers and 8 from the row headers, then find the cell that overlaps the chosen row and column.

0.025 F Table	Numerator DF									
Denom. DF	1	2	3	4	5	6	7	8	9	10
1	647.78901	799.50000	864.16297	899.58331	921.84790	937.11108	948.21689	956.65622	963.28458	968.62744
2	38.50633	39.00000	39.16549	39.24842	39.29823	39.33146	39.35521	39.37302	39.38688	39.39797
3	17.44344	16.04411	15.43918	15.10098	14.88482	14.73472	14.62440	14.53989	14.47308	14.41894
4	12.21786	10.64911	9.97920	9.60453	9.36447	9.19731	9.07414	8.97958	8.90468	8.84388
5	10.00698	8.43362	7.76359	7.38789	7.14638	6.97770	6.85308	6.75717	6.68105	6.61915
6	8.81310	7.25986	6.59880	6.22716	5.98757	5.81976	5.69547	5.59962	5.52341	5.46132
7	8.07267	6.54152	5.88982	5.52259	5.28524	5.11860	4.99491	4.89934	4.82322	4.76112
8	7.57088	6.05947	5.41596	5.05263	4.81728	4.65170	4.52856	4.43326	4.35723	4.29513
9	7.20928	5.71471	5.07812	4.71808	4.48441	4.31972	4.19705	4.10196	4.02599	3.96387
10	6.93673	5.45640	4.82562	4.46834	4.23609	4.07213	3.94982	3.85489	3.77896	3.71679

Hence, $F_{0.025}(6, 8) = 4.65170$. Putting all the values into the formula, the lower and upper limits are

$$\frac{s_1^2}{s_2^2 F_{0.025}(6, 8)} = \frac{21.9024}{2.9241 \times 4.65170} = 1.610229531$$

$$\frac{s_1^2}{s_2^2 F_{0.975}(6, 8)} = \frac{21.9024}{2.9241 \times 0.17858} = 41.94369307$$

Hence, the 95% confidence interval for the ratio of variances is (rounded to five decimals)

$$\left(\frac{s_1^2}{s_2^2 F_{\alpha/2}(n_1 - 1, n_2 - 1)}, \frac{s_1^2}{s_2^2 F_{1-\alpha/2}(n_1 - 1, n_2 - 1)}\right) = (1.61023, 41.94369)$$

Note that the sample ratio variances s_1^2/s_2^2 is equal to 7.490304709, which is inside the confidence interval, as we expect. It is not at the center of the interval, but that is expected because the F-distribution is not symmetric (cf. the chi-square distribution). If you instead need a 95% confidence interval for the ratio of the population standard deviations, then square root both sides to get

$$\left(\sqrt{1.610229531}, \sqrt{41.94369307}\right) = (1.26895, 6.47640)$$

To interpret the interval, we are 95% confident that the ratio of population variances is between 1.61023 and 41.94369. Observe that 1 is not inside the interval, which means the variances most likely are not equal. Further, since the whole interval is above 1, that means that the first population variance (boys' heights) most likely is larger than the second population variance (girls' heights).

You might be wondering what would happen if we had reversed the order of the groups. The answer is that we would get a different confidence interval since the ratio has been reversed (since now we would be studying s_s^2/s_1^2). This new interval would still not contain 1, but now the whole interval would be less than 1, implying that the variance of girls' heights is smaller than the variance of boys' heights. That is in fact the same conclusion we already made, only worded differently.

Δ

As before, we next turn our attention to hypothesis testing. The steps are similar to what we have used before, except in Step 4 we will create a rejection region, just like we did for hypothesis testing of one variance. (Again, the TI-84 can find the p-value for a left-tailed or right-tailed test, but the two-tailed p-value is harder to do although not impossible. For that reason, we stick to using rejection regions here. As before, different computer programs will find the p-values.)

Here are the five steps to follow for hypothesis testing.

Step 1: Set up the hypotheses.
Suppose we want to test whether the variances from two different populations are equal to each other. The null hypothesis is

$$H_0: \sigma_1^2 = \sigma_2^2$$

The alternative hypothesis is one of the following:

$$H_A: \sigma_1^2 > \sigma_2^2 \quad \text{(right-tailed test)}$$
$$H_A: \sigma_1^2 < \sigma_2^2 \quad \text{(left-tailed test)}$$
$$H_A: \sigma_1^2 \neq \sigma_2^2 \quad \text{(two-tailed test)}$$

Note that alternatively, we could write the hypotheses using standard deviations instead of variances. If you do that, the following would be an example of how to write it (however, as before, I recommend you stick with variance notation for consistency):

$$H_0: \sigma_1 = \sigma_2$$
$$H_A: \sigma_1 > \sigma_2$$

Step 2: Check the assumptions.
For the hypothesis test to be valid, four assumptions need to be true, assuming the sample sizes n_1 and n_2:

1) The data must be quantitative (meaning they are numbers that can be averaged).
2) The subjects must be randomly selected.
3) The two groups of subjects must be independent of each other.
4) The data from both groups must come from normally distributed populations.

Step 3: Compute the test statistic.
Assuming we are comparing Group 1 to Group 2 in that order, the test statistic for the ratio of two population variances is

$$F = \frac{s_1^2}{s_2^2}$$

Simply stated, you find the first group's sample variance and divide it by the second group's sample variance.

Step 4: Determine the rejection region.

The rejection region is the part of the F-distribution that is the extreme upper (and/or lower side). If the test statistic falls inside this region, then we reject the null hypothesis. If the test statistic falls anywhere else, we do not reject the null hypothesis. Once again, there are three ways of sketching the rejection region, and they all depend on the choice of alternative hypothesis.

For a right-tailed test, we find the F-value from the Appendix F table that gives probability α to the right. That means we need $F_\alpha(n_1 - 1, n_2 - 1)$. If F lies above this value, we reject the null hypothesis, and if it lies below, we don't reject it.

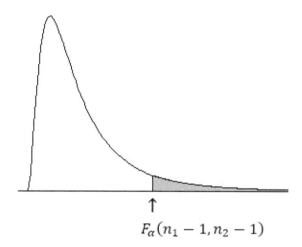

$$F_\alpha(n_1 - 1, n_2 - 1)$$

For a left-tailed test, we find the F-value from the Appendix F table that gives probability α to the left (and therefore $1 - \alpha$ to the right). That means we need $F_{1-\alpha}(n_1 - 1, n_2 - 1)$. If F lies below this value, we reject the null hypothesis, and if it lies above, we don't reject it.

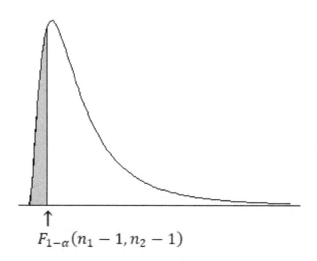

$$F_{1-\alpha}(n_1 - 1, n_2 - 1)$$

For a two-tailed test, we find the F-value from the Appendix F table that gives probability $\alpha/2$ to the right, which is $F_{\alpha/2}(n_1 - 1, n_2 - 1)$. We also need the value that gives probability $\alpha/2$ to the left (and therefore $1 - \alpha/2$ to the right), which is $F_{1-\alpha/2}(n_1 - 1, n_2 - 1)$. If F lies below the lower value or above the upper value, we reject the null hypothesis, and if it lies in between, we don't reject it.

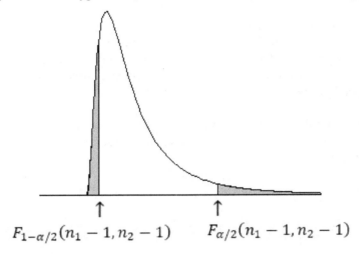

$$F_{1-\alpha/2}(n_1 - 1, n_2 - 1) \qquad F_{\alpha/2}(n_1 - 1, n_2 - 1)$$

Step 5: State the conclusion.
Finally, we determine the outcome. If the test statistic falls inside the rejection region, then…

1) We reject the null hypothesis.
2) There is sufficient evidence against the null hypothesis.
3) There is sufficient evidence for the alternative hypothesis.

If the test statistic falls outside the rejection region, then…

1) We fail to reject the null hypothesis.
2) There is insufficient evidence against the null hypothesis.
3) There is insufficient evidence for the alternative hypothesis.

REVIEW: HYPOTHESIS TESTING FOR RATO OF TWO POPULATION VARIANCES
Step 1: Set up the hypotheses.

$$H_0: \sigma_1^2 = \sigma_2^2$$
$$H_A: \sigma_1^2 > \sigma_2^2 \quad \text{or} \quad H_A: \sigma_1^2 < \sigma_2^2 \quad \text{or} \quad H_A: \sigma_1^2 \neq \sigma_2^2$$

Step 2: Check the assumptions.

1) Quantitative data
2) Random samples
3) Two groups are independent of each other
4) Data come from normal populations

Step 3: Compute the test statistic.

$$F = \frac{s_1^2}{s_2^2}$$

Step 4: Determine the rejection region.

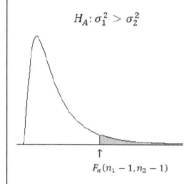

$H_A: \sigma_1^2 > \sigma_2^2$

$F_\alpha(n_1 - 1, n_2 - 1)$

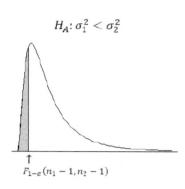

$H_A: \sigma_1^2 < \sigma_2^2$

$F_{1-\alpha}(n_1 - 1, n_2 - 1)$

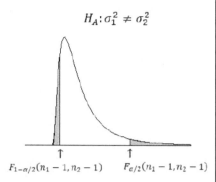

$H_A: \sigma_1^2 \neq \sigma_2^2$

$F_{1-\alpha/2}(n_1 - 1, n_2 - 1)$ $F_{\alpha/2}(n_1 - 1, n_2 - 1)$

Step 5: State the conclusion.

If the test statistic falls inside the rejection region, then…
   1) We reject the null hypothesis.
   2) There is sufficient evidence against the null hypothesis.
   3) There is sufficient evidence for the alternative hypothesis.

If the test statistic falls outside the rejection region, then…
   1) We fail to reject the null hypothesis.
   2) There is insufficient evidence against the null hypothesis.
   3) There is insufficient evidence for the alternative hypothesis.

And now … for some examples!

EXAMPLE

Let's continue the previous example about heights of fifth-grade boys and girls. Recall that for boys, $s_1^2 = 21.9024$ and $n_1 = 7$, while for girls, $s_2^2 = 2.9241$ and $n_2 = 9$. Test whether the population variance for boys is greater than the population variance for girls, then whether they are different from each other, both at the $\alpha = 0.05$ significance level.

Solution: First, here are the hypotheses for a right-tailed test.

$$H_0: \sigma_1^2 = \sigma_2^2$$
$$H_A: \sigma_1^2 > \sigma_2^2$$

Remember we assumed that the heights represented random selections and that they were from two different normal populations. The test statistic is

$$F = \frac{s_1^2}{s_2^2} = \frac{21.9024}{2.9241} = 7.490304709$$

Here comes the rejection region! First, drawing a sketch of the situation, we see that since this is a right-tailed test, we need the F-value with $DF_1 = 7 - 1 = 6$ and $DF_2 = 9 - 1 = 8$ that has probability 0.05 to the right.

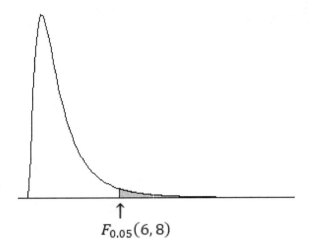

$$F_{0.05}(6, 8)$$

That means we need to find $F_{0.05}(6, 8)$. Consulting the 0.05 table, we discover that it is 3.58058. Now let's redraw our sketch but with the rejection region and the computed F:

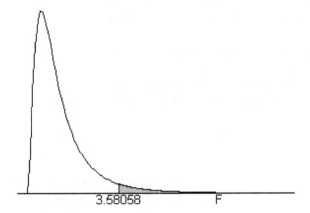

The null hypothesis is rejected if F is above 3.58058, and we see that the test statistic ($F = 7.490304709$) does indeed fall inside the rejection region. That means that we reject the null hypothesis; there is sufficient evidence that the population variance of heights for boys is greater than the population variance of heights for girls.

Next, let's repeat this exercise for a two-tailed test. The hypotheses are

$$H_0: \sigma_1^2 = \sigma_2^2$$
$$H_A: \sigma_1^2 \neq \sigma_2^2$$

The test statistic is still the same: $F = 7.490304709$. However, we need to redraw our rejection region so that probability $\alpha/2$ is in the lower tail and another probability $\alpha/2$ is in the upper tail.

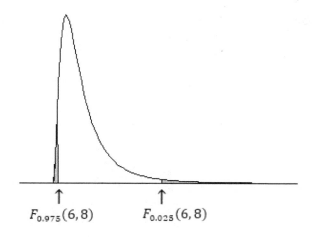

$$F_{0.975}(6,8) \qquad F_{0.025}(6,8)$$

Since $\alpha = 0.05$, we need the F-values at $1 - \alpha/2 = 0.975$ and $\alpha/2 = 0.025$ for $DF_1 = 6$ and $DF_2 = 8$. From the earlier example, we had already computed these values as $F_{0.975}(6,8) = 0.17858$ and $F_{0.025}(6,8) = 4.65170$. Let's add everything to our sketch:

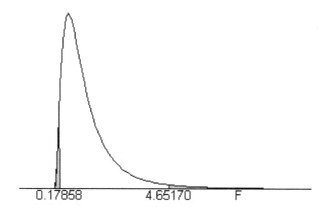

The null hypothesis is rejected if F falls below 0.17858 or above 4.65170, and we discover that the test statistic ($F = 7.490304709$) is above 4.65170. That means that we reject the null hypothesis; there is sufficient evidence that the population variances are different from each other.

As a side note, if we actually did compute the p-values in this problem, we would have discovered that they are both less than $\alpha = 0.05$, which again would lead to rejecting the null hypothesis. Although we won't show the work here, the p-value for the right-tailed test is 0.00605, while the p-value for the two-tailed test is 0.00606 (and again, note that it is not double the right-tailed p-value due to the F-distribution not being symmetric).

Δ

EXAMPLE
An ornithologist wants to study the lengths of eggs (in centimeters) of House Finches (*Haemorhous mexicanus*) and Common Redpolls (*Acanthis flammea*). It is of interest to see if the variance of the House Finch egg lengths is smaller than the variance of the Common Redpoll egg lengths. The ornithologist takes a random sample of eggs from both species and carefully measures their lengths. A sample of 11 House Finch eggs produced a sample standard deviation of 0.08 cm, while a sample of 8 Common Redpoll eggs resulted in a sample standard deviation of 0.09 cm. Assuming that egg lengths of both species follow normal distributions, conduct a hypothesis test at the $\alpha = 0.05$ significance level.

Solution: First, let Group 1 be the House Finch eggs and Group 2 be the Common Redpoll eggs. We want to see whether the variance of Group 1 is less than Group 2, so this is a left-tailed test. The hypotheses are

$$H_0: \sigma_1^2 = \sigma_2^2$$
$$H_A: \sigma_1^2 < \sigma_2^2$$

We have $s_1 = 0.08$, $n_1 = 11$, $s_2 = 0.09$, and $n_2 = 8$. This means the sample variances are $s_1^2 = 0.0064$ and $s_2^2 = 0.0081$, so the test statistic is

$$F = \frac{s_1^2}{s_2^2} = \frac{0.0064}{0.0081} = 0.7901234568$$

We now need the rejection region. Drawing a sketch, since this is a left-tailed test, we need the F-value that has probability 0.05 to the left (and therefore probability 0.95 to the right). The degrees of freedom to use are $DF_1 = 11 - 1 = 10$ and $DF_2 = 8 - 1 = 7$.

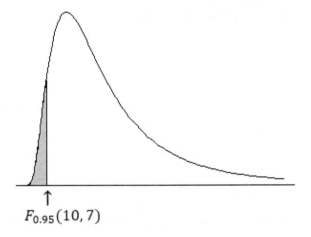

$$F_{0.95}(10, 7)$$

Now we go to the 0.95 F-table (because $1 - \alpha = 0.95$) and look up $F_{0.95}(10, 7)$ by looking in the 10 column and the 7 row. Consulting the table, we get 0.31893. Now let's redraw our sketch but with the rejection region and the computed F:

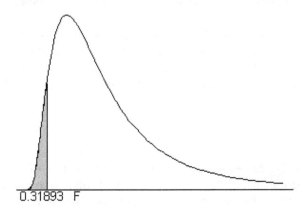

0.31893   F

The null hypothesis is rejected if F falls below 0.31893. We see that the test statistic ($F = 0.7901234568$) actually falls above 0.31893 and therefore outside the rejection region. That means that we don't reject the null hypothesis; there is insufficient evidence that the first population variance is less than the second population variance. In context of the problem, the population variance of House Finch egg lengths is not significantly smaller than the population variance of Common Redpoll egg lengths. (If you bother to compute the left-tailed p-value, you will see that it is 0.35509, which is greater than $\alpha = 0.05$, as expected.)

Δ

There is also a TI-84 command available for the hypothesis test (not the confidence interval).

TI-84 COMMAND: HYPOTHESIS TESTING FOR RATIO OF TWO VARIANCES

To conduct a hypothesis test for the ratio of two population variance, press $\boxed{\text{STAT}}$, scroll right to TESTS, and select Option E: $2 - SampFTest$. For input, if your data are already stored in a list (say L_1 and L_2), select Data, but if you instead have the sample standard deviations and sizes, select Stats.

If you chose Data, type L_1 for List1 and L_2 for List2, but if you chose Stats, type the numbers for s_1, n_1, s_2, and n_2. Select the appropriate symbol for the alternative hypothesis ($\neq \sigma_2, < \sigma_2, > \sigma_2$), then scroll down to Calculate and press $\boxed{\text{ENTER}}$. The resulting output shows the following:

The alternative hypothesis selected.
The F-statistic.
The p-value (denoted as p).
The two sample standard deviations and sample sizes.

Caution: The TI-84 gives slightly different p-values for a two-tailed test. Depending what your instructor says, you may be able to use it as an approximate answer, but realize that different computer programs could give different, more accurate results.

EXAMPLE

Repeating the previous example about egg lengths, select Option E: $2 - SampFTest$. Under Stats, enter $s_1 = 0.08$, $n_1 = 11$, $s_2 = 0.09$, and $n_2 = 8$. Select $\sigma_1 < \sigma_2$ for the alternative hypothesis and choose Calculate. The results are $F = 0.7901234568$ and $p = 0.3550908601$, and notice that the F-statistic matches what we computed by hand. We didn't compute the p-value, but it is given on the output, and you can see that it is greater than $\alpha = 0.05$.

Δ

Section 11.5 – One-Way ANOVA*

Congratulations – you have made it to the final topic covered in these notes! To give you a little incentive to make it through this last section, I will give you a joke: What do you get if you cross a statistician with an astronomer? You will have to finish reading the section to see the answer!

We are going to give a very brief introduction to a test called Analysis of Variance (abbreviated as ANOVA). There are several different types of ANOVA used in statistics, but the one that is most frequently taught in introductory classes is called one-way ANOVA, so we concentrate on that one here. (Again, your introductory class may or may not cover this topic.)

In Chapter 9 we did hypothesis testing for one population mean μ. In Chapter 10 we extended the hypothesis testing to see if two population means μ_1 and μ_2 were significantly different from each other. ANOVA testing generalizes the hypothesis test to see whether many (three or more) population means are significantly different from one another. (In a similar way, chi-square goodness of fit testing extends the same concepts for population proportions.)

The process of conducting an ANOVA test is quite different from other tests we have seen before since we need to fill in some entries on an ANOVA table, all of which are computed with specific equations. To make matters worse, a lot of the terms vary in name depending what statistical source you use. We shall go through these terms and equations carefully. First, the following is an ANOVA table before any numbers or equations are shown (so don't worry – we will go through all the terms below!).

Source of Variation	Sum of Squares	DF	Mean Square	Test Statistic	P-Value
Treatment	SSR	r - 1	MSR	F	p-value
Error	SSE	n - r	MSE		
Total	SST	n - 1			

As you can see, the end goal is to compute an F-statistic and consequently a p-value, with which we decide whether to reject the null hypothesis. On that note, let's discuss the steps to ANOVA.

Step 1: Set up the hypotheses.
Suppose we want to test whether the population means from r total groups are equal to one another against the alternative, that at least one of the means is significantly different from the rest, at the α significance level. The hypotheses are

$$H_0: \mu_1 = \mu_2 = \dots = \mu_r$$
$$H_A: \text{At least one mean is not equal to the others.}$$

Step 2: Check the assumptions.
For the ANOVA test to be valid, four assumptions need to be true, assuming a sample size n:

1) The data must be quantitative (meaning they are numbers that can be averaged).
2) The samples from all groups must be randomly selected and independent of one another.
3) The samples must all come from normally distributed populations.
4) The population variances must all be equal.

The last assumption about equal population variances is necessary for ANOVA to be valid. This simply means that even though they are unknown, we assume that $\sigma_1^2 = \sigma_2^2 = \dots = \sigma_r^2$. If this assumption were false, then we would need to use a non-parametric test on the dataset (which we won't cover here).

Step 3: Compute the overall sample mean and the sample group means.
We first identify the sample sizes of the r groups, calling them $n_1, n_2, \dots, n_r$. Also let n denote the total number of subjects, or in other words $n = n_1 + n_2 + \dots + n_r$. Next, we compute the overall sample mean $\bar{x}$ on all n subjects, then we compute the sample group means $\bar{x}_1, \bar{x}_2, \dots, \bar{x}_r$.

To be clear, the sample group means are computed individually per group. For instance, $\bar{x}_1$ is just the sample average of the n_1 subjects in Group 1 and nowhere else. (Note that the sample sizes don't necessarily all have to be equal to one another, although a lot of examples you might find with ANOVA will have them that way.)

Step 4: Compute the sum of squares.

The notation can get a bit confusing here since there are multiple ways of labeling these three quantities (and multiple ways of writing the equations). The following are what I believe are the most straightforward equations.

First, we compute the **Treatment Sum of Squares** (labeled SSR, which stands for Sum of Squares Treatment, where R is used instead of T because T is used for the next sum of squares). This is also known as the Between Sum of Squares. The Treatment Sum of Squares is computed over the r groups:

$$SSR = \sum_{i=1}^{r} n_i(\overline{x}_i - \overline{x})^2$$
$$= n_1(\overline{x}_1 - \overline{x})^2 + n_2(\overline{x}_2 - \overline{x})^2 + \cdots + n_r(\overline{x}_r - \overline{x})^2$$

Second, we find the **Total Sum of Squares** (labeled SST, which stands for Sum of Squares Total). The Total Sum of Squares is computed over all n observations:

$$SST = \sum_{All\ Obs} (x_i - \overline{x})^2$$

Third, we compute the **Error Sum of Squares** (labeled SSE, which stands for Sum of Squares Error). This is also known as the Within Sum of Squares. There are two formulas to compute it, but the easier of the two (much easier!) is

$$SSE = SST - SSR$$

In case you are interested, the other formula is

$$SSE = \sum_{i=1}^{n_1} (x_i - \overline{x}_1)^2 + \sum_{i=1}^{n_2} (x_i - \overline{x}_2)^2 + \cdots + \sum_{i=1}^{n_r} (x_i - \overline{x}_r)^2$$

Step 5: Compute the degrees of freedom.

There are three different degrees of freedom in an ANOVA table, although only two of them are used in subsequent calculations. They are denoted DF_R, DF_E, and DF_T, one for each of Treatment, Error, and Total. The formulas are simple:

$$DF_R = r - 1$$
$$DF_E = n - r$$
$$DF_T = n - 1$$

The only two we actually need are DF_R and DF_E, but we state DF_T just for completeness, and also to illustrate the fact that $DF_R + DF_E = DF_T$ (just like the sum of squares formulas).

Step 6: Compute the mean squares.

There are two different mean squares we need, the Mean Square Treatment (labeled MSR, again using R instead of T) and the Mean Square Error (labeled MSE). These are found just by dividing the corresponding sum of squares by its degrees of freedom:

$$MSR = \frac{SSR}{DF_R} = \frac{SSR}{r - 1}$$

$$MSE = \frac{SSE}{DF_E} = \frac{SSE}{n - r}$$

Step 7: Compute the F-statistic.
The F-statistic is computed by dividing MSR by MSE:

$$F = \frac{MSR}{MSE}$$

Step 8: Compute the p-value.
Since we have an F-statistic, we must use the F-distribution to find the p-value. Unlike with most earlier hypothesis tests (except the first two chi-square tests), for an ANOVA test we always find the right-tailed p-value. We compute the probability to the right of F, as in the following graph.

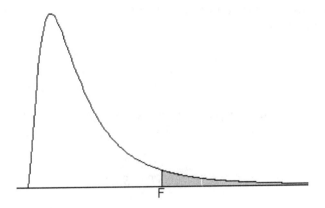

Step 9: State the conclusion.
Finally, we determine the outcome. If the p-value is less than α, then…

1) We reject the null hypothesis.
2) There is sufficient evidence against the null hypothesis.
3) There is sufficient evidence that at least one the population means is significantly different from the others.

If the p-value is greater than α, then…
1) We fail to reject the null hypothesis.
2) There is insufficient evidence against the null hypothesis.
3) There is insufficient evidence that at least one the population means is significantly different from the others.

Step 10: Determine which population means are different from one another (if applicable).
If we fail to reject the null hypothesis, then we are finished because none of the population means are significantly different from one another. However, if we reject the null hypothesis, then we need to investigate specifically which means are the "offenders." This requires a separate statistical test called Least Significant Difference, which we will cover later in this section.

REVIEW: ANOVA TEST
Assume we have a dataset of n subjects divided into r groups where each group has sample size n_1, n_2, …, n_r.

Step 1: Set up the hypotheses.

$$H_0: \mu_1 = \mu_2 = \ldots = \mu_r$$
H_A: At least one mean is not equal to the others.

Step 2: Check the assumptions.

1) Quantitative data
2) Random samples independent of one another
3) Data come from normally distributed populations
4) Population variances are all equal

Step 3: Compute the overall sample mean $\bar{x}$ (on all n subjects) and the sample group means $\bar{x}_1, \bar{x}_2, \ldots, \bar{x}_r$.

Step 4: Compute the sum of squares.

$$SSR = n_1(\bar{x}_1 - \bar{x})^2 + n_2(\bar{x}_2 - \bar{x})^2 + \cdots + n_r(\bar{x}_r - \bar{x})^2$$
$$SST = \sum_{All\ Obs} (x_i - \bar{x})^2$$
$$SSE = SST - SSR$$

Step 5: Compute the degrees of freedom.

$$DF_R = r - 1$$
$$DF_E = n - r$$
$$DF_T = n - 1$$

Step 6: Compute the mean squares.

$$MSR = \frac{SSR}{DF_R} = \frac{SSR}{r - 1}$$
$$MSE = \frac{SSE}{DF_E} = \frac{SSE}{n - r}$$

Step 7: Compute the F-statistic.

$$F = \frac{MSR}{MSE}$$

Step 8: Compute the p-value by finding the probability above F on the F-distribution with numerator degrees of freedom $(r - 1)$ and denominator degrees of freedom $(n - r)$. This is always a right-tailed test.

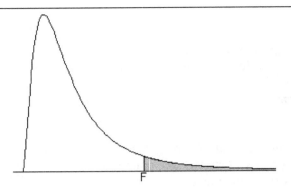

Step 9: State the conclusion.

If the *p*-value is below the significance level α, we reject the null hypothesis.
There is evidence that at least one of the population means is different from the others.

If the *p*-value is above the significance level α, we fail to reject the null hypothesis.
There is no evidence that the population means are different from one another.

Step 10: Determine which population means are different from one another (if applicable). If Step 9 resulted in rejecting the null hypothesis, then conduct the Least Significant Difference test (described later).

Let's do an example!

EXAMPLE
Given three local cupcake shops, we want to see if the mean amount of sugar (in grams) used per cupcake is different from each shop (and all shops are independent of one another). We randomly select a sample of five cupcakes from each of the shops and record how many grams of sugar were used per cupcake. Assume that the amount of sugar used is normally distributed in each case, and further assume that the population variances of used sugar are the same for all three shops. Perform an appropriate ANOVA test at the $\alpha = 0.05$ significance level using the data below.

Shop A	Shop B	Shop C
28	28	30
30	32	36
32	33	32
29	30	37
30	29	34

Solution: The first thing to do is set up the hypotheses to test, noting that there are three shops and therefore three population mean sugar measurements.

$$H_0: \mu_1 = \mu_2 = \mu_3$$
$$H_A: \text{At least one mean is not equal to the others.}$$

Noting that the assumptions are satisfied, we need to compute a series of calculations. We begin by writing down the sample sizes as well as the total sample size and number of groups. Each shop provided five cupcakes, so $n_1 = 5$, $n_2 = 5$, and $n_3 = 5$, and therefore $n = 15$. There are three groups (the cupcake shops) and therefore $r = 3$.

We compute the overall sample mean $\bar{x}$, as well as the sample group means $\bar{x}_1$, $\bar{x}_2$, and $\bar{x}_3$. The overall mean is

$$\bar{x} = \frac{28 + 30 + 32 + 29 + 30 + 28 + 32 + 33 + 30 + 29 + 30 + 36 + 32 + 37 + 34}{15}$$
$$= 31.33333333$$

The group means are

$$\bar{x}_1 = \frac{28 + 30 + 32 + 29 + 30}{5} = 29.8$$
$$\bar{x}_2 = \frac{28 + 32 + 33 + 30 + 29}{5} = 30.4$$
$$\bar{x}_3 = \frac{30 + 36 + 32 + 37 + 34}{5} = 33.8$$

Next, we need the Treatment Sum of Squares (SSR), the Error Sum of Squares (SSE), and the Total Sum of Squares (SST). We go for SSR first:

$$\begin{aligned} SSR &= n_1(\bar{x}_1 - \bar{x})^2 + n_2(\bar{x}_2 - \bar{x})^2 + n_3(\bar{x}_3 - \bar{x})^2 \\ &= 5(29.8 - 31.33333333)^2 + 5(30.4 - 31.33333333)^2 + 5(33.8 - 31.33333333)^2 \\ &= 46.53333333 \end{aligned}$$

Noting the shortcut to finding SSE, we instead compute SST:

$$\begin{aligned} SST = \sum (x_i - \bar{x})^2 \\ = (28 - 31.33333333)^2 + (30 - 31.33333333)^2 + (32 - 31.33333333)^2 \\ + (29 - 31.33333333)^2 + (30 - 31.33333333)^2 + (28 - 31.33333333)^2 \\ + (32 - 31.33333333)^2 + (33 - 31.33333333)^2 + (30 - 31.33333333)^2 \\ + (29 - 31.33333333)^2 + (30 - 31.33333333)^2 + (36 - 31.33333333)^2 \\ + (32 - 31.33333333)^2 + (37 - 31.33333333)^2 + (34 - 31.33333333)^2 \\ = 105.33333333 \end{aligned}$$

The Error Sum of Squares is then the difference between SST and SSR:

$$\begin{aligned} SSE = SST - SSR &= 105.33333333 - 46.33333333 \\ &= 58.8 \end{aligned}$$

The ANOVA table now looks like the following:

Source of Variation	Sum of Squares	DF	Mean Square	Test Statistic	P-Value
Treatment	46.53333333	r - 1	MSR	F	p-value
Error	58.80000000	n - r	MSE		
Total	105.33333333	n - 1			

We also need the corresponding degrees of freedom DF_R and DF_E (and we will compute DF_T as well, even though we don't need it in later calculations):

$$DF_R = r - 1 = 3 - 1 = 2$$
$$DF_E = n - r = 15 - 3 = 12$$
$$DF_T = n - 1 = 15 - 1 = 14$$

Here is the updated table:

Source of Variation	Sum of Squares	DF	Mean Square	Test Statistic	P-Value
Treatment	46.53333333	2	MSR	F	p-value
Error	58.80000000	12	MSE		
Total	105.33333333	14			

We now need the two mean squared error terms, Mean Square Treatment (MSR) and Mean Square Error (MSE), now that we have the Sum of Squares and corresponding degrees of freedom. They are computed as

$$MSR = \frac{SSR}{DF_R} = \frac{46.53333333}{2} = 23.26666667$$
$$MSE = \frac{SSE}{DF_E} = \frac{58.8}{12} = 4.9$$

The updated ANOVA table awaits:

Source of Variation	Sum of Squares	DF	Mean Square	Test Statistic	P-Value
Treatment	46.53333333	2	23.26666667	F	p-value
Error	58.80000000	12	4.90000000		
Total	105.33333333	14			

Next, the F-statistic is MSR divided by MSE:

$$F = \frac{MSR}{MSE} = \frac{23.26666667}{4.9} = 4.74829932$$

We are nearly there!

Source of Variation	Sum of Squares	DF	Mean Square	Test Statistic	P-Value
Treatment	46.53333333	2	23.26666667	4.74829932	p-value
Error	58.80000000	12	4.90000000		
Total	105.33333333	14			

Finally, to get the p-value, notice that the numerator degrees of freedom is 2 and the denominator degrees of freedom is 12. For an ANOVA test, we always find the probability to the right of F, as in the following sketch:

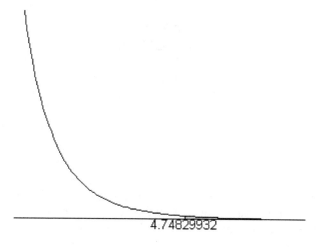

The lower limit is 4.74829932 and the upper limit is 999999, and so we can use the TI-84 to get the p-value:

$$Fcdf(4.74829932, 999999, 2, 12) = 0.03026$$

Here is the completed ANOVA table:

Source of Variation	Sum of Squares	DF	Mean Square	Test Statistic	P-Value
Treatment	46.53333333	2	23.26666667	4.74829932	0.03026
Error	58.80000000	12	4.90000000		
Total	105.33333333	14			

The p-value is below $\alpha = 0.05$, so we reject the null hypothesis. There is strong evidence that at least one of the population means is different from the others. Put another way, given the three population average amounts of grams of sugar used per cupcake per shop, at least one of those average amounts is different from the others. However, the ANOVA test alone will not tell us specifically which means are different from the others.

Δ

I'll go ahead and answer your next question – yes, the TI-84 will quickly perform an ANOVA test for us!

TI-84 COMMAND: ANOVA

To run an ANOVA test, first enter your data into L_1, L_2, and L_3, or more lists as needed (as many lists as there are groups). Next, press STAT, scroll right to TESTS, and choose Option H: $ANOVA(\ )$. Enter each list name separated by commas (for instance, $ANOVA(L_1, L_2, L_3)$ and press ENTER.

There is a lot of output, but the two most important lines are the first two, the F-statistic and the p-value (written as p). If you are interested, the next group of lines is for the Treatment row (DF_R, SSR, and MSR), while the group of lines after that is for the Error row (DF_E, SSE, and MSE).

EXAMPLE

Let's use the TI-84 to conduct the cupcake ANOVA example above. Using the command $ANOVA(L_1, L_2, L_3)$, we obtain the following output, all of which matches what we computed by hand.

$$F = 4.74829932$$
$$p = 0.0302600046$$
$$DF_R = 2$$
$$SSR = 46.5333333$$
$$MSR = 23.2666667$$
$$DF_E = 12$$
$$SSE = 58.8$$
$$MSE = 4.9$$

Δ

Now that we have established that at least one of the population means is significantly different from the others, the obvious next question is exactly how do we determine which mean (or means) is significantly different than the others? There are a number of methods to do this, but the only one we show here is the Least Significant Difference, or the LSD. We run it on each possible pair of groups – for instance, with three groups, we would compare Group 1 with Group 2, then Group 1 with Group 3, and lastly Group 2 with Group 3. (In general, with r groups we would have $\binom{r}{2}$ pairs to examine.)

The following steps are used to conduct the Least Significant Difference test. It is important to note that you only do this if the ANOVA test gave a significant result with a p-value below α, otherwise LSD would be unnecessary since none of the means would be significantly different from one other.

LEAST SIGNIFICANT DIFFERENCE TEST

First perform an ANOVA test, and do the following steps only if the p-value is less than the significance level α.

Step 1: Compute the T-score $T_{\alpha/2}(n - r)$, where the degrees of freedom are equal to those from the SSE row on the ANOVA table.

Step 2: For each possible pair of groups (call them Group A and Group B), compute the following quantity:

$$LSD_{A,B} = T_{\alpha/2}(n - r) \times \sqrt{MSE\left(\frac{1}{n_A} + \frac{1}{n_B}\right)}$$

Step 3: For the two groups in question, compute $|\bar{x}_A - \bar{x}_B|$, the absolute value of the difference of the two sample means (this means if the answer is negative, make it positive).

Step 4: If $|\bar{x}_A - \bar{x}_B| > LSD_{A,B}$, then conclude that the two population means μ_A and μ_B are significantly different from each other. If $|\bar{x}_A - \bar{x}_B| \leq LSD_{A,B}$, then conclude that the two population means μ_A and μ_B are not significantly different from each other.

Step 5: Repeat Steps 2 – 4 for all possible pairs of groups, so there will be $\binom{r}{2}$ pairs to check.

EXAMPLE

Returning to the delicious cupcake example, we have $n = 15$ total cupcakes and $r = 3$ groups, with $n_1 = n_2 = n_3 = 5$, representing 5 cupcakes per shop. We had computed the sample means $\bar{x}_1 = 29.8$, $\bar{x}_2 = 30.4$, and $\bar{x}_3 = 33.8$, and the mean squared error was $MSE = 4.9$. Having concluded that at least one of the population means is different from the others, let's use the *LSD* test to find which means are different from the rest at the $\alpha = 0.05$ significance level.

Solution: First we compute the *T*-score with $n - r = 15 - 3 = 12$ degrees of freedom, noting that $\alpha/2 = 0.05/2 = 0.025$:

$$invT(0.025, 12) = -2.178812801$$

Dropping the negative sign, we have $T_{0.025}(12) = 2.178812801$. Next, since there are 3 groups, we will compare μ_1 to μ_2, μ_1 to μ_3, and μ_2 to μ_3. Let's compare Group 1 to Group 2 first:

$$LSD_{1,2} = T_{0.025}(12) \times \sqrt{MSE\left(\frac{1}{n_1} + \frac{1}{n_2}\right)} = 2.178812801 \times \sqrt{4.9 \times \left(\frac{1}{5} + \frac{1}{5}\right)} = 2.178812801 \times 1.4$$
$$= 3.05034$$

We now check whether the absolute value of the difference of sample means is greater than 3.05034:

$$|\overline{x}_1 - \overline{x}_2| = |29.8 - 30.4| = |-0.6| = 0.6$$

Since 0.6 is less than 3.05034, we conclude that the population means for Group 1 and Group 2 are not significantly different from each other. The next step is to repeat this exercise for the other possible pairs. Actually, since the three sample sizes are all equal, $LSD_{1,3}$ and $LSD_{2,3}$ are both equal to 3.05034, the same as $LSD_{1,2}$ (if the sample sizes were unequal, we would just recalculate the *LSD* thresholds). Examining Group 1 and Group 3,

$$|\overline{x}_1 - \overline{x}_3| = |29.8 - 33.8| = |-4| = 4$$

This time 4 is greater than 3.05034, so we conclude that the population means for Group 1 and Group 3 are significantly different from each other. Finally, examining Group 2 and Group 3,

$$|\overline{x}_2 - \overline{x}_3| = |30.4 - 33.8| = |-3.4| = 3.4$$

Once again, 3.4 is greater than 3.05034, so we conclude that the population means for Group 2 and Group 3 are significantly different from each other.

To recap, we have determined that μ_1 and μ_2 are not significantly different from each other, but μ_1 and μ_3 are significantly different from each other, and so are μ_2 and μ_3.

Δ

You might have wondered how to perform an ANOVA test when the sample sizes are unequal. Let's look at an example of that now. I am including one here because it seems surprisingly hard to find online examples of this situation. However, realize that the technique is still similar to what we already did.

EXAMPLE
Let's repeat the cupcake example, where we had five cupcakes per shop, and we want to measure the average grams of sugar per cupcake. However, this time the researcher keeps the five cupcakes from Shop A, but he accidentally drops one of the Shop B cupcakes, ruining it (so it is not included anymore). As for the Shop C cupcakes, the researcher fancies a sugary snack and eats two cupcakes from that sample. Thus, the following is the new dataset, where three cupcakes have been removed from consideration.

Assume again that the amount of sugar used is normally distributed in each case and that the population variances of used sugar are the same for all three shops. Perform an appropriate ANOVA test at the $\alpha = 0.05$ significance level using the data below.

Shop A	Shop B	Shop C
28	28	30
30	32	36
32	33	32
29	30	
30		

Solution: The hypotheses are still the same, noting that there are three shops and therefore three population mean sugar measurements.

$$H_0: \mu_1 = \mu_2 = \mu_3$$
$$H_A: \text{At least one mean is not equal to the others.}$$

Noting that the assumptions are satisfied, we need to compute a series of calculations. The sample sizes are now different because a cupcake was ruined and two more were eaten. Now $n_1 = 5, n_2 = 4$, and $n_3 = 3$, and therefore $n = 12$. There are three groups (the cupcake shops) and therefore $r = 3$.

We compute the overall sample mean $\overline{x}$, as well as the sample group means $\overline{x}_1, \overline{x}_2$, and $\overline{x}_3$. The overall mean is

$$\overline{x} = \frac{28 + 30 + 32 + 29 + 30 + 28 + 32 + 33 + 30 + 30 + 36 + 32}{12}$$
$$= 30.83333333$$

The group means are

$$\overline{x}_1 = \frac{28 + 30 + 32 + 29 + 30}{5} = 29.8$$
$$\overline{x}_2 = \frac{28 + 32 + 33 + 30}{4} = 30.75$$
$$\overline{x}_3 = \frac{30 + 36 + 32}{3} = 32.66666667$$

Next, we need the Treatment Sum of Squares (SSR), the Error Sum of Squares (SSE), and the Total Sum of Squares (SST). We go for SSR first:
$$SSR = n_1(\overline{x}_1 - \overline{x})^2 + n_2(\overline{x}_2 - \overline{x})^2 + n_3(\overline{x}_3 - \overline{x})^2$$
$$= 5(29.8 - 30.83333333)^2 + 4(30.75 - 30.83333333)^2 + 3(32.66666667 - 30.83333333)^2$$
$$= 15.45$$

Noting the shortcut to finding SSE, we instead compute SST:

$$SST = \sum (x_i - \overline{x})^2$$

$$= (28 - 30.83333333)^2 + (30 - 30.83333333)^2 + (32 - 30.83333333)^2$$
$$+ (29 - 30.83333333)^2 + (30 - 30.83333333)^2 + (28 - 30.83333333)^2$$
$$+ (32 - 30.83333333)^2 + (33 - 30.83333333)^2 + (30 - 30.83333333)^2$$
$$+ (30 - 30.83333333)^2 + (36 - 30.83333333)^2 + (32 - 30.83333333)^2$$
$$= 57.66666667$$

The Error Sum of Squares is the difference between SST and SSR:

$$SSE = SST - SSR = 57.66666667 - 15.45$$
$$= 42.21666667$$

The ANOVA table now looks like the following:

Source of Variation	Sum of Squares	DF	Mean Square	Test Statistic	P-Value
Treatment	15.45000000	r - 1	MSR	F	p-value
Error	42.21666667	n - r	MSE		
Total	57.66666667	n - 1			

We also need the corresponding degrees of freedom:

$$DF_R = r - 1 = 3 - 1 = 2$$
$$DF_E = n - r = 12 - 3 = 9$$
$$DF_T = n - 1 = 12 - 1 = 11$$

Here is the updated table:

Source of Variation	Sum of Squares	DF	Mean Square	Test Statistic	P-Value
Treatment	15.45000000	2	MSR	F	p-value
Error	42.21666667	9	MSE		
Total	57.66666667	11			

We now need the two mean squared error terms, Mean Square Treatment (MSR) and Mean Square Error (MSE). They are computed as

$$MSR = \frac{SSR}{DF_R} = \frac{15.45}{2} = 7.725$$
$$MSE = \frac{SSE}{DF_E} = \frac{42.21666667}{9} = 4.69074074$$

The updated ANOVA table is below:

Source of Variation	Sum of Squares	DF	Mean Square	Test Statistic	P-Value
Treatment	15.45000000	2	7.72500000	F	p-value
Error	42.21666667	9	4.69074074		
Total	57.66666667	11			

Next, the F-statistic is MSR divided by MSE:

$$F = \frac{MSR}{MSE} = \frac{7.725}{4.69074074} = 1.64686143$$

Source of Variation	Sum of Squares	DF	Mean Square	Test Statistic	P-Value
Treatment	15.45000000	2	7.72500000	1.64686143	p-value
Error	42.21666667	9	4.69074074		
Total	57.66666667	11			

Finally, to get the p-value, notice that the numerator degrees of freedom is 2 and the denominator degrees of freedom is 9. For an ANOVA test, we always find the probability to the right of F, as in the following sketch:

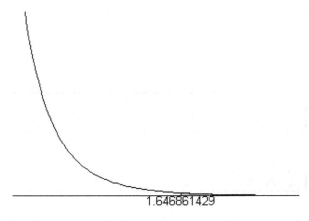

1.646861429

The lower limit is 1.646861429 and the upper limit is 999999, and so we can use the TI-84 to get the p-value:

$$Fcdf(1.646861429, 999999, 2, 9) = 0.24576$$

Here is the completed ANOVA table:

Source of Variation	Sum of Squares	DF	Mean Square	Test Statistic	P-Value
Treatment	15.45000000	2	7.72500000	1.64686143	0.24576
Error	42.21666667	9	4.69074074		
Total	57.66666667	11			

The p-value is above $\alpha = 0.05$, so we don't reject the null hypothesis. There is insufficient evidence that at least one of the population means is different from the others. Put another way, given the three population average amounts of grams of sugar used per cupcake per shop, the three means are not significantly different from one another (so there is no need to do the Least Significance Test). Now let's check our work with the TI-84 by doing $ANOVA(L_1, L_2, L_3)$:

$$F = 1.646861429$$
$$p = 0.245762666$$

We get the same answers with more decimals.

Δ

And now back to that joke – what do you get if you cross a statistician with an astronomer? The answer is … a nova! ☺

References

Chapter 2 – Summary Statistics
[1] – Universe Today: How Far Are The Planets From The Sun? (2014). https://www.universetoday.com/15462/how-far-are-the-planets-from-the-sun/.

Chapter 4 – Sampling Methods and Collecting Data
[1] – Here's the Final 2016 Electoral College Map (2016). https://www.businessinsider.com/final-electoral-college-map-trump-clinton-2016-11.
[2] – Wendt, Lloyd (1979). *Chicago Tribune: The Rise of a Great American Newspaper*. Chicago: Rand McNally.

Chapter 5 – Probability
[1] – Lewand, Robert (2000). *Cryptological Mathematics*. The Mathematical Association of America.
[2] – Perec, Georges, and Adair, Gilbert (translator) (1995). *A Void*. The Harvill Press.
[3] – Perec, Georges (1969). *La Disparition*. Gallimard.
[4] – Venn, John (1880). On the diagrammatic and mechanical representation of propositions and reasonings. *The London, Edinburgh, and Dublin Philosophical Magazine and Journal of Science, Fifth Series*. 10:59, 1 – 18.
[5] – "Two Letter Scrabble Words" (2019). https://scrabblewordfinder.org/two-letter-scrabble-words.
[6] – "Frequency of Easter Sundays." https://www.staff.science.uu.nl/~gent0113/easter/easter_text2b.htm.
[7] – vos Savant, Marilyn (1990). "Game Show Problem." marilynvossavant.com.
[8] – Selvin, Steve (1975). "A Problem in Probability (Letter to the Editor)." *American Statistician*. **29** (1): 67.
[9] – Selvin, Steve (1975). "On the Monty Hall Problem (Letter to the Editor)." *American Statistician*. **29** (3): 134.
[10] – Tierney, John (1991). "Behind Monty Hall's Doors: Puzzle, Debate and Answer?" *The New York Times*.
[11] – Haddon, Mark (2003). *The Curious Incident of the Dog in the Night-Time*. Vintage Books.
[12] – vos Savant, Marilyn (1992). "Ask Marilyn." *Parade*.

Chapter 6 – Probability Distributions
[1] – 6 Things You May Not Know About the Gregorian Calendar (2012). https://www.history.com/news/6-things-you-may-not-know-about-the-gregorian-calendar.
[2] – Highest Recorded Temperature (2019). http://www.guinnessworldrecords.com/world-records/highest-recorded-temperature/.

Appendices

Appendix A – Statistics Formulas

Various Statistical Formulas

The following tables contain various statistical formulas that appear in these notes. Formulas relating to confidence intervals and hypothesis tests appear in their own tables.

Topic	Formula
Sample Mean	$\overline{x} = \dfrac{x_1 + x_2 + \cdots + x_n}{n} = \dfrac{\sum x_i}{n}$
Median	Middlemost data value, or 50th percentile
Mode	Date value that occurs most frequently
Range	Highest data value minus lowest data value
Sample Variance	$s^2 = \dfrac{\sum(x_i - \overline{x})^2}{n-1}$
Sample Standard Deviation	$s = \sqrt{\dfrac{\sum(x_i - \overline{x})^2}{n-1}}$
pth Percentile	The value such that $p\%$ of all observations fall below or at that value
Q_1	First quartile, or 25th percentile
Q_3	Third quartile, or 75th percentile
Z-score	$Z = \dfrac{(\text{data value}) - (\text{mean})}{\text{standard deviation}} = \dfrac{x - \mu}{\sigma} = \dfrac{x - \overline{x}}{s}$
Correlation (r)	$r = \dfrac{\sum\left(\frac{x_i - \overline{x}}{s_x}\right)\left(\frac{y_i - \overline{y}}{s_y}\right)}{n-1} = \dfrac{\sum z_x z_y}{n-1}$
Linear Regression	$\hat{y} = a + bx$ where $b = \dfrac{\sum(x_i - \overline{x})(y_i - \overline{y})}{\sum(x_i - \overline{x})^2}$ and $a = \overline{y} - b\overline{x}$
Residual	$\text{residual} = y - \hat{y} = \text{observed} - \text{predicted}$
Relative Risk	$\text{Relative Risk} = \dfrac{\text{Conditional proportion for 1st group (larger proportion)}}{\text{Conditional proportion for 2nd group (smaller proportion)}}$
Basic Probability	$P(A) = \dfrac{\text{Number of ways event } A \text{ can happen}}{\text{Total number of possible outcomes}}$
Complement Probability	$P(A^c) = 1 - P(A)$
$P(A \text{ or } B)$	$P(A \text{ or } B) = P(A) + P(B) - P(A \text{ and } B)$
Disjoint Probability	$P(A \text{ or } B) = P(A) + P(B)$
Conditional Probability	$P(A \mid B) = \dfrac{P(A \text{ and } B)}{P(B)}$
Independent Probability	$P(A \text{ and } B) = P(A) \times P(B)$
n factorial	$n! = n \times (n-1) \times (n-2) \times \cdots \times 2 \times 1$
Combination of n items k at a time	$\binom{n}{k} = \dfrac{n!}{(n-k)!\,k!}$
Expected Value of Discrete Distribution	$\text{Mean} = \sum x_i \times P(x_i)$
Standard Deviation of Discrete Distribution	$\text{St. Dev.} = \sqrt{\sum x_i^2 \times P(x_i) - (\text{Mean})^2}$
Binomial Probability that X equals x	$P(X = x) = \binom{n}{x} p^x (1-p)^{n-x}$

Topic	Formula
Mean of Binomial	$\text{Mean} = np$
St. Dev. Of Binomial	$\text{St. Dev.} = \sqrt{np(1-p)}$
Standard Error of Sampling Distribution of Sample Means	$\text{standard error} = \dfrac{\sigma}{\sqrt{n}}$
Standard Error of Sampling Dist. Of Sample Proportions	$\text{standard error} = \sqrt{\dfrac{p(1-p)}{n}}$
Estimating Sample Size for a Proportion	$n = \dfrac{\hat{p}(1-\hat{p})\left(Z_{\alpha/2}\right)^2}{m^2}$
Estimating Sample Size for a Mean	$n = \dfrac{\sigma^2\left(Z_{\alpha/2}\right)^2}{m^2}$
Residual Standard Error	$\hat{\sigma} = \sqrt{\dfrac{\sum(y_i-\hat{y}_i)^2}{n-2}}$
Slope Standard Error	$SE_b = \dfrac{\hat{\sigma}}{s_x\sqrt{n-1}}$
Intercept Standard Error	$SE_a = SE_b\sqrt{\dfrac{\sum x_i^2}{n}}$

Confidence Interval Formulas

The following table contains the important confidence interval formulas.

Topic	$100(1-\alpha)\%$ Confidence Interval
One Proportion p	$\hat{p} \pm Z_{\alpha/2}\sqrt{\dfrac{\hat{p}(1-\hat{p})}{n}}$
One Mean μ	$\overline{x} \pm T_{\alpha/2}(n-1)\times\dfrac{s}{\sqrt{n}}$
Matched Pairs Difference μ_d	$\overline{x}_d \pm T_{\alpha/2}(n_d-1)\times\dfrac{s_d}{\sqrt{n}}$
Difference of Proportions $p_1 - p_2$	$(\hat{p}_1 - \hat{p}_2) \pm Z_{\alpha/2}\sqrt{\dfrac{\hat{p}_1(1-\hat{p}_1)}{n_1} + \dfrac{\hat{p}_2(1-\hat{p}_2)}{n_2}}$
Difference of Means $\mu_1 - \mu_2$ (unpooled)	$(\overline{x}_1 - \overline{x}_2) \pm T_{\alpha/2}(DF)\sqrt{\dfrac{s_1^2}{n_1} + \dfrac{s_2^2}{n_2}}$ where DF is the ugly formula
Regression Slope β	$b \pm T_{\alpha/2}(n-2)\times SE_b$ where SE_b is standard error of slope
Correlation Coefficient ρ	$\left(\dfrac{\exp(2Z_L)-1}{\exp(2Z_L)+1}, \dfrac{\exp(2Z_U)-1}{\exp(2Z_U)+1}\right)$ where $Z_L = \dfrac{1}{2}\ln\left(\dfrac{1+r}{1-r}\right) - \dfrac{Z_{\alpha/2}}{\sqrt{n-3}}$ and $Z_U = \dfrac{1}{2}\ln\left(\dfrac{1+r}{1-r}\right) + \dfrac{Z_{\alpha/2}}{\sqrt{n-3}}$
Average Value of y at x (confidence interval)	$(a+bx) \pm T_{\alpha/2}(n-2)\times\hat{\sigma}\sqrt{\dfrac{1}{n} + \dfrac{(x-\overline{x})^2}{(n-1)s_x^2}}$ where $\hat{\sigma} = \sqrt{\dfrac{\sum(y_i-\hat{y}_i)^2}{n-2}}$
Individual Value of y at x (prediction interval)	$(a+bx) \pm T_{\alpha/2}(n-2)\times\hat{\sigma}\sqrt{1 + \dfrac{1}{n} + \dfrac{(x-\overline{x})^2}{(n-1)s_x^2}}$ where $\hat{\sigma} = \sqrt{\dfrac{\sum(y_i-\hat{y}_i)^2}{n-2}}$
One Variance σ^2	$\left(\dfrac{(n-1)s^2}{\chi_{\alpha/2}^2(n-1)}, \dfrac{(n-1)s^2}{\chi_{1-\alpha/2}^2(n-1)}\right)$
Ratio of Variances σ_1^2/σ_2^2	$\left(\dfrac{s_1^2}{s_2^2 F_{\alpha/2}(n_1-1,n_2-1)}, \dfrac{s_1^2}{s_2^2 F_{1-\alpha/2}(n_1-1,n_2-1)}\right)$

Hypothesis Test Statistic Formulas

The following table contains the important formulas for test statistics used in hypothesis testing.

Topic	Hypothesis Test Statistic
One Proportion p	$Z = \dfrac{\hat{p}-p_0}{SE}$ where $SE = \sqrt{\dfrac{p_0(1-p_0)}{n}}$
One Mean μ	$T = \dfrac{\bar{x}-\mu_0}{SE}$ where $SE = \dfrac{s}{\sqrt{n}}$
Matched Pairs Difference μ_d	$T = \dfrac{\bar{x}_d-0}{SE}$ where $SE = \dfrac{s_d}{\sqrt{n_d}}$
Difference of Proportions $p_1 - p_2$	$Z = \dfrac{(\hat{p}_1-\hat{p}_2)-0}{SE}$ where $SE = \sqrt{\hat{p}(1-\hat{p})\left(\dfrac{1}{n_1}+\dfrac{1}{n_2}\right)}$ and $\hat{p} = \dfrac{x_1+x_2}{n_1+n_2}$
Difference of Means $\mu_1 - \mu_2$ (unpooled)	$T = \dfrac{(\bar{x}_1-\bar{x}_2)-0}{SE}$ where $SE = \sqrt{\dfrac{s_1^2}{n_1}+\dfrac{s_2^2}{n_2}}$
Regression Slope β	$T = \dfrac{b-0}{SE_b}$ where SE_b is standard error of slope
Correlation Coefficient ρ	$T = r\sqrt{\dfrac{n-2}{1-r^2}}$
One Variance σ^2	$X^2 = \dfrac{(n-1)s^2}{\sigma_0^2}$
Ratio of Variances σ_1^2/σ_2^2	$F = \dfrac{s_1^2}{s_2^2}$

Appendix B – TI-84 Commands

Statistical Calculations

To enter a list of numbers, press $\boxed{\text{STAT}}$, choose Option 1: *Edit* ..., and type the numbers into the L_1 column. Type other numbers into extra columns as needed (L_2, L_3, etc.)

To compute specific statistical calculations including summary statistics and linear regression, press $\boxed{\text{STAT}}$, scroll right to CALC, and select the appropriate option below.

Option #	Command	Description of Probability Command
Option 1	$1 - Var\ Stats$	Summary statistics (choose $1 - Var\ Stats$ then type list name)
Option 2	$2 - Var\ Stats$	NOT USED IN THESE NOTES
Option 3	$Med - Med$	NOT USED IN THESE NOTES
Option 4	$LinReg(ax + b)$	Regression to fit $\hat{y} = ax + b$ (Option 8 recommended instead)
Option 5	$QuadReg$	NOT USED IN THESE NOTES
Option 6	$CubicReg$	NOT USED IN THESE NOTES
Option 7	$QuartReg$	NOT USED IN THESE NOTES
Option 8	$LinReg(a + bx)$	Regression to fit $\hat{y} = a + bx$

For linear regression calculations, if you don't see correlation (r) as part of the output, go into the Catalog (press $\boxed{\text{2nd}}$ and $\boxed{0}$), scroll down to *DiagnosticOn*, and press $\boxed{\text{ENTER}}$ twice. When you see "Done" on the home screen, you are all set and should not have to do this again. Now repeat the above steps and you should now see r.

Probability Distribution Calculations

To compute a probability associated with a specific distribution (or to find a Z-score or T-score that gives a specific probability below that value), press $\boxed{\text{2nd}}$ and $\boxed{\text{VARS}}$ to pull up the Distribution menu, and select the appropriate option below. Use the correct commands as needed.

Option #	Command	Description of Probability Command
Option 1	$normalpdf(\ \ )$	NOT USED IN THESE NOTES
Option 2	$normalcdf(L, U, \text{mean}, \text{sd})$	Probability on normal distribution between L and U
Option 3	$invNorm(p, \text{mean}, \text{sd})$	Z-score (or data value) that gives probability p below
Option 4	$invT(p, DF)$	T-score that gives probability p below
Option 5	$tpdf(\ \ )$	NOT USED IN THESE NOTES
Option 6	$tcdf(L, U, DF)$	Probability on T-distribution between L and U
Option 7	$\chi^2 pdf(\ \ )$	NOT USED IN THESE NOTES
Option 8	$\chi^2 cdf(L, U, DF)$	Probability on χ^2-distribution between L and U
Option 9	$Fpdf(\ \ )$	NOT USED IN THESE NOTES
Option 0	$Fcdf(L, U, DF_1, DF_2)$	Probability on F-distribution between L and U
Option A	$binompdf(n, p, x)$	Binomial probability of exactly x successes
Option B	$binomcdf(n, p, x)$	Binomial probability of at most x successes

Confidence Intervals and Hypothesis Tests

To compute a confidence interval or conduct a hypothesis test, press $\boxed{\text{STAT}}$, scroll right to TESTS, and select the appropriate option below.

Option #	Command	Type of Interval / Test
Option 1	$Z-Test$	NOT USED IN THESE NOTES
Option 2	$T-Test$	Hypothesis test for one mean μ (and difference of dependent means μ_d)
Option 3	$2-SampZTest$	NOT USED IN THESE NOTES
Option 4	$2-SampTTest$	Hypothesis test for difference of independent means $\mu_1 - \mu_2$
Option 5	$1-PropZTest$	Hypothesis test for one proportion p
Option 6	$2-PropZTest$	Hypothesis test for difference of independent proportions $p_1 - p_2$
Option 7	$ZInterval$	NOT USED IN THESE NOTES
Option 8	$TInterval$	Interval for one mean μ (and difference of dependent means μ_d)
Option 9	$2-SampZInt$	NOT USED IN THESE NOTES
Option 0	$2-SampTInt$	Interval for difference of independent means $\mu_1 - \mu_2$
Option A	$1-PropZInt$	Interval for one proportion p
Option B	$2-PropZInt$	Interval for difference of independent proportions $p_1 - p_2$
Option C	χ^2-Test	Chi-square independence test
Option D	$\chi^2 GOF-Test$	Chi-square goodness of fit test
Option E	$2-SampFTest$	Hypothesis test for ratio of two variances
Option F	$LinRegTTest$	Hypothesis test for slope of regression equation/correlation
Option G	$LinRegTInt$	Interval for slope of regression equation
Option H	$ANOVA$	ANOVA Test

Other Probability Calculations

To compute a calculation associated with mathematical aspects of probability, press $\boxed{\text{MATH}}$, scroll right to PRB, and select the appropriate option below.

Option #	Command	Description of Probability Command
Option 1	$rand$	NOT USED IN THESE NOTES
Option 2	nPr	NOT USED IN THESE NOTES
Option 3	nCr	Combination of n items r at a time (type n, then nCr, then r)
Option 4	$!$	Factorial of n (type n, then $!$)
Option 5	$randInt(L, U, n)$	Randomly chose n numbers between L and U, inclusive

Appendix C – Normal Table

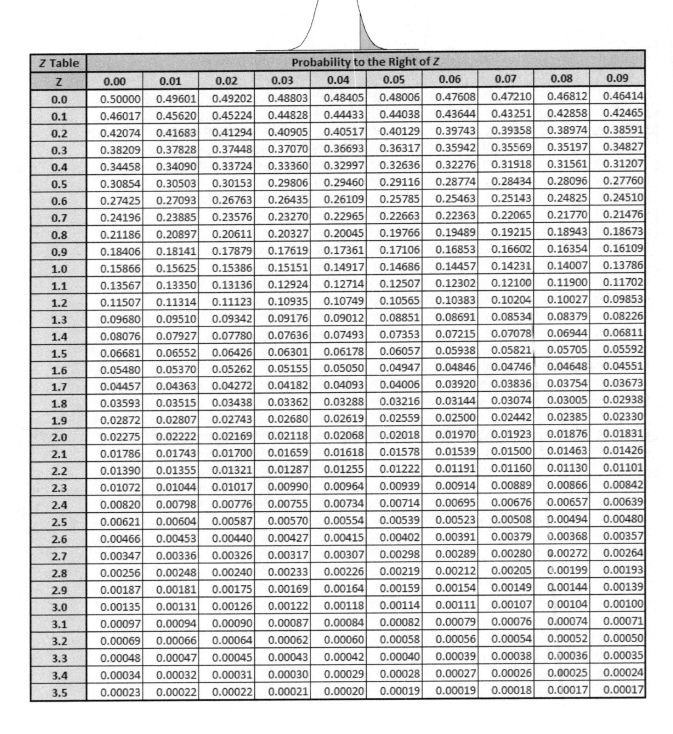

Z Table	Probability to the Right of Z									
Z	0.00	0.01	0.02	0.03	0.04	0.05	0.06	0.07	0.08	0.09
0.0	0.50000	0.49601	0.49202	0.48803	0.48405	0.48006	0.47608	0.47210	0.46812	0.46414
0.1	0.46017	0.45620	0.45224	0.44828	0.44433	0.44038	0.43644	0.43251	0.42858	0.42465
0.2	0.42074	0.41683	0.41294	0.40905	0.40517	0.40129	0.39743	0.39358	0.38974	0.38591
0.3	0.38209	0.37828	0.37448	0.37070	0.36693	0.36317	0.35942	0.35569	0.35197	0.34827
0.4	0.34458	0.34090	0.33724	0.33360	0.32997	0.32636	0.32276	0.31918	0.31561	0.31207
0.5	0.30854	0.30503	0.30153	0.29806	0.29460	0.29116	0.28774	0.28434	0.28096	0.27760
0.6	0.27425	0.27093	0.26763	0.26435	0.26109	0.25785	0.25463	0.25143	0.24825	0.24510
0.7	0.24196	0.23885	0.23576	0.23270	0.22965	0.22663	0.22363	0.22065	0.21770	0.21476
0.8	0.21186	0.20897	0.20611	0.20327	0.20045	0.19766	0.19489	0.19215	0.18943	0.18673
0.9	0.18406	0.18141	0.17879	0.17619	0.17361	0.17106	0.16853	0.16602	0.16354	0.16109
1.0	0.15866	0.15625	0.15386	0.15151	0.14917	0.14686	0.14457	0.14231	0.14007	0.13786
1.1	0.13567	0.13350	0.13136	0.12924	0.12714	0.12507	0.12302	0.12100	0.11900	0.11702
1.2	0.11507	0.11314	0.11123	0.10935	0.10749	0.10565	0.10383	0.10204	0.10027	0.09853
1.3	0.09680	0.09510	0.09342	0.09176	0.09012	0.08851	0.08691	0.08534	0.08379	0.08226
1.4	0.08076	0.07927	0.07780	0.07636	0.07493	0.07353	0.07215	0.07078	0.06944	0.06811
1.5	0.06681	0.06552	0.06426	0.06301	0.06178	0.06057	0.05938	0.05821	0.05705	0.05592
1.6	0.05480	0.05370	0.05262	0.05155	0.05050	0.04947	0.04846	0.04746	0.04648	0.04551
1.7	0.04457	0.04363	0.04272	0.04182	0.04093	0.04006	0.03920	0.03836	0.03754	0.03673
1.8	0.03593	0.03515	0.03438	0.03362	0.03288	0.03216	0.03144	0.03074	0.03005	0.02938
1.9	0.02872	0.02807	0.02743	0.02680	0.02619	0.02559	0.02500	0.02442	0.02385	0.02330
2.0	0.02275	0.02222	0.02169	0.02118	0.02068	0.02018	0.01970	0.01923	0.01876	0.01831
2.1	0.01786	0.01743	0.01700	0.01659	0.01618	0.01578	0.01539	0.01500	0.01463	0.01426
2.2	0.01390	0.01355	0.01321	0.01287	0.01255	0.01222	0.01191	0.01160	0.01130	0.01101
2.3	0.01072	0.01044	0.01017	0.00990	0.00964	0.00939	0.00914	0.00889	0.00866	0.00842
2.4	0.00820	0.00798	0.00776	0.00755	0.00734	0.00714	0.00695	0.00676	0.00657	0.00639
2.5	0.00621	0.00604	0.00587	0.00570	0.00554	0.00539	0.00523	0.00508	0.00494	0.00480
2.6	0.00466	0.00453	0.00440	0.00427	0.00415	0.00402	0.00391	0.00379	0.00368	0.00357
2.7	0.00347	0.00336	0.00326	0.00317	0.00307	0.00298	0.00289	0.00280	0.00272	0.00264
2.8	0.00256	0.00248	0.00240	0.00233	0.00226	0.00219	0.00212	0.00205	0.00199	0.00193
2.9	0.00187	0.00181	0.00175	0.00169	0.00164	0.00159	0.00154	0.00149	0.00144	0.00139
3.0	0.00135	0.00131	0.00126	0.00122	0.00118	0.00114	0.00111	0.00107	0.00104	0.00100
3.1	0.00097	0.00094	0.00090	0.00087	0.00084	0.00082	0.00079	0.00076	0.00074	0.00071
3.2	0.00069	0.00066	0.00064	0.00062	0.00060	0.00058	0.00056	0.00054	0.00052	0.00050
3.3	0.00048	0.00047	0.00045	0.00043	0.00042	0.00040	0.00039	0.00038	0.00036	0.00035
3.4	0.00034	0.00032	0.00031	0.00030	0.00029	0.00028	0.00027	0.00026	0.00025	0.00024
3.5	0.00023	0.00022	0.00022	0.00021	0.00020	0.00019	0.00019	0.00018	0.00017	0.00017

Appendix D – *T* Table

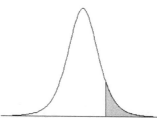

T Table	Probability to the Right of *T*									
DF	0.25	0.20	0.15	0.10	0.05	0.025	0.01	0.005	0.001	0.0005
1	1.00000	1.37638	1.96261	3.07768	6.31375	12.70620	31.82052	63.65674	318.30884	636.61925
2	0.81650	1.06066	1.38621	1.88562	2.91999	4.30265	6.96456	9.92484	22.32712	31.59905
3	0.76489	0.97847	1.24978	1.63774	2.35336	3.18245	4.54070	5.84091	10.21453	12.92398
4	0.74070	0.94096	1.18957	1.53321	2.13185	2.77645	3.74695	4.60409	7.17318	8.61030
5	0.72669	0.91954	1.15577	1.47588	2.01505	2.57058	3.36493	4.03214	5.89343	6.86883
6	0.71756	0.90570	1.13416	1.43976	1.94318	2.44691	3.14267	3.70743	5.20763	5.95882
7	0.71114	0.89603	1.11916	1.41492	1.89458	2.36462	2.99795	3.49948	4.78529	5.40788
8	0.70639	0.88889	1.10815	1.39682	1.85955	2.30600	2.89646	3.35539	4.50079	5.04131
9	0.70272	0.88340	1.09972	1.38303	1.83311	2.26216	2.82144	3.24984	4.29681	4.78091
10	0.69981	0.87906	1.09306	1.37218	1.81246	2.22814	2.76377	3.16927	4.14370	4.58689
11	0.69745	0.87553	1.08767	1.36343	1.79588	2.20099	2.71808	3.10581	4.02470	4.43698
12	0.69548	0.87261	1.08321	1.35622	1.78229	2.17881	2.68100	3.05454	3.92963	4.31779
13	0.69383	0.87015	1.07947	1.35017	1.77093	2.16037	2.65031	3.01228	3.85198	4.22083
14	0.69242	0.86805	1.07628	1.34503	1.76131	2.14479	2.62449	2.97684	3.78739	4.14045
15	0.69120	0.86624	1.07353	1.34061	1.75305	2.13145	2.60248	2.94671	3.73283	4.07277
16	0.69013	0.86467	1.07114	1.33676	1.74588	2.11991	2.58349	2.92078	3.68615	4.01500
17	0.68920	0.86328	1.06903	1.33338	1.73961	2.10982	2.56693	2.89823	3.64577	3.96513
18	0.68836	0.86205	1.06717	1.33039	1.73406	2.10092	2.55238	2.87844	3.61048	3.92165
19	0.68762	0.86095	1.06551	1.32773	1.72913	2.09302	2.53948	2.86093	3.57940	3.88341
20	0.68695	0.85996	1.06402	1.32534	1.72472	2.08596	2.52798	2.84534	3.55181	3.84952
21	0.68635	0.85907	1.06267	1.32319	1.72074	2.07961	2.51765	2.83136	3.52715	3.81928
22	0.68581	0.85827	1.06145	1.32124	1.71714	2.07387	2.50832	2.81876	3.50499	3.79213
23	0.68531	0.85753	1.06034	1.31946	1.71387	2.06866	2.49987	2.80734	3.48496	3.76763
24	0.68485	0.85686	1.05932	1.31784	1.71088	2.06390	2.49216	2.79694	3.46678	3.74540
25	0.68443	0.85624	1.05838	1.31635	1.70814	2.05954	2.48511	2.78744	3.45019	3.72514
26	0.68404	0.85567	1.05752	1.31497	1.70562	2.05553	2.47863	2.77871	3.43500	3.70661
27	0.68368	0.85514	1.05673	1.31370	1.70329	2.05183	2.47266	2.77068	3.42103	3.68959
28	0.68335	0.85465	1.05599	1.31253	1.70113	2.04841	2.46714	2.76326	3.40816	3.67391
29	0.68304	0.85419	1.05530	1.31143	1.69913	2.04523	2.46202	2.75639	3.39624	3.65941
30	0.68276	0.85377	1.05466	1.31042	1.69726	2.04227	2.45726	2.75000	3.38518	3.64596
40	0.68067	0.85070	1.05005	1.30308	1.68385	2.02108	2.42326	2.70446	3.30688	3.55097
50	0.67943	0.84887	1.04729	1.29871	1.67591	2.00856	2.40327	2.67779	3.26141	3.49601
60	0.67860	0.84765	1.04547	1.29582	1.67065	2.00030	2.39012	2.66028	3.23171	3.46020
70	0.67801	0.84679	1.04417	1.29376	1.66691	1.99444	2.38081	2.64790	3.21079	3.43501
80	0.67757	0.84614	1.04320	1.29222	1.66412	1.99006	2.37387	2.63869	3.19526	3.41634
90	0.67723	0.84563	1.04244	1.29103	1.66196	1.98667	2.36850	2.63157	3.18327	3.40194
100	0.67695	0.84523	1.04184	1.29007	1.66023	1.98397	2.36422	2.62589	3.17374	3.39049
1000	0.67474	0.84198	1.03697	1.28240	1.64638	1.96234	2.33008	2.58075	3.09840	3.30028
Infinity	0.67449	0.84162	1.03643	1.28155	1.64485	1.95996	2.32635	2.57583	3.09023	3.29053

Appendix E – Chi-Square Table

X^2 Table	Probability to the Right of X^2									
DF	0.995	0.99	0.975	0.95	0.9	0.1	0.05	0.025	0.01	0.005
1	0.00004	0.00016	0.00098	0.00393	0.01579	2.70554	3.84146	5.02389	6.63490	7.87944
2	0.01003	0.02010	0.05064	0.10259	0.21072	4.60517	5.99146	7.37776	9.21034	10.59663
3	0.07172	0.11483	0.21580	0.35185	0.58437	6.25139	7.81473	9.34840	11.34487	12.83816
4	0.20699	0.29711	0.48442	0.71072	1.06362	7.77944	9.48773	11.14329	13.27670	14.86026
5	0.41174	0.55430	0.83121	1.14548	1.61031	9.23636	11.07050	12.83250	15.08627	16.74960
6	0.67573	0.87209	1.23734	1.63538	2.20413	10.64464	12.59159	14.44938	16.81189	18.54758
7	0.98926	1.23904	1.68987	2.16735	2.83311	12.01704	14.06714	16.01276	18.47531	20.27774
8	1.34441	1.64650	2.17973	2.73264	3.48954	13.36157	15.50731	17.53455	20.09024	21.95495
9	1.73493	2.08790	2.70039	3.32511	4.16816	14.68366	16.91898	19.02277	21.66599	23.58935
10	2.15586	2.55821	3.24697	3.94030	4.86518	15.98718	18.30704	20.48318	23.20925	25.18818
11	2.60322	3.05348	3.81575	4.57481	5.57778	17.27501	19.67514	21.92005	24.72497	26.75685
12	3.07382	3.57057	4.40379	5.22603	6.30380	18.54935	21.02607	23.33666	26.21697	28.29952
13	3.56503	4.10692	5.00875	5.89186	7.04150	19.81193	22.36203	24.73560	27.68825	29.81947
14	4.07467	4.66043	5.62873	6.57063	7.78953	21.06414	23.68479	26.11895	29.14124	31.31935
15	4.60092	5.22935	6.26214	7.26094	8.54676	22.30713	24.99579	27.48839	30.57791	32.80132
16	5.14221	5.81221	6.90766	7.96165	9.31224	23.54183	26.29623	28.84535	31.99993	34.26719
17	5.69722	6.40776	7.56419	8.67176	10.08519	24.76904	27.58711	30.19101	33.40866	35.71847
18	6.26480	7.01491	8.23075	9.39046	10.86494	25.98942	28.86930	31.52638	34.80531	37.15645
19	6.84397	7.63273	8.90652	10.11701	11.65091	27.20357	30.14353	32.85233	36.19087	38.58226
20	7.43384	8.26040	9.59078	10.85081	12.44261	28.41198	31.41043	34.16961	37.56623	39.99685
21	8.03365	8.89720	10.28290	11.59131	13.23960	29.61509	32.67057	35.47888	38.93217	41.40106
22	8.64272	9.54249	10.98232	12.33801	14.04149	30.81328	33.92444	36.78071	40.28936	42.79565
23	9.26042	10.19572	11.68855	13.09051	14.84796	32.00690	35.17246	38.07563	41.63840	44.18128
24	9.88623	10.85636	12.40115	13.84843	15.65868	33.19624	36.41503	39.36408	42.97982	45.55851
25	10.51965	11.52398	13.11972	14.61141	16.47341	34.38159	37.65248	40.64647	44.31410	46.92789
26	11.16024	12.19815	13.84390	15.37916	17.29188	35.56317	38.88514	41.92317	45.64168	48.28988
27	11.80759	12.87850	14.57338	16.15140	18.11390	36.74122	40.11327	43.19451	46.96294	49.64492
28	12.46134	13.56471	15.30786	16.92788	18.93924	37.91592	41.33714	44.46079	48.27824	50.99338
29	13.12115	14.25645	16.04707	17.70837	19.76774	39.08747	42.55697	45.72229	49.58788	52.33562
30	13.78672	14.95346	16.79077	18.49266	20.59923	40.25602	43.77297	46.97924	50.89218	53.67196
40	20.70654	22.16426	24.43304	26.50930	29.05052	51.80506	55.75848	59.34171	63.69074	66.76596
50	27.99075	29.70668	32.35736	34.76425	37.68865	63.16712	67.50481	71.42020	76.15389	79.48998
60	35.53449	37.48485	40.48175	43.18796	46.45889	74.39701	79.08194	83.29767	88.37942	91.95170
70	43.27518	45.44172	48.75756	51.73928	55.32894	85.52704	90.53123	95.02318	100.42518	104.21490
80	51.17193	53.54008	57.15317	60.39148	64.27784	96.57820	101.87947	106.62857	112.32879	116.32106
90	59.19630	61.75408	65.64662	69.12603	73.29109	107.56501	113.14527	118.13589	124.11632	128.29894
100	67.32756	70.06489	74.22193	77.92947	82.35814	118.49800	124.34211	129.56120	135.80672	140.16949

Appendix F – *F* Tables

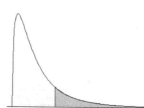

0.005 F Table	Numerator DF									
Denom. DF	**1**	**2**	**3**	**4**	**5**	**6**	**7**	**8**	**9**	**10**
1	16210.72272	19999.50000	21614.74140	22499.58333	23055.79823	23437.11111	23714.56580	23925.40625	24091.00411	24224.48685
2	198.50125	199.00000	199.16643	199.24969	199.29965	199.33296	199.35676	199.37461	199.38849	199.39960
3	55.55196	49.79928	47.46723	46.19462	45.39165	44.83847	44.43410	44.12557	43.88240	43.68580
4	31.33277	26.28427	24.25912	23.15450	22.45643	21.97458	21.62169	21.35198	21.13908	20.96673
5	22.78478	18.31383	16.52977	15.55606	14.93961	14.51326	14.20045	13.96096	13.77165	13.61818
6	18.63500	14.54411	12.91660	12.02753	11.46370	11.07304	10.78592	10.56576	10.39149	10.25004
7	16.23556	12.40396	10.88245	10.05049	9.52206	9.15534	8.88539	8.67811	8.51382	8.38033
8	14.68820	11.04241	9.59647	8.80513	8.30180	7.95199	7.69414	7.49591	7.33860	7.21064
9	13.61361	10.10671	8.71706	7.95589	7.47116	7.13385	6.88491	6.69330	6.54109	6.41716
10	12.82647	9.42700	8.08075	7.34281	6.87237	6.54463	6.30249	6.11592	5.96757	5.84668
12	11.75423	8.50963	7.22576	6.52114	6.07113	5.75703	5.52453	5.34507	5.20213	5.08548
15	10.79805	7.70076	6.47604	5.80291	5.37214	5.07080	4.84726	4.67436	4.53637	4.42354
20	9.94393	6.98646	5.81770	5.17428	4.76157	4.47215	4.25689	4.08997	3.95644	3.84700
25	9.47531	6.59820	5.46152	4.83509	4.43267	4.14999	3.93937	3.77577	3.64468	3.53705
30	9.17968	6.35469	5.23879	4.62336	4.22758	3.94921	3.74156	3.58006	3.45048	3.34396
40	8.82786	6.06643	4.97584	4.37378	3.98605	3.71291	3.50881	3.34979	3.22198	3.11675
50	8.62576	5.90162	4.82587	4.23163	3.84860	3.57850	3.37645	3.21886	3.09205	2.98752
60	8.49462	5.79499	4.72899	4.13989	3.75995	3.49183	3.29111	3.13444	3.00827	2.90418
120	8.17883	5.53929	4.49717	3.92065	3.54823	3.28494	3.08744	2.93296	2.80828	2.70520
1000	7.91453	5.32649	4.30481	3.73905	3.37304	3.11384	2.91904	2.76635	2.64287	2.54055

0.005 F Table	Numerator DF									
Denom. DF	**12**	**15**	**20**	**25**	**30**	**40**	**50**	**60**	**120**	**1000**
1	24426.36618	24630.20515	24835.97091	24960.34045	25043.62767	25148.15323	25211.08879	25253.13690	25358.57345	25451.72802
2	199.41626	199.43292	199.44959	199.45958	199.46625	199.47458	199.47958	199.48292	199.49125	199.49858
3	43.38739	43.08466	42.77750	42.59103	42.46580	42.30821	42.21309	42.14944	41.98948	41.84771
4	20.70469	20.43827	20.16728	20.00240	19.89150	19.75175	19.66729	19.61072	19.46838	19.34200
5	13.38447	13.14633	12.90349	12.75540	12.65564	12.52974	12.45353	12.40245	12.27373	12.15923
6	10.03429	9.81399	9.58877	9.45112	9.35824	9.24085	9.16969	9.12194	9.00146	8.89407
7	8.17641	7.96777	7.75396	7.62299	7.53449	7.42245	7.35443	7.30875	7.19332	7.09020
8	7.01492	6.81428	6.60820	6.48171	6.39609	6.28754	6.22155	6.17718	6.06490	5.96439
9	6.22737	6.03246	5.83184	5.70844	5.62479	5.51858	5.45392	5.41041	5.30011	5.20116
10	5.66133	5.47066	5.27402	5.15282	5.07055	4.96594	4.90216	4.85919	4.75013	4.65206
12	4.90625	4.72134	4.52992	4.41151	4.33092	4.22815	4.16532	4.12292	4.01495	3.91743
15	4.24975	4.06978	3.88259	3.76623	3.68675	3.58499	3.52254	3.48027	3.37218	3.27388
20	3.67791	3.50196	3.31779	3.20254	3.12341	3.02153	2.95863	2.91588	2.80580	2.70457
25	3.37038	3.19634	3.01327	2.89812	2.81871	2.71598	2.65224	2.60875	2.49605	2.39127
30	3.17873	3.00573	2.82304	2.70764	2.62778	2.52406	2.45940	2.41515	2.29977	2.19139
40	2.95310	2.78108	2.59842	2.48229	2.40148	2.29584	2.22951	2.18384	2.06356	1.94834
50	2.82470	2.65310	2.47016	2.35332	2.27169	2.16444	2.09671	2.04986	1.92537	1.80401
60	2.74186	2.57046	2.38720	2.26975	2.18743	2.07887	2.00999	1.96217	1.83411	1.70725
120	2.54393	2.37271	2.18811	2.06856	1.98395	1.87095	1.79811	1.74685	1.60551	1.45496
1000	2.37995	2.20848	2.02191	1.89963	1.81207	1.69317	1.61481	1.55848	1.39447	1.17708

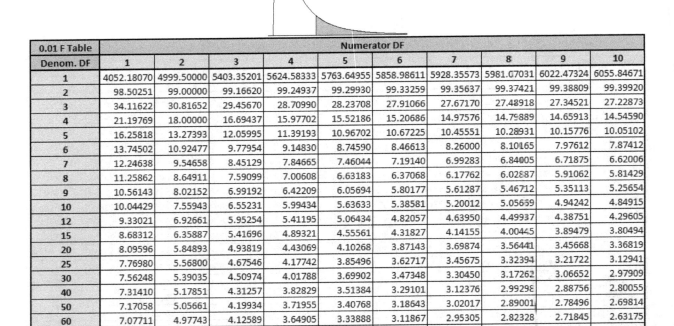

0.01 F Table	Numerator DF									
Denom. DF	1	2	3	4	5	6	7	8	9	10
1	4052.18070	4999.50000	5403.35201	5624.58333	5763.64955	5858.98611	5928.35573	5981.07031	6022.47324	6055.84671
2	98.50251	99.00000	99.16620	99.24937	99.29930	99.33259	99.35637	99.37421	99.38809	99.39920
3	34.11622	30.81652	29.45670	28.70990	28.23708	27.91066	27.67170	27.48918	27.34521	27.22873
4	21.19769	18.00000	16.69437	15.97702	15.52186	15.20686	14.97576	14.79889	14.65913	14.54590
5	16.25818	13.27393	12.05995	11.39193	10.96702	10.67225	10.45551	10.28931	10.15776	10.05102
6	13.74502	10.92477	9.77954	9.14830	8.74590	8.46613	8.26000	8.10165	7.97612	7.87412
7	12.24638	9.54658	8.45129	7.84665	7.46044	7.19140	6.99283	6.84005	6.71875	6.62006
8	11.25862	8.64911	7.59099	7.00608	6.63183	6.37068	6.17762	6.02887	5.91062	5.81429
9	10.56143	8.02152	6.99192	6.42209	6.05694	5.80177	5.61287	5.46712	5.35113	5.25654
10	10.04429	7.55943	6.55231	5.99434	5.63633	5.38581	5.20012	5.05659	4.94242	4.84915
12	9.33021	6.92661	5.95254	5.41195	5.06434	4.82057	4.63950	4.49937	4.38751	4.29605
15	8.68312	6.35887	5.41696	4.89321	4.55561	4.31827	4.14155	4.00445	3.89479	3.80494
20	8.09596	5.84893	4.93819	4.43069	4.10268	3.87143	3.69874	3.56441	3.45668	3.36819
25	7.76980	5.56800	4.67546	4.17742	3.85496	3.62717	3.45675	3.32394	3.21722	3.12941
30	7.56248	5.39035	4.50974	4.01788	3.69902	3.47348	3.30450	3.17262	3.06652	2.97909
40	7.31410	5.17851	4.31257	3.82829	3.51384	3.29101	3.12376	2.99298	2.88756	2.80055
50	7.17058	5.05661	4.19934	3.71955	3.40768	3.18643	3.02017	2.89001	2.78496	2.69814
60	7.07711	4.97743	4.12589	3.64905	3.33888	3.11867	2.95305	2.82328	2.71845	2.63175
120	6.85089	4.78651	3.94910	3.47953	3.17355	2.95585	2.79176	2.66291	2.55857	2.47208
1000	6.66029	4.62644	3.80125	3.33795	3.03555	2.81999	2.65717	2.52903	2.42504	2.33863

0.01 F Table	Numerator DF									
Denom. DF	12	15	20	25	30	40	50	60	120	1000
1	6106.32071	6157.28462	6208.73022	6239.82511	6260.64858	6286.78205	6302.51719	6313.03005	6339.39127	6362.68175
2	99.41585	99.43251	99.44917	99.45917	99.46583	99.47416	99.47916	99.48250	99.49083	99.49816
3	27.05182	26.87219	26.68979	26.57898	26.50453	26.41081	26.35423	26.31635	26.22114	26.13672
4	14.37359	14.19820	14.01961	13.91085	13.83766	13.74538	13.68958	13.65220	13.55810	13.47451
5	9.88828	9.72222	9.55265	9.44912	9.37933	9.29119	9.23781	9.20201	9.11177	9.03144
6	7.71833	7.55899	7.39583	7.29597	7.22853	7.14322	7.09148	7.05674	6.96902	6.89077
7	6.46909	6.31433	6.15544	6.05795	5.99201	5.90845	5.85768	5.82357	5.73729	5.66014
8	5.66672	5.51512	5.35909	5.26314	5.19813	5.11561	5.06540	5.03162	4.94605	4.86936
9	5.11143	4.96208	4.80800	4.71303	4.64858	4.56665	4.51671	4.48309	4.39777	4.32112
10	4.70587	4.55814	4.40539	4.31106	4.24693	4.16529	4.11545	4.08186	3.99648	3.91960
12	4.15526	4.00962	3.85843	3.76469	3.70079	3.61918	3.56922	3.53547	3.44944	3.37159
15	3.66624	3.52219	3.37189	3.27822	3.21411	3.13191	3.08137	3.04713	2.95945	2.87954
20	3.23112	3.08804	2.93774	2.84340	2.77848	2.69475	2.64295	2.60771	2.51678	2.43294
25	2.99306	2.85019	2.69932	2.60411	2.53831	2.45299	2.39994	2.36369	2.26956	2.18178
30	2.84310	2.70018	2.54866	2.45260	2.38597	2.29921	2.24501	2.20785	2.11076	2.01924
40	2.66483	2.52162	2.36888	2.27140	2.20338	2.11423	2.05811	2.01941	1.91719	1.81889
50	2.56250	2.41896	2.26524	2.16666	2.09759	2.00659	1.94896	1.90903	1.80260	1.69837
60	2.49612	2.35230	2.19781	2.09837	2.02848	1.93602	1.87719	1.83626	1.72632	1.61687
120	2.33630	2.19150	2.03459	1.93249	1.86001	1.76285	1.70002	1.65569	1.53299	1.40146
1000	2.20252	2.05650	1.89673	1.79149	1.71584	1.61271	1.54448	1.49529	1.35133	1.15863

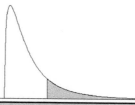

0.025 F Table	Numerator DF									
Denom. DF	1	2	3	4	5	6	7	8	9	10
1	647.78901	799.50000	864.16297	899.58331	921.84790	937.11108	948.21689	956.65622	963.28458	968.62744
2	38.50633	39.00000	39.16549	39.24842	39.29823	39.33146	39.35521	39.37302	39.38688	39.39797
3	17.44344	16.04411	15.43918	15.10098	14.88482	14.73472	14.62440	14.53989	14.47308	14.41894
4	12.21786	10.64911	9.97920	9.60453	9.36447	9.19731	9.07414	8.97958	8.90468	8.84388
5	10.00698	8.43362	7.76359	7.38789	7.14638	6.97770	6.85308	6.75717	6.68105	6.61915
6	8.81310	7.25986	6.59880	6.22716	5.98757	5.81976	5.69547	5.59962	5.52341	5.46132
7	8.07267	6.54152	5.88982	5.52259	5.28524	5.11860	4.99491	4.89934	4.82322	4.76112
8	7.57088	6.05947	5.41596	5.05263	4.81728	4.65170	4.52856	4.43326	4.35723	4.29513
9	7.20928	5.71471	5.07812	4.71808	4.48441	4.31972	4.19705	4.10196	4.02599	3.96387
10	6.93673	5.45640	4.82562	4.46834	4.23609	4.07213	3.94982	3.85489	3.77896	3.71679
12	6.55377	5.09587	4.47418	4.12121	3.89113	3.72829	3.60651	3.51178	3.43585	3.37355
15	6.19950	4.76505	4.15280	3.80427	3.57642	3.41466	3.29336	3.19874	3.12271	3.06020
20	5.87149	4.46126	3.85870	3.51470	3.28906	3.12834	3.00742	2.91280	2.83655	2.77367
25	5.68637	4.29093	3.69427	3.35301	3.12868	2.96855	2.84780	2.75311	2.67664	2.61347
30	5.56753	4.18206	3.58936	3.24993	3.02647	2.86670	2.74603	2.65126	2.57461	2.51119
40	5.42394	4.05099	3.46326	3.12611	2.90372	2.74438	2.62378	2.52886	2.45194	2.38816
50	5.34032	3.97493	3.39019	3.05441	2.83265	2.67355	2.55297	2.45794	2.38082	2.31679
60	5.28561	3.92527	3.34252	3.00766	2.78631	2.62737	2.50679	2.41167	2.33441	2.27020
120	5.15233	3.80464	3.22689	2.89431	2.67399	2.51540	2.39479	2.29941	2.22173	2.15701
1000	5.03905	3.70252	3.12918	2.79859	2.57915	2.42084	2.30017	2.20449	2.12638	2.06113

0.025 F Table	Numerator DF									
Denom. DF	12	15	20	25	30	40	50	60	120	1000
1	976.70795	984.86684	993.10280	998.08079	1001.41441	1005.59810	1008.11712	1009.80011	1014.02024	1017.74877
2	39.41462	39.43126	39.44791	39.45790	39.46457	39.47290	39.47789	39.48123	39.48956	39.49689
3	14.33655	14.25271	14.16738	14.11545	14.08052	14.03651	14.00991	13.99210	13.94728	13.90751
4	8.75116	8.65654	8.55994	8.50100	8.46127	8.41113	8.38078	8.36044	8.30917	8.26358
5	6.52455	6.42773	6.32856	6.26786	6.22688	6.17505	6.14362	6.12253	6.06929	6.02183
6	5.36624	5.26867	5.16840	5.10686	5.06523	5.01247	4.98042	4.95889	4.90445	4.85579
7	4.66583	4.56779	4.46674	4.40455	4.36239	4.30888	4.27631	4.25440	4.19890	4.14918
8	4.19967	4.10121	3.99945	3.93666	3.89402	3.83978	3.80672	3.78445	3.72794	3.67718
9	3.86822	3.76936	3.66691	3.60353	3.56041	3.50547	3.47192	3.44930	3.39180	3.34001
10	3.62095	3.52167	3.41854	3.35460	3.31102	3.25540	3.22137	3.19840	3.13991	3.08710
12	3.27728	3.17720	3.07277	3.00774	2.96328	2.90635	2.87141	2.84777	2.78737	2.73253
15	2.96328	2.86209	2.75590	2.68940	2.64374	2.58501	2.54880	2.52423	2.46112	2.40340
20	2.67583	2.57310	2.46448	2.39594	2.34860	2.28732	2.24929	2.22336	2.15624	2.09407
25	2.51489	2.41095	2.30045	2.23030	2.18162	2.11826	2.07872	2.05164	1.98106	1.91490
30	2.41203	2.30715	2.19516	2.12372	2.07394	2.00887	1.96806	1.94001	1.86642	1.79665
40	2.28816	2.18190	2.06771	1.99434	1.94292	1.87520	1.83238	1.80277	1.72420	1.64814
50	2.21621	2.10901	1.99329	1.91856	1.86594	1.79627	1.75195	1.72114	1.63862	1.55721
60	2.16919	2.06131	1.94447	1.86872	1.81520	1.74405	1.69855	1.66679	1.58103	1.49497
120	2.05482	1.94499	1.82492	1.74617	1.68994	1.61415	1.56485	1.52994	1.43268	1.32732
1000	1.95772	1.84586	1.72231	1.64021	1.58083	1.49935	1.44507	1.40577	1.28978	1.13205

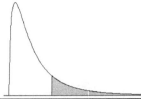

0.05 F Table	Numerator DF									
Denom. DF	1	2	3	4	5	6	7	8	9	10
1	161.44764	199.50000	215.70735	224.58324	230.16188	233.98600	236.76840	238.88269	240.54325	241.88175
2	18.51282	19.00000	19.16429	19.24679	19.29641	19.32953	19.35322	19.37099	19.38483	19.39590
3	10.12796	9.55209	9.27663	9.11718	9.01346	8.94065	8.88674	8.84524	8.81230	8.78552
4	7.70865	6.94427	6.59138	6.38823	6.25606	6.16313	6.09421	6.04104	5.99878	5.96437
5	6.60789	5.78614	5.40945	5.19217	5.05033	4.95029	4.87587	4.81832	4.77247	4.73506
6	5.98738	5.14325	4.75706	4.53368	4.38737	4.28387	4.20666	4.14580	4.09902	4.05996
7	5.59145	4.73741	4.34683	4.12031	3.97152	3.86597	3.78704	3.72573	3.67667	3.63652
8	5.31766	4.45897	4.06618	3.83785	3.68750	3.58058	3.50046	3.43810	3.38813	3.34716
9	5.11736	4.25649	3.86255	3.63309	3.48166	3.37375	3.29275	3.22958	3.17889	3.13728
10	4.96460	4.10282	3.70826	3.47805	3.32583	3.21717	3.13546	3.07166	3.02038	2.97824
12	4.74723	3.88529	3.49029	3.25917	3.10588	2.99612	2.91336	2.84857	2.79638	2.75339
15	4.54308	3.68232	3.28738	3.05557	2.90129	2.79046	2.70663	2.64080	2.58763	2.54372
20	4.35124	3.49283	3.09839	2.86608	2.71089	2.59898	2.51401	2.44705	2.39281	2.34788
25	4.24170	3.38519	2.99124	2.75871	2.60299	2.49041	2.40473	2.33706	2.28210	2.23647
30	4.17088	3.31583	2.92228	2.68963	2.53355	2.42052	2.33434	2.26616	2.21070	2.16458
40	4.08475	3.23173	2.83875	2.60597	2.44947	2.33585	2.24902	2.18017	2.12403	2.07725
50	4.03431	3.18261	2.79001	2.55718	2.40041	2.28644	2.19920	2.12992	2.07335	2.02614
60	4.00119	3.15041	2.75808	2.52522	2.36827	2.25405	2.16654	2.09697	2.04010	1.99259
120	3.92012	3.07178	2.68017	2.44724	2.28985	2.17501	2.08677	2.01643	1.95876	1.91046
1000	3.85077	3.00472	2.61380	2.38083	2.22305	2.10763	2.01872	1.94765	1.88923	1.84015

0.05 F Table	Numerator DF									
Denom. DF	12	15	20	25	30	40	50	60	120	1000
1	243.90604	245.94993	248.01308	249.26008	250.09515	251.14315	251.77416	252.19574	253.25285	254.18682
2	19.41251	19.42914	19.44577	19.45575	19.46241	19.47074	19.47573	19.47906	19.48739	19.49473
3	8.74464	8.70287	8.66019	8.63414	8.61658	8.59441	8.58100	8.57200	8.54935	8.52921
4	5.91173	5.85781	5.80254	5.76872	5.74588	5.71700	5.69949	5.68774	5.65811	5.63170
5	4.67770	4.61876	4.55813	4.52090	4.49571	4.46379	4.44441	4.43138	4.39845	4.36904
6	3.99994	3.93806	3.87419	3.83484	3.80816	3.77429	3.75367	3.73980	3.70467	3.67320
7	3.57468	3.51074	3.44452	3.40361	3.37581	3.34043	3.31886	3.30432	3.26745	3.23432
8	3.28394	3.21841	3.15032	3.10813	3.07941	3.04278	3.02040	3.00530	2.96692	2.93235
9	3.07295	3.00610	2.93646	2.89318	2.86365	2.82593	2.80284	2.78725	2.74752	2.71164
10	2.91298	2.84502	2.77402	2.72978	2.69955	2.66086	2.63712	2.62108	2.58012	2.54302
12	2.68664	2.61685	2.54359	2.49773	2.46628	2.42588	2.40102	2.38417	2.34099	2.30167
15	2.47531	2.40345	2.32754	2.27973	2.24679	2.20428	2.17799	2.16011	2.11406	2.07176
20	2.27758	2.20327	2.12416	2.07392	2.03909	1.99382	1.96563	1.94636	1.89632	1.84974
25	2.16489	2.08889	2.00747	1.95545	1.91919	1.87180	1.84211	1.82173	1.76840	1.71813
30	2.09206	2.01480	1.93165	1.87825	1.84087	1.79179	1.76088	1.73957	1.68345	1.62993
40	2.00346	1.92446	1.83886	1.78346	1.74443	1.69280	1.66000	1.63725	1.57661	1.51750
50	1.95153	1.87138	1.78412	1.72734	1.68716	1.63368	1.59950	1.57565	1.51147	1.44767
60	1.91740	1.83644	1.74798	1.69019	1.64914	1.59427	1.55901	1.53431	1.46727	1.39943
120	1.83370	1.75050	1.65868	1.59796	1.55434	1.49520	1.45652	1.42901	1.35189	1.26747
1000	1.76185	1.67639	1.58106	1.51713	1.47059	1.40630	1.36320	1.33184	1.23854	1.10969

0.10 F Table	Numerator DF									
Denom. DF	1	2	3	4	5	6	7	8	9	10
1	39.86346	49.50000	53.59324	55.83296	57.24008	58.20442	58.90595	59.43898	59.85759	60.19498
2	8.52632	9.00000	9.16179	9.24342	9.29263	9.32553	9.34908	9.36677	9.38054	9.39157
3	5.53832	5.46238	5.39077	5.34264	5.30916	5.28473	5.26619	5.25167	5.24000	5.23041
4	4.54477	4.32456	4.19086	4.10725	4.05058	4.00975	3.97897	3.95494	3.93567	3.91988
5	4.06042	3.77972	3.61948	3.52020	3.45298	3.40451	3.36790	3.33928	3.31628	3.29740
6	3.77595	3.46330	3.28876	3.18076	3.10751	3.05455	3.01446	2.98304	2.95774	2.93693
7	3.58943	3.25744	3.07407	2.96053	2.88334	2.82739	2.78493	2.75158	2.72468	2.70251
8	3.45792	3.11312	2.92380	2.80643	2.72645	2.66833	2.62413	2.58935	2.56124	2.53804
9	3.36030	3.00645	2.81286	2.69268	2.61061	2.55086	2.50531	2.46941	2.44034	2.41632
10	3.28502	2.92447	2.72767	2.60534	2.52164	2.46058	2.41397	2.37715	2.34731	2.32260
12	3.17655	2.80680	2.60552	2.48010	2.39402	2.33102	2.28278	2.24457	2.21352	2.18776
15	3.07319	2.69517	2.48979	2.36143	2.27302	2.20808	2.15818	2.11853	2.08621	2.05932
20	2.97465	2.58925	2.38009	2.24893	2.15823	2.09132	2.03970	1.99853	1.96485	1.93674
25	2.91774	2.52831	2.31702	2.18424	2.09216	2.02406	1.97138	1.92925	1.89469	1.86578
30	2.88069	2.48872	2.27607	2.14223	2.04925	1.98033	1.92692	1.88412	1.84896	1.81949
40	2.83535	2.44037	2.22609	2.09095	1.99682	1.92688	1.87252	1.82886	1.79290	1.76269
50	2.80866	2.41195	2.19673	2.06082	1.96600	1.89543	1.84050	1.79630	1.75984	1.72915
60	2.79107	2.39325	2.17741	2.04099	1.94571	1.87472	1.81939	1.77483	1.73802	1.70701
120	2.74781	2.34734	2.12999	1.99230	1.89587	1.82381	1.76748	1.72196	1.68425	1.65238
1000	2.71056	2.30790	2.08928	1.95049	1.85304	1.78001	1.72275	1.67635	1.63779	1.60511

0.10 F Table	Numerator DF									
Denom. DF	12	15	20	25	30	40	50	60	120	1000
1	60.70521	61.22034	61.74029	62.05454	62.26497	62.52905	62.68805	62.79428	63.06064	63.29596
2	9.40813	9.42471	9.44131	9.45128	9.45793	9.46624	9.47124	9.47456	9.48289	9.49022
3	5.21562	5.20031	5.18448	5.17473	5.16811	5.15972	5.15462	5.15119	5.14251	5.13476
4	3.89553	3.87036	3.84434	3.82830	3.81742	3.80361	3.79522	3.78957	3.77527	3.76249
5	3.26824	3.23801	3.20665	3.18726	3.17408	3.15732	3.14711	3.14023	3.12279	3.10715
6	2.90472	2.87122	2.83634	2.81470	2.79996	2.78117	2.76969	2.76195	2.74229	2.72460
7	2.66811	2.63223	2.59473	2.57139	2.55546	2.53510	2.52263	2.51422	2.49279	2.47346
8	2.50196	2.46422	2.42464	2.39992	2.38302	2.36136	2.34808	2.33910	2.31618	2.29544
9	2.37888	2.33962	2.29832	2.27246	2.25472	2.23196	2.21797	2.20849	2.18427	2.16228
10	2.28405	2.24351	2.20074	2.17388	2.15543	2.13169	2.11707	2.10716	2.08176	2.05864
12	2.14744	2.10485	2.05968	2.03116	2.01149	1.98610	1.97040	1.95973	1.93228	1.90712
15	2.01707	1.97222	1.92431	1.89387	1.87277	1.84539	1.82837	1.81676	1.78672	1.75895
20	1.89236	1.84494	1.79384	1.76108	1.73822	1.70833	1.68962	1.67678	1.64326	1.61183
25	1.82000	1.77083	1.71752	1.68310	1.65895	1.62718	1.60715	1.59335	1.55703	1.52252
30	1.77270	1.72227	1.66731	1.63163	1.60648	1.57323	1.55215	1.53757	1.49891	1.46172
40	1.71456	1.66241	1.60515	1.56767	1.54108	1.50562	1.48296	1.46716	1.42476	1.38302
50	1.68017	1.62690	1.56811	1.52940	1.50180	1.46478	1.44094	1.42424	1.37894	1.33342
60	1.65743	1.60337	1.54349	1.50389	1.47554	1.43734	1.41261	1.39520	1.34757	1.29881
120	1.60120	1.54500	1.48207	1.43992	1.40938	1.36760	1.34005	1.32034	1.26457	1.20264
1000	1.55239	1.49406	1.42799	1.38308	1.35007	1.30403	1.27287	1.25004	1.18135	1.08446

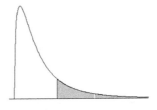

0.90 F Table	Numerator DF									
Denom. DF	1	2	3	4	5	6	7	8	9	10
1	0.02509	0.11728	0.18056	0.22003	0.24628	0.26483	0.27860	0.28919	0.29759	0.30441
2	0.02020	0.11111	0.18307	0.23124	0.26457	0.28874	0.30699	0.32122	0.33262	0.34194
3	0.01866	0.10915	0.18550	0.23861	0.27628	0.30407	0.32530	0.34202	0.35551	0.36661
4	0.01791	0.10819	0.18717	0.24347	0.28408	0.31439	0.33778	0.35633	0.37138	0.38383
5	0.01747	0.10761	0.18835	0.24688	0.28960	0.32180	0.34682	0.36678	0.38305	0.39657
6	0.01718	0.10723	0.18922	0.24939	0.29373	0.32738	0.35368	0.37477	0.39203	0.40641
7	0.01698	0.10696	0.18989	0.25132	0.29692	0.33173	0.35908	0.38108	0.39915	0.41426
8	0.01682	0.10676	0.19042	0.25285	0.29947	0.33523	0.36343	0.38620	0.40496	0.42067
9	0.01671	0.10660	0.19084	0.25409	0.30154	0.33810	0.36702	0.39044	0.40978	0.42602
10	0.01661	0.10648	0.19119	0.25511	0.30327	0.34049	0.37003	0.39401	0.41385	0.43055
12	0.01647	0.10629	0.19173	0.25670	0.30598	0.34427	0.37480	0.39969	0.42037	0.43782
15	0.01633	0.10610	0.19230	0.25837	0.30883	0.34828	0.37991	0.40581	0.42742	0.44573
20	0.01620	0.10592	0.19288	0.26012	0.31185	0.35257	0.38540	0.41243	0.43510	0.45439
25	0.01611	0.10581	0.19325	0.26121	0.31375	0.35528	0.38889	0.41668	0.44005	0.46001
30	0.01606	0.10573	0.19349	0.26196	0.31505	0.35715	0.39132	0.41964	0.44351	0.46395
40	0.01599	0.10564	0.19381	0.26291	0.31672	0.35956	0.39446	0.42348	0.44804	0.46911
50	0.01595	0.10558	0.19400	0.26349	0.31775	0.36105	0.39641	0.42588	0.45086	0.47235
60	0.01593	0.10555	0.19413	0.26388	0.31845	0.36206	0.39774	0.42752	0.45280	0.47457
120	0.01586	0.10545	0.19446	0.26488	0.32023	0.36466	0.40116	0.43175	0.45782	0.48036
1000	0.01580	0.10537	0.19475	0.26578	0.32184	0.36703	0.40429	0.43565	0.46248	0.48576

0.90 F Table	Numerator DF									
Denom. DF	12	15	20	25	30	40	50	60	120	1000
1	0.31481	0.32540	0.33617	0.34273	0.34714	0.35269	0.35604	0.35829	0.36393	0.36893
2	0.35628	0.37103	0.38621	0.39552	0.40181	0.40977	0.41460	0.41784	0.42601	0.43330
3	0.38380	0.40164	0.42015	0.43159	0.43935	0.44922	0.45522	0.45926	0.46949	0.47863
4	0.40321	0.42347	0.44466	0.45782	0.46680	0.47825	0.48524	0.48996	0.50193	0.51269
5	0.41771	0.43994	0.46334	0.47797	0.48798	0.50080	0.50865	0.51395	0.52746	0.53965
6	0.42900	0.45288	0.47817	0.49406	0.50497	0.51897	0.52758	0.53341	0.54830	0.56179
7	0.43806	0.46335	0.49027	0.50726	0.51896	0.53404	0.54333	0.54963	0.56578	0.58047
8	0.44552	0.47203	0.50037	0.51834	0.53075	0.54679	0.55670	0.56343	0.58073	0.59653
9	0.45177	0.47934	0.50894	0.52779	0.54085	0.55776	0.56823	0.57537	0.59374	0.61058
10	0.45709	0.48560	0.51633	0.53597	0.54961	0.56732	0.57832	0.58582	0.60519	0.62301
12	0.46567	0.49577	0.52844	0.54945	0.56411	0.58324	0.59518	0.60334	0.62453	0.64417
15	0.47509	0.50704	0.54202	0.56471	0.58063	0.60154	0.61467	0.62369	0.64725	0.66932
20	0.48551	0.51967	0.55746	0.58223	0.59977	0.62299	0.63771	0.64788	0.67473	0.70028
25	0.49233	0.52802	0.56783	0.59414	0.61288	0.63789	0.65385	0.66494	0.69448	0.72302
30	0.49714	0.53397	0.57530	0.60279	0.62248	0.64890	0.66587	0.67772	0.70953	0.74070
40	0.50350	0.54189	0.58537	0.61456	0.63564	0.66418	0.68270	0.69573	0.73121	0.76685
50	0.50751	0.54693	0.59185	0.62222	0.64427	0.67433	0.69399	0.70791	0.74624	0.78563
60	0.51027	0.55043	0.59638	0.62761	0.65038	0.68159	0.70213	0.71674	0.75738	0.79998
120	0.51752	0.55968	0.60855	0.64225	0.66715	0.70187	0.72519	0.74208	0.79078	0.84649
1000	0.52435	0.56852	0.62041	0.65681	0.68413	0.72306	0.74995	0.76993	0.83150	0.92212

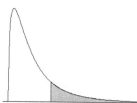

0.95 F Table	Numerator DF									
Denom. DF	1	2	3	4	5	6	7	8	9	10
1	0.00619	0.05402	0.09874	0.12972	0.15133	0.16702	0.17884	0.18805	0.19541	0.20143
2	0.00501	0.05263	0.10469	0.14400	0.17283	0.19443	0.21109	0.22427	0.23494	0.24373
3	0.00464	0.05218	0.10780	0.15171	0.18486	0.21021	0.23005	0.24593	0.25890	0.26967
4	0.00445	0.05196	0.10968	0.15654	0.19260	0.22057	0.24270	0.26056	0.27525	0.28752
5	0.00434	0.05182	0.11095	0.15985	0.19801	0.22793	0.25179	0.27119	0.28722	0.30068
6	0.00427	0.05173	0.11185	0.16226	0.20201	0.23343	0.25867	0.27928	0.29641	0.31083
7	0.00422	0.05167	0.11253	0.16409	0.20509	0.23772	0.26406	0.28568	0.30370	0.31893
8	0.00419	0.05162	0.11306	0.16553	0.20754	0.24115	0.26840	0.29086	0.30964	0.32556
9	0.00416	0.05159	0.11348	0.16670	0.20954	0.24396	0.27198	0.29515	0.31457	0.33108
10	0.00413	0.05156	0.11382	0.16766	0.21119	0.24631	0.27499	0.29876	0.31875	0.33577
12	0.00410	0.05151	0.11436	0.16916	0.21378	0.25000	0.27975	0.30451	0.32542	0.34329
15	0.00407	0.05147	0.11490	0.17071	0.21651	0.25393	0.28484	0.31071	0.33266	0.35149
20	0.00403	0.05143	0.11547	0.17234	0.21939	0.25812	0.29032	0.31743	0.34055	0.36049
25	0.00401	0.05140	0.11582	0.17335	0.22119	0.26077	0.29381	0.32174	0.34564	0.36633
30	0.00400	0.05138	0.11606	0.17404	0.22243	0.26259	0.29623	0.32474	0.34920	0.37043
40	0.00398	0.05136	0.11635	0.17492	0.22402	0.26495	0.29936	0.32865	0.35387	0.37582
50	0.00397	0.05135	0.11654	0.17545	0.22500	0.26641	0.30131	0.33108	0.35678	0.37920
60	0.00397	0.05134	0.11666	0.17582	0.22566	0.26739	0.30263	0.33275	0.35878	0.38152
120	0.00395	0.05132	0.11697	0.17674	0.22735	0.26993	0.30605	0.33705	0.36396	0.38758
1000	0.00393	0.05130	0.11724	0.17757	0.22888	0.27224	0.30918	0.34102	0.36878	0.39323

0.95 F Table	Numerator DF									
Denom. DF	12	15	20	25	30	40	50	60	120	1000
1	0.21065	0.22012	0.22982	0.23575	0.23976	0.24481	0.24787	0.24993	0.25509	0.25969
2	0.25738	0.27157	0.28630	0.29540	0.30158	0.30943	0.31421	0.31742	0.32554	0.33281
3	0.28651	0.30419	0.32275	0.33431	0.34220	0.35227	0.35842	0.36257	0.37311	0.38258
4	0.30683	0.32727	0.34891	0.36249	0.37180	0.38373	0.39106	0.39601	0.40862	0.42002
5	0.32197	0.34467	0.36888	0.38417	0.39470	0.40825	0.41660	0.42225	0.43671	0.44983
6	0.33376	0.35836	0.38477	0.40154	0.41313	0.42811	0.43736	0.44365	0.45977	0.47447
7	0.34325	0.36946	0.39777	0.41585	0.42839	0.44464	0.45471	0.46157	0.47921	0.49536
8	0.35105	0.37867	0.40865	0.42789	0.44127	0.45868	0.46950	0.47688	0.49593	0.51344
9	0.35761	0.38645	0.41792	0.43819	0.45235	0.47080	0.48231	0.49017	0.51053	0.52932
10	0.36319	0.39313	0.42592	0.44713	0.46198	0.48141	0.49355	0.50186	0.52343	0.54343
12	0.37221	0.40399	0.43906	0.46192	0.47800	0.49914	0.51242	0.52154	0.54535	0.56759
15	0.38214	0.41607	0.45387	0.47872	0.49633	0.51963	0.53436	0.54453	0.57127	0.59652
20	0.39315	0.42964	0.47078	0.49814	0.51769	0.54382	0.56050	0.57209	0.60289	0.63249
25	0.40036	0.43865	0.48218	0.51139	0.53241	0.56071	0.57892	0.59165	0.62580	0.65914
30	0.40547	0.44508	0.49042	0.52105	0.54322	0.57325	0.59271	0.60638	0.64336	0.68000
40	0.41222	0.45366	0.50155	0.53424	0.55810	0.59074	0.61211	0.62725	0.66881	0.71108
50	0.41649	0.45914	0.50874	0.54286	0.56790	0.60241	0.62520	0.64143	0.68657	0.73357
60	0.41943	0.46294	0.51378	0.54893	0.57485	0.61078	0.63466	0.65176	0.69978	0.75084
120	0.42717	0.47302	0.52734	0.56548	0.59402	0.63427	0.66161	0.68154	0.73971	0.80741
1000	0.43447	0.48268	0.54062	0.58203	0.61352	0.65898	0.69076	0.71458	0.78897	0.90115

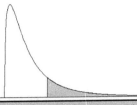

0.975 F Table	Numerator DF									
Denom. DF	1	2	3	4	5	6	7	8	9	10
1	0.00154	0.02597	0.05733	0.08185	0.09993	0.11347	0.12387	0.13209	0.13871	0.14416
2	0.00125	0.02564	0.06233	0.09390	0.11857	0.13774	0.15287	0.16503	0.17499	0.18327
3	0.00116	0.02553	0.06477	0.10021	0.12881	0.15154	0.16978	0.18464	0.19692	0.20723
4	0.00111	0.02548	0.06622	0.10412	0.13536	0.16059	0.18107	0.19792	0.21195	0.22380
5	0.00108	0.02545	0.06718	0.10679	0.13993	0.16701	0.18921	0.20759	0.22299	0.23607
6	0.00107	0.02542	0.06787	0.10873	0.14331	0.17183	0.19537	0.21498	0.23150	0.24557
7	0.00105	0.02541	0.06838	0.11020	0.14592	0.17558	0.20020	0.22082	0.23826	0.25318
8	0.00105	0.02540	0.06878	0.11136	0.14799	0.17858	0.20411	0.22537	0.24379	0.25941
9	0.00104	0.02539	0.06909	0.11230	0.14968	0.18105	0.20733	0.22950	0.24839	0.26462
10	0.00103	0.02538	0.06935	0.11307	0.15108	0.18311	0.21003	0.23282	0.25228	0.26905
12	0.00102	0.02537	0.06975	0.11427	0.15327	0.18635	0.21432	0.23811	0.25852	0.27617
15	0.00102	0.02536	0.07016	0.11552	0.15558	0.18980	0.21892	0.24383	0.26530	0.28396
20	0.00101	0.02535	0.07058	0.11682	0.15801	0.19348	0.22388	0.25003	0.27271	0.29252
25	0.00100	0.02534	0.07084	0.11763	0.15954	0.19582	0.22704	0.25402	0.27751	0.29810
30	0.00100	0.02534	0.07102	0.11819	0.16059	0.19742	0.22923	0.25680	0.28087	0.30202
40	0.00099	0.02533	0.07124	0.11889	0.16194	0.19950	0.23208	0.26043	0.28527	0.30718
50	0.00099	0.02533	0.07138	0.11932	0.16277	0.20079	0.23385	0.26269	0.28802	0.31043
60	0.00099	0.02533	0.07147	0.11961	0.16333	0.20166	0.23505	0.26424	0.28991	0.31266
120	0.00099	0.02532	0.07170	0.12035	0.16476	0.20390	0.23816	0.26824	0.29483	0.31848
1000	0.00098	0.02532	0.07190	0.12101	0.16606	0.20594	0.24101	0.27195	0.29940	0.32393

0.975 F Table	Numerator DF									
Denom. DF	12	15	20	25	30	40	50	60	120	1000
1	0.15258	0.16130	0.17031	0.17586	0.17961	0.18437	0.18725	0.18919	0.19409	0.19845
2	0.19624	0.20986	0.22415	0.23305	0.23912	0.24685	0.25158	0.25476	0.26284	0.27009
3	0.22350	0.24080	0.25915	0.27069	0.27860	0.28875	0.29497	0.29918	0.30990	0.31957
4	0.24265	0.26286	0.28452	0.29824	0.30770	0.31989	0.32739	0.33248	0.34551	0.35732
5	0.25699	0.27961	0.30404	0.31962	0.33042	0.34439	0.35303	0.35890	0.37397	0.38772
6	0.26822	0.29285	0.31966	0.33686	0.34883	0.36438	0.37403	0.38061	0.39755	0.41308
7	0.27728	0.30364	0.33251	0.35115	0.36416	0.38113	0.39170	0.39892	0.41757	0.43475
8	0.28476	0.31262	0.34331	0.36323	0.37718	0.39543	0.40684	0.41465	0.43489	0.45362
9	0.29105	0.32023	0.35254	0.37360	0.38841	0.40784	0.42002	0.42837	0.45010	0.47028
10	0.29642	0.32678	0.36053	0.38263	0.39822	0.41873	0.43163	0.44049	0.46360	0.48517
12	0.30513	0.33746	0.37372	0.39763	0.41459	0.43703	0.45122	0.46100	0.48666	0.51080
15	0.31474	0.34939	0.38864	0.41477	0.43343	0.45832	0.47416	0.48513	0.51414	0.54175
20	0.32544	0.36286	0.40576	0.43470	0.45555	0.48363	0.50168	0.51428	0.54797	0.58062
25	0.33248	0.37183	0.41737	0.44837	0.47087	0.50142	0.52122	0.53513	0.57268	0.60968
30	0.33746	0.37825	0.42579	0.45838	0.48217	0.51469	0.53592	0.55090	0.59174	0.63258
40	0.34407	0.38685	0.43719	0.47209	0.49779	0.53328	0.55671	0.57338	0.61952	0.66696
50	0.34826	0.39234	0.44458	0.48107	0.50811	0.54574	0.57079	0.58874	0.63904	0.69201
60	0.35115	0.39616	0.44977	0.48742	0.51546	0.55470	0.58101	0.59996	0.65362	0.71136
120	0.35876	0.40632	0.46377	0.50478	0.53579	0.57998	0.61027	0.63250	0.69799	0.77533
1000	0.36596	0.41608	0.47754	0.52222	0.55659	0.60674	0.64218	0.66891	0.75340	0.88335

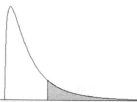

0.99 F Table	Numerator DF									
Denom. DF	1	2	3	4	5	6	7	8	9	10
1	0.00025	0.01015	0.02931	0.04717	0.06151	0.07275	0.08166	0.08882	0.09468	0.09956
2	0.00020	0.01010	0.03245	0.05556	0.07534	0.09154	0.10475	0.11562	0.12466	0.13229
3	0.00019	0.01008	0.03395	0.05990	0.08292	0.10225	0.11833	0.13174	0.14302	0.15262
4	0.00018	0.01008	0.03483	0.06259	0.08778	0.10931	0.12744	0.14273	0.15571	0.16682
5	0.00017	0.01007	0.03541	0.06443	0.09118	0.11434	0.13404	0.15079	0.16510	0.17742
6	0.00017	0.01007	0.03583	0.06576	0.09370	0.11812	0.13905	0.15697	0.17236	0.18567
7	0.00017	0.01006	0.03614	0.06677	0.09564	0.12107	0.14300	0.16187	0.17816	0.19230
8	0.00017	0.01006	0.03638	0.06757	0.09719	0.12343	0.14620	0.16587	0.18291	0.19776
9	0.00017	0.01006	0.03657	0.06822	0.09845	0.12537	0.14884	0.16919	0.18688	0.20233
10	0.00017	0.01006	0.03673	0.06875	0.09949	0.12700	0.15106	0.17199	0.19024	0.20622
12	0.00016	0.01006	0.03697	0.06957	0.10113	0.12956	0.15458	0.17647	0.19564	0.21250
15	0.00016	0.01006	0.03721	0.07043	0.10286	0.13229	0.15837	0.18132	0.20153	0.21939
20	0.00016	0.01006	0.03747	0.07133	0.10468	0.13521	0.16246	0.18660	0.20799	0.22699
25	0.00016	0.01005	0.03762	0.07189	0.10583	0.13706	0.16507	0.19000	0.21218	0.23196
30	0.00016	0.01005	0.03773	0.07227	0.10662	0.13834	0.16689	0.19238	0.21512	0.23546
40	0.00016	0.01005	0.03786	0.07275	0.10763	0.13999	0.16925	0.19548	0.21898	0.24008
50	0.00016	0.01005	0.03794	0.07305	0.10825	0.14101	0.17072	0.19742	0.22140	0.24299
60	0.00016	0.01005	0.03800	0.07325	0.10867	0.14171	0.17172	0.19874	0.22306	0.24499
120	0.00016	0.01005	0.03814	0.07376	0.10975	0.14349	0.17430	0.20218	0.22739	0.25022
1000	0.00016	0.01005	0.03826	0.07421	0.11072	0.14512	0.17667	0.20537	0.23142	0.25513

0.99 F Table	Numerator DF									
Denom. DF	12	15	20	25	30	40	50	60	120	1000
1	0.10718	0.11517	0.12352	0.12870	0.13223	0.13672	0.13946	0.14130	0.14597	0.15014
2	0.14437	0.15726	0.17097	0.17960	0.18552	0.19311	0.19776	0.20091	0.20892	0.21615
3	0.16800	0.18461	0.20250	0.21388	0.22174	0.23188	0.23813	0.24237	0.25322	0.26307
4	0.18478	0.20436	0.22570	0.23938	0.24889	0.26121	0.26885	0.27404	0.28740	0.29958
5	0.19746	0.21951	0.24374	0.25941	0.27034	0.28459	0.29345	0.29950	0.31510	0.32943
6	0.20744	0.23157	0.25830	0.27570	0.28790	0.30386	0.31383	0.32065	0.33831	0.35461
7	0.21554	0.24146	0.27036	0.28929	0.30262	0.32013	0.33111	0.33863	0.35820	0.37634
8	0.22225	0.24972	0.28055	0.30085	0.31520	0.33412	0.34602	0.35420	0.37553	0.39541
9	0.22792	0.25675	0.28930	0.31083	0.32610	0.34631	0.35907	0.36786	0.39084	0.41236
10	0.23277	0.26282	0.29690	0.31955	0.33567	0.35707	0.37063	0.37998	0.40452	0.42760
12	0.24066	0.27276	0.30949	0.33411	0.35173	0.37526	0.39024	0.40062	0.42803	0.45403
15	0.24940	0.28391	0.32383	0.35085	0.37035	0.39657	0.41340	0.42512	0.45631	0.48626
20	0.25917	0.29657	0.34040	0.37046	0.39236	0.42214	0.44145	0.45500	0.49150	0.52722
25	0.26563	0.30504	0.35169	0.38401	0.40773	0.44026	0.46154	0.47656	0.51747	0.55820
30	0.27021	0.31113	0.35991	0.39396	0.41912	0.45385	0.47674	0.49298	0.53763	0.58280
40	0.27631	0.31929	0.37109	0.40767	0.43493	0.47298	0.49836	0.51652	0.56726	0.62007
50	0.28017	0.32453	0.37836	0.41668	0.44543	0.48588	0.51309	0.53271	0.58823	0.64747
60	0.28285	0.32818	0.38348	0.42307	0.45293	0.49519	0.52383	0.54459	0.60398	0.66877
120	0.28990	0.33790	0.39733	0.44061	0.47376	0.52160	0.55476	0.57927	0.65232	0.74001
1000	0.29660	0.34728	0.41103	0.45834	0.49524	0.54979	0.58880	0.61848	0.71354	0.86309

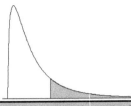

0.995 F Table	Numerator DF									
Denom. DF	1	2	3	4	5	6	7	8	9	10
1	0.00006	0.00504	0.01800	0.03192	0.04389	0.05366	0.06159	0.06808	0.07346	0.07796
2	0.00005	0.00503	0.02008	0.03805	0.05460	0.06876	0.08062	0.09056	0.09894	0.10608
3	0.00005	0.00502	0.02107	0.04122	0.06050	0.07742	0.09189	0.10420	0.11472	0.12375
4	0.00004	0.00502	0.02165	0.04319	0.06428	0.08314	0.09950	0.11357	0.12569	0.13619
5	0.00004	0.00502	0.02203	0.04453	0.06694	0.08723	0.10502	0.12046	0.13385	0.14551
6	0.00004	0.00502	0.02230	0.04551	0.06890	0.09031	0.10923	0.12575	0.14018	0.15280
7	0.00004	0.00502	0.02251	0.04625	0.07042	0.09271	0.11254	0.12997	0.14525	0.15867
8	0.00004	0.00502	0.02266	0.04683	0.07163	0.09465	0.11523	0.13341	0.14940	0.16351
9	0.00004	0.00502	0.02279	0.04731	0.07261	0.09623	0.11746	0.13627	0.15288	0.16757
10	0.00004	0.00502	0.02289	0.04769	0.07343	0.09756	0.11933	0.13868	0.15583	0.17104
12	0.00004	0.00501	0.02305	0.04830	0.07471	0.09966	0.12230	0.14255	0.16058	0.17664
15	0.00004	0.00501	0.02321	0.04893	0.07607	0.10190	0.12551	0.14675	0.16577	0.18279
20	0.00004	0.00501	0.02338	0.04959	0.07750	0.10429	0.12897	0.15133	0.17147	0.18961
25	0.00004	0.00501	0.02348	0.04999	0.07840	0.10581	0.13118	0.15428	0.17518	0.19407
30	0.00004	0.00501	0.02355	0.05027	0.07902	0.10686	0.13272	0.15635	0.17778	0.19722
40	0.00004	0.00501	0.02364	0.05063	0.07981	0.10822	0.13473	0.15904	0.18121	0.20137
50	0.00004	0.00501	0.02369	0.05085	0.08030	0.10905	0.13597	0.16073	0.18335	0.20399
60	0.00004	0.00501	0.02373	0.05099	0.08063	0.10963	0.13682	0.16189	0.18483	0.20580
120	0.00004	0.00501	0.02382	0.05137	0.08147	0.11109	0.13902	0.16488	0.18868	0.21052
1000	0.00004	0.00501	0.02390	0.05170	0.08224	0.11243	0.14104	0.16766	0.19226	0.21496

0.995 F Table	Numerator DF									
Denom. DF	12	15	20	25	30	40	50	60	120	1000
1	0.08508	0.09261	0.10056	0.10554	0.10894	0.11328	0.11593	0.11772	0.12227	0.12635
2	0.11751	0.12986	0.14313	0.15156	0.15736	0.16484	0.16945	0.17256	0.18053	0.18774
3	0.13839	0.15442	0.17189	0.18310	0.19088	0.20097	0.20722	0.21146	0.22236	0.23230
4	0.15335	0.17233	0.19326	0.20682	0.21629	0.22864	0.23632	0.24155	0.25506	0.26745
5	0.16471	0.18615	0.21001	0.22560	0.23654	0.25088	0.25983	0.26596	0.28183	0.29647
6	0.17370	0.19721	0.22361	0.24096	0.25321	0.26933	0.27945	0.28638	0.30442	0.32115
7	0.18101	0.20630	0.23491	0.25385	0.26727	0.28500	0.29617	0.30385	0.32389	0.34258
8	0.18709	0.21393	0.24450	0.26485	0.27932	0.29853	0.31067	0.31904	0.34095	0.36149
9	0.19223	0.22044	0.25275	0.27437	0.28981	0.31037	0.32341	0.33242	0.35609	0.37838
10	0.19664	0.22606	0.25994	0.28272	0.29905	0.32085	0.33473	0.34433	0.36966	0.39362
12	0.20382	0.23531	0.27189	0.29670	0.31459	0.33863	0.35402	0.36472	0.39309	0.42018
15	0.21180	0.24571	0.28555	0.31286	0.33270	0.35957	0.37692	0.38904	0.42146	0.45280
20	0.22075	0.25756	0.30141	0.33187	0.35423	0.38485	0.40483	0.41890	0.45702	0.49458
25	0.22668	0.26552	0.31225	0.34505	0.36933	0.40285	0.42493	0.44058	0.48343	0.52642
30	0.23090	0.27124	0.32016	0.35477	0.38055	0.41641	0.44020	0.45716	0.50404	0.55185
40	0.23651	0.27894	0.33096	0.36819	0.39619	0.43557	0.46201	0.48103	0.53449	0.59061
50	0.24008	0.28389	0.33799	0.37704	0.40660	0.44853	0.47694	0.49752	0.55614	0.61927
60	0.24255	0.28733	0.34295	0.38332	0.41405	0.45791	0.48784	0.50964	0.57246	0.64165
120	0.24907	0.29654	0.35640	0.40063	0.43483	0.48460	0.51938	0.54522	0.62286	0.71712
1000	0.25527	0.30545	0.36975	0.41819	0.45633	0.51326	0.55432	0.58574	0.68730	0.84956

CPSIA information can be obtained
at www.ICGtesting.com
Printed in the USA
LVHW061554030620
657245LV00009BA/619